P9-CNC-797

WITHDRAWN

INTRODUCTION TO
PROBABILITY
AND
MATHEMATICAL
STATISTICS

▲▲▲▲▲▲▲▲▲▲▲▲▲▲▲▲▲▲▲▲▲

HARPER & BROTHERS, PUBLISHERS, NEW YORK

INTRODUCTION TO

PROBABILITY

AND

MATHEMATICAL

STATISTICS

▲▲▲

Z. W. Birnbaum

Professor of Mathematics
University of Washington

WITHDRAWN

INTRODUCTION TO PROBABILITY AND MATHEMATICAL STATISTICS

Copyright © 1962 by Z. W. Birnbaum

Printed in the United States of America

*All rights in this book are reserved. No part of the book
may be used or reproduced in any manner whatsoever
without written permission except in the case of brief
quotations embodied in critical articles and reviews.*

*For information address Harper & Brothers,
49 East 33rd Street, New York 16, N.Y.*

Library of Congress catalog card number: 62-7140

519
B619i

Contents

v

22619

Preface

THIS BOOK IS WRITTEN FOR A VERY DEFINITE PURPOSE: to serve as a text
for an introductory course in calculus of probabilities and in the mathematical
theory of statistics for students who have a firm grasp of calculus and some
knowledge of the theory of matrices and determinants. The plan of the book
has been tried out in actual class work over a number of years. The students
were better juniors and seniors majoring in mathematics and intending to
specialize in statistics and better graduate students specializing in various
fields in which some knowledge of the theory of statistics appeared desirable.

This specific aim of the book imposed very definite limitations on the
selection of topics and the method of presentation. An attempt was made to
make the book satisfactory to a mathematician, with emphasis on careful
formulation of assumptions and rigorous derivations. Only a few major
theorems appeared important enough to be stated and used extensively
although their proofs seemed too difficult to be presented: the central limit
theorem (Theorem 7.5.4 and the two preceding theorems), Fisher's theorem
on sampling from bivariate normal distributions (Theorem 14.1.6), and the
theorem on χ^2 with parameters estimated from the sample (Theorem 15.4.3).
The presentation is limited to discrete random variables and random variables
with probability densities only; the general theory of random variables,
which would require the use of Stieltjes integrals, is not included. Statements
involving integrals are so formulated that the student will interpret them
correctly and with sufficient generality if he thinks of the integrands as
continuous functions with, at the utmost, a finite number of discontinuities,
or, in the case of multiple integrals, as functions which may have a finite
number of arcs of discontinuity; these same statements are, however, correct
if the student interprets the integrands as measurable functions and the
integrals as Lebesgue integrals.

Two self-imposed limitations in the choice of the material deserve to be
called explicitly to the attention of the reader. They consist in excluding
quite elementary and quite advanced topics. This is not a book from which a
beginner can learn the elements of statistical technique; in fact, familiarity
with simple statistical routines is assumed. On the other hand, only a very

brief sketch of the general theory of statistical inference is presented in the concluding Chapter 17.

Some parts of statistical theory had to be excluded in order to keep the book down to the size appropriate for an introductory text. Such topics as analysis of variance, sequential analysis, applications to quality control, multivariate analysis, were omitted for this reason. For many of these special topics the reader may turn to monographic treatments which are already available.

Experience has shown that a number of concepts and theorems used in this presentation, although quite elementary and considered part of the general education of a mathematician, are often not familiar to students for whom this book is intended. Two groups of topics of this kind are dealt with separately in appendixes, in order to avoid lengthy interruptions in the exposition of the main subject: the elementary concepts of the theory of sets (Appendix A), and the inequalities traditionally connected with the names of Schwarz and Cauchy. It would seem advisable for the student to acquaint himself with Appendix A as early as possible.

The material presented can be studied in the order in which it appears in the book, but it also may be grouped in several ways. Dividing it into the following courses has been found quite expedient:

Calculus of probabilities: Chapters 1–7, and sections 8.1 and 10.1.

Introduction to statistical inference: Chapter 11, sections 10.2 and 10.3, and Chapters 12, 13, and 17.

Introduction to the theory of correlation, and distribution-free t echniques: Chapters 9, 14, 15, and 16.

Starred sections contain material which is not required for the understanding of the rest.

It is hoped that the student who finds the patience to read this book will have developed enough interest in the subject to wish to continue his studies by reading more advanced books and monographs. If, concurrently with reading this book, he improves his knowledge of mathematical theory by completing a course in the theory of functions of real variables and of complex variables, he should find himself well equipped for this task.

Several pages of numerical tables are given at the end of this book. They are intended for use in solving exercises and simple practical problems but would not be sufficient for extensive numerical work in probability and statistics. A student interested in such work will have to make use of one of the excellent volumes of statistical tables which are now available. I am indebted to Professor Sir Ronald A. Fisher, F.R.S., Cambridge, to Dr. Frank Yates, F.R.S., Rothamsted, and to Messrs. Oliver & Boyd Ltd., Edinburgh, for permission to reprint Tables III and IV from their book, *Statistical Tables for Biological, Agricultural and Medical Research*. I am also grateful for the generous support of the Office of Naval Research.

June, 1961   Z. W. B.

PART I

Fundamentals
of Calculus
of Probabilities

The Object of Calculus
of Probabilities:
Intuitive Approach

1.1 Random Phenomena

The aim of the calculus of probabilities is to give a mathematical theory of some of the occurrences in the empirical world which are usually referred to as random phenomena. No attempt will be made here to give an accurate description of this class of occurrences. We shall, instead, rely on the intuitive concept of randomness, as illustrated by the following examples.

To begin with, it is easy to name occurrences which one would not call random in the usual sense of the word. If a deck of cards is ordered so that the four aces are on top, and this fact is known, then the value of the card drawn from the top of the deck will hardly be considered as random. When a stone is dropped from a known height, the length of time it needs to reach the ground can be computed with reasonable accuracy by a known formula, and one will not call this time a random quantity. If a metal rod is required which is $2\frac{1}{4}$ inches long, and $2\frac{1}{4}$ inches is accurately marked off on a longer rod and then sawed off with care, the length of the resulting piece will not be, except possibly for very small deviations, a random occurrence in the everyday meaning of "random."

If, however, a deck of cards has been well shuffled, then the outcome of drawing the top card will be considered a random occurrence. When a stone is thrown at a target, the distance by which it may miss the target usually cannot be predicted beforehand, and it will be considered a quantity of a random character. When an electric bulb is installed in a socket, the total time until it burns out cannot be foretold, and the life length of such a bulb will be considered random.

From these examples one may infer that a random phenomenon must have the property of being unpredictable. This, in turn, may depend on the information available to those who have to do the predicting. When a coin is tossed, the ordinary person will not be able to predict whether the outcome will be heads or tails, and thus tossing of a coin will generally be considered a random phenomenon. It cannot be denied, however, that an individual endowed with extraordinary skill may be able to control the initial conditions (position of the coin, velocity, etc.) so that he can predict the outcome and hence make it a non-random phenomenon.

1.2 Random Experiments

Among random phenomena we shall single out a class of occurrences which can happen repeatedly, for a practically unlimited number of times, under essentially unchanged conditions, and these will be called *random experiments*. The judgment whether an occurrence is, first, a random phenomenon, and, secondly, a random experiment, will be reserved to common sense. Rolling a die, for example, will generally be considered a random experiment, since it is a random phenomenon and can be repeated as many times as one may wish under essentially unchanged conditions. Observing the life length of a mass-produced electronic tube would also be considered a random experiment, provided there have been enough such tubes produced to make it possible to repeat this observation (which ends in the burning out of the tube) practically on as many tubes as we please. If an occurrence is unpredictable, but cannot be repeated as often as desired, it will not be considered a random experiment.

1.3 Outcome-Space

A random experiment X will, whenever it is performed, lead to an outcome, which we will also call *an observation of X*. For example, the rolling of a die may lead to one of the possible outcomes: 1, 2, 3, 4, 5, 6. The crossbreeding of peas in Mendel's classical experiments may lead to outcomes of crimped leaves or straight leaves. Obtaining a random sample of 100 individuals listed in a directory and classifying them according to whether they are high school graduates or not may lead to any one of the possible outcomes: 0 high school (h.s.) graduates, 1 h.s. graduate, 2 h.s. graduates, $\cdots$, 98 h.s. graduates, 99 h.s. graduates, 100 h.s. graduates.

The set of all possible outcomes for a random experiment X will be called the *outcome space* for X. This terminology does not imply that every outcome space is necessarily a space in the sense of elementary geometry, although in most cases we shall be able to use simple geometrical representations of outcome spaces.

1.4 Random Variables: Geometric Representation

The outcomes of various random experiments are perceivable by different senses and may be described accordingly in terms of sounds, colors, shapes, sizes, temperatures, etc. In all practical situations, either the possible out-comes are already real numbers or it is possible to describe them in a code made of real numbers. For example, drawing an individual at random from the population of a city and recording his age is a random experiment whose outcome always is a number. If, in addition to his age, one wishes to record the color of his eyes, this outcome is not a number, but it could be put on record by using a numerical code such as: 1 for blue, 2 for brown, and 3 for green. An outcome would then be recorded as a pair of numbers so that, for example, the pair (27,3) would mean: "age 27, eye color green."

Random experiments whose outcomes are real numbers, or pairs of real numbers, or triples of real numbers or, generally, n-tuples of real numbers, are called *random variables* or, more specifically, one-dimensional random variables, two-dimensional random variables, three-dimensional random variables, and, generally, n-dimensional random variables. As was already mentioned, all random experiments occurring in practical applications can be coded in real numbers, so that practically, without loss of generality, we may limit ourselves to the study of random variables.

Since the possible outcomes of an n-dimensional random variable are n-tuples of real numbers, each such possible outcome may be represented by a point in n-dimensional Euclidean space R_n; hence, the outcome space for an n-dimensional random variable is a set of points in R_n. This geometric representation will be illustrated in the examples of the next section.

1.5   Examples

1.5.1. The random experiment consisting of tossing a coin has the outcome space composed of two outcomes, heads and tails. If these outcomes are coded in num-bers so that 1 stands for heads and 0 for tails, then the outcome space can be represented by the set consisting of the points $x_1 = 0$ and $x_2 = 1$ on the real number line R_1 (Fig. 1.5.1).

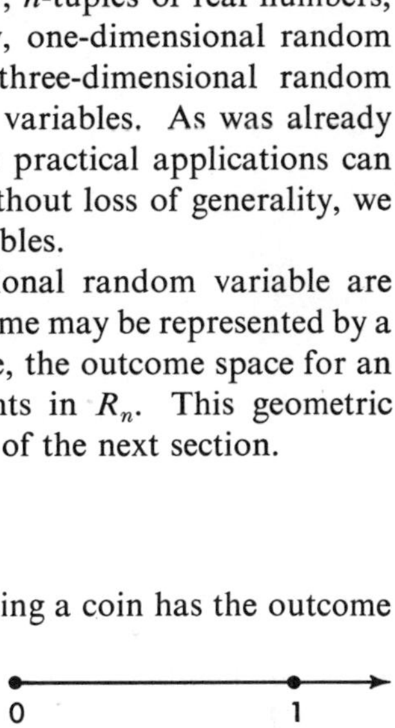

Fig. 1.5.1

1.5.2. The possible outcomes of the two-dimensional random variable defined by rolling a white and a black die and reading off the number U of points on the white die, and the number V of points on the black die are represented by the 36 points in the (U,V) plane indicated in Fig. 1.5.2. The set of these 36 points represents the outcome space for the random variable (U,V).

1.5.3. Bolts are manufactured on a machine set to produce them with a diameter of $\frac{3}{8}$ inch. On account of unavoidable inaccuracies in the manu-facturing process, the bolts produced vary in thickness. Every bolt goes through an inspection process and it is rejected if its diameter differs from $\frac{3}{8}$ inch by more than $\frac{1}{100}$ inch. The bolts which pass inspection are packaged and sold. Let D be the diameter of a bolt selected at random from a package; it is a one-dimensional random variable. Knowing the production and inspection process, we conclude that the outcome space for D is represented by the

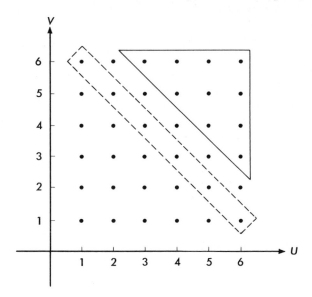

Fig. 1.5.2

set of all points on the real number line whose coordinates D satisfy the inequalities

$$\tfrac{3}{8} - \tfrac{1}{100} = 0.365 \leq D \leq \tfrac{3}{8} + \tfrac{1}{100} = 0.385$$

hence by a line segment described by these inequalities.

1.5.4.   A dart thrown at a circular target of radius 1 foot with the aim of hitting the center determines the polar coordinates R, Φ of the point actually hit, and (R,Φ) is a two-dimensional random variable. If we agree to disregard entirely the outcomes with $R > 1$, i.e., those throws in which the dart fell outside of the target, then all possible outcomes are represented by those points of the Cartesian plane with the coordinates R, Φ, for which $0 \leq R \leq 1$ and $0 \leq \Phi \leq 2\pi$. The circle described by these inequalities represents the outcome space of the random variable (R,Φ).

1.5.5.   A random variable X is defined by the following rule. A coin is tossed repeatedly until heads appears for the first time. If this happens in the first throw, we put $X = 0$; if it happens in the nth throw with $n > 1$, we put $X = n - 1$; in other words X is the number of throws preceding the first heads. Any non-negative integer is a possible outcome for X, and the outcome space is the set of all non-negative integers and can be represented by the sequence of points with the coordinates $0, 1, 2, 3, \cdots$ on the real number line.

1.6 Events

If X is a random experiment, and S_X the outcome space for X, it often is of interest to study different subsets of S_X. For example, in discussing the random variable of 1.5.2 one may pay special attention to the subset of the outcome space consisting of those six points for which $U + V = 7$, or to the subset consisting of the one point $U = 1$, $V = 1$.

We agree to call any subset of the outcome space for a random experiment an *event* for that random experiment.

It should be pointed out that this definition is a generalization of what is understood by an event in everyday language. For example, in the outcome space for the random experiment of 1.5.4, the subset defined by $\{R, \Phi: R < \frac{1}{10}\}$ may be described in words as "the dart hits the target within $\frac{1}{10}$ foot of the center," which would be an event in the colloquial use of the word. But the subset of the outcome space defined by $\{R, \Phi: R = \text{irrational number}\}$ has little intuitive meaning and would hardly be called an event by anybody interested in dart throwing, although it is an event according to our definition.

If E is an event for a random experiment X, one says that E *occurred* if the observed outcome of X is an element of the set E, and that *non-E* (in symbols $\bar{E}$) occurred if the observed outcome is not an element of E. One also refers to any outcome contained in E as an outcome *favorable* to the event E, and to any outcome not contained in E as *unfavorable* to E (or favorable to $\bar{E}$).

1.7 Probabilities

If one is familiar with a certain random experiment, he may form an opinion that some events for this experiment are more likely to occur than some others, or that some events are extremely unlikely to occur at all, and he will say this by using such phrases as "event A is more probable than event B," or "event C is highly improbable." Some random experiments have been studied and are known so well that it is possible to be more specific and to ascribe to certain events numbers which indicate an estimate of how likely it is that these events occur. These numbers ascribed to events for a random experiment are called *probabilities*. They are customarily chosen between 0 and 1 in such a manner that, if one event is considered less likely than another, the first is assigned a smaller probability than the second; that an event whose occurrence is considered practically impossible is given the probability 0; and that an event which is considered practically certain to occur has probability 1. Further requirements which probabilities must satisfy will be discussed in Chapter 2.

There are two main ways by which probabilities are ascribed to events: (a) by using accumulated experience and (b) by mathematical argument.

The phenomena which we agreed to call random experiments have, in addition to the property that the outcome of each repetition cannot be predicted beforehand, another important property which may best be illustrated by examples.

When a coin is tossed n times, and heads are obtained n_H times, the ratio $f_n(H) = n_H/n$ is called the relative frequency of heads in n throws. It has been found by many repetitions of the experiment that, although the outcome of a single throw of a coin cannot be predicted, one can be practically sure that for large n the relative frequency $f_n(H)$ will be close to a constant value which, for a symmetrical coin, is $\frac{1}{2}$. Similarly, when a mass production process for an electronic tube is well established and stable from the point of view of quality control (which may be a practical problem of considerable difficulty), the number of those tubes which have a life length of less than, say, 250 hours will in the long run be a practically constant fraction of the total number of tubes produced.

In general, if A is an event for a random experiment, and if that experiment is repeated n times and A is observed in n_A of these n repetitions, then the *relative frequency* of the event A, defined by

(1.7.1)
$$f_n(A) = n_A/n$$

approaches for large n some constant value $p(A)$. Since $0 \le n_A \le n$, hence $0 \le f_n(A) \le 1$, we have $0 \le p(A) \le 1$. This behavior of relative frequencies has been observed in many sequences of repetitions of random experiments, and is the empirical basis of a procedure for ascribing probabilities to events according to the following *frequency limit principle:* If in a large number n of repetitions of a random experiment the relative frequencies $f_n(A)$ of an event A approach a number $p(A)$, then this number is ascribed to A as its probability.

There are other ways of utilizing accumulated experience to assign probabilities to events. For example, if it is known that a mass-produced component of a mechanism has probability r of failing when first put to use, and this component is replaced by a similar component made of stronger material, then it is reasonable to assume that these new components have a probability r' of failure such that $r' < r$. Many rules of thumb are in use for assigning probabilities empirically, but the frequency limit principle is the most fundamental.

Once probabilities for some events are assumed to be known, from experience or otherwise, it often is possible to obtain probabilities of other events by mathematical argument. For example, if the probability of an event A is known to be p, one can conclude that the probability of the event $\bar{A}$ is $1 - p$, and this can be done without further reference to experience. Similarly, knowing for each component of a mechanism the probability that it will fail makes it possible under certain additional assumptions to compute the probability that the entire mechanism will perform (not fail), by using only mathematical reasoning and without further empirical evidence.

The situation described here for the calculus of probabilities is well known in other fields of applied mathematics, such as geometry or mechanics. There, too, certain quantities are determined by empirical means, while certain other quantities can be found from those already known by mathematical argument. For example, the area of a triangle can be computed by formula if base and height are known (either by direct measurement or from a preceding computation). Similarly, the trajectory of a projectile can be computed by theoretical means, if the initial position and velocity are given and some additional information is available on the gravitation field, air currents, etc. These initial conditions and additional information, in turn, may be obtained empirically (e.g., initial position and velocity can be preset by the experimenter) or else may be obtained by applying theoretical reasoning to some other quantities which are given. In fact, geometry, mechanics, and other branches of applied mathematics are principally concerned with the mathematical relationships between various quantities and objects, showing how some of them are determined by others. Similarly, the main object of the calculus of probabilities is to derive relationships between probabilities of various events. All its theorems can be reduced to the logical scheme: If the probabilities of certain events for the random experiments $X_1, X_2, \cdots$ are given, and if the random experiment Y is connected with $X_1, X_2, \cdots$ in a given manner, then the probabilities of certain events for Y are such and such. A theorem of this structure holds true regardless of whether the probabilities given were estimated from experience or were themselves computed from other probabilities by using some similar theorems. The conclusions obtained by correctly applying such a theorem may still be found sometimes not to agree with experiment and observation. The reasons for such disagreement may be manifold: the probabilities assumed as given may have been incorrectly estimated, or the relationships between the events considered may be different than assumed, or the occurrences studied may not be random. These sources of possible discrepancies between observation and conclusions based on mathematical theory are again quite analogous to what may happen in specific applications of geometry or mechanics. If, for example, a projectile follows a path which differs substantially from the theoretically computed trajectory, one will suspect errors such as actual initial velocity or position different than assumed, presence of factors not considered in the theory such as friction or aircurrents. In using any branch of applied mathematics it is therefore a matter of commonsense, good judgment, and experience, not of mathematics, to decide whether an empirical situation is such that a certain mathematical theory may be applied.

The next chapter will contain an introduction to the mathematical theory of probabilities. It will deal with such concepts as outcome space, events, and probabilities as mathematical entities, will describe relationships between them and formulate properties that these relationships are assumed to have, and will form the foundation of the mathematical theory that will be developed throughout Part I of this book and will also be amply used in Part II. Whenever this mathematical theory is applied to a problem in the empirical world, one will have to establish a correspondence between some experimental outcomes and the elements of an abstract mathematical outcome space, some empirical events and some subsets of the outcome space, etc., so that it may be reasonably assumed that the relationships between the mathematical entities and their empirical counterparts parallel each other. If this is the case, then mathematical derivations will lead to conclusions which may have practically meaningful counterparts in the empirical world.

EXERCISES

1.1. The distribution of ages (at last birthday) of students in a class is given in the following table:

Age	Frequency
18	6
19	8
20	11
21	7
22	6
23	5
24	5

Five students are selected at random, and the arithmetic mean $\bar{X}$ of their ages is computed. Plot the set of possible values of $\bar{X}$.

1.2. A die is rolled and the number P of points is recorded. Then a needle is dropped on a board of width $\frac{1}{2}$ inch, and the distance D of the needle point from the left-hand edge of the board is measured. Consider the two-dimensional random variable (P, D) and plot the set of its possible values by using 1 inch for the unit on the P axis. Then consider the one-dimensional random variable $S = P + D$ and plot the set of its possible values.

1.3. From the class of Exercise 1.1 two students are selected in succession, and the age of the first is called X, the age of the second Y. Plot the set of possible values of the two-dimensional random variable (X, Y). Indicate (by circling with closed curves) the sets representing the following events:

E_1, both are of equal age,

E_2, the second is older than the first,

E_3, the second is at least two years older than the first,

E_4, the second is not older than the first,

E_5, the average age of the two is not more than 20,

E_6, the second is five years younger than the first.

1.4. The vertical lines $x = 0$, $x = d$, $x = 2d, \cdots, x = kd$ are drawn in the (x,y) plane. A very thin needle of length $l < d$ is thrown at random on the (x,y) plane. Only those throws are recorded in which some point of the needle falls on the vertical strip $0 \leq x \leq kd$. The position of the needle is described by giving X as the abscissa of the midpoint of the needle and θ as the slope angle. We consider the random variable (X,θ). In the (X,θ) plane, plot the set of all its possible values and the set representing the event E: {The needle intersects one of the vertical lines}.

1.5. In the random experiment of Exercise 1.4 the position of the needle is described by giving X_1 as the abscissa of that end which has the smaller ordinate and X_2 as the abscissa of the end with the larger ordinate; if both ends have the same ordinate, X_1 shall be the smaller and X_2 the larger abscissa. Consider the random variable (X_1, X_2), plot the set of all possible values and the set representing the event E of Exercise 1.4.

CHAPTER 2

Formal Approach to the Calculus of Probabilities

2.1 Outcome Space. Borel Field of Events

Following an approach due to Kolmogorov* the theory of probability will be formally developed from a set of axioms. As in all axiomatic systems, we shall deal with certain undefined objects. These objects will be called *outcomes* of a random experiment and will be denoted by small letters such as x, y, x_i, y_j, z_{ik}. We consider the set S of all outcomes and call it the *outcome space*. An outcome space may contain a finite number of outcomes, or it may be countably infinite, or non-countably infinite, and we shall have occasion to consider examples of each kind.

We assume that a family $\mathscr{B}$ of certain subsets of S is given which will be called *events*, and that this family satisfies the following axioms:

B_1. The outcome space and the empty set are in $\mathscr{B}$:

$$S \in \mathscr{B}, \qquad \theta \in \mathscr{B}$$

B_2. If each set of the finite or countable sequence $A_1, A_2, \cdots, A_j, \cdots$ is in $\mathscr{B}$, then their union and their intersection is in $\mathscr{B}$:

$$A_i \in \mathscr{B} \text{ for } i = 1, 2, \cdots \rightarrow \bigcup_{(i)} A_i \in \mathscr{B}$$

$$A_i \in \mathscr{B} \text{ for } i = 1, 2, \cdots \rightarrow \bigcap_{(i)} A_i \in \mathscr{B}$$

B_3. If a set A is in $\mathscr{B}$ then its complement is in $\mathscr{B}$:

$$A \in \mathscr{B} \rightarrow \bar{A} = S - A \in \mathscr{B}$$

---

* A. N. Kolmogorov, *Foundations of the Theory of Probability*, 2nd English edition, Chelsea Publishing Company, New York, 1956.

A family of subsets of a set S which satisfies axioms B_1, B_2, B_3 is called a *Borel field* on S. Our assumptions on the family $\mathscr{B}$ of events may therefore be summarized by saying that $\mathscr{B}$ is a Borel field on the outcome space S.

It is customary to refer to S as the *certain event*, to θ as the *impossible event*, and to $\bar{A}$ as the *event non-A*.

Events A and B are called *disjoint* or *mutually exclusive*, if the subsets A and B of $\mathscr{B}$ have no elements in common, that is, if $A \cap B = \theta$. A sequence (finite or countable) of events A_1, A_2, $\cdots$, A_j, $\cdots$ is said to consist of disjoint events, if every pair of its events is disjoint.

For any two events A, B, the event $A \cup B$ will be sometimes called *event A or B*, and the event $A \cap B$ *event A and B*.

2.2 Probability Measure for a Borel Field

For a given outcome space S and Borel field $\mathscr{B}$, we consider a set function $P(A)$ on $\mathscr{B}$, that is, a rule which ascribes to every $A \in \mathscr{B}$ a real number $P(A)$. This set function shall be called a *probability measure* on $\mathscr{B}$ if it satisfies the following axioms:

P_1. For every A in $\mathscr{B}$ its value is a non-negative real number:

$$P(A) \geq 0 \text{ for } A \in \mathscr{B}$$

P_2. $P(S) = 1$

P_3. If $A_1, A_2, \cdots, A_j, \cdots$ is a finite or countable sequence of mutually exclusive events, then

$$P \left(\bigcup_{(j)} A_j \right) = \sum_{(j)} P(A_j)$$

For $A \in \mathscr{B}$, the number $P(A)$ will be called the *probability of the event A*.

2.2.1. Theorem. For any event A we have

(2.2.1.1.) $$P(A) + P(\bar{A}) = 1$$

Proof. Since A and $\bar{A}$ are mutually exclusive and $A \cup \bar{A} = S$, it follows from P_3 that $P(S) = P(A) + P(\bar{A})$ and from P_2 that $1 = P(A) + P(\bar{A})$.

From 2.2.1.1. and P_1 it follows immediately

(2.2.1.2) $$0 \leq P(A) \leq 1 \text{ for any event } A$$

2.2.2.1. Theorem. The probability of the impossible event θ is zero:

(2.2.2.1) $$P(\theta) = 0$$

Proof. The events S and θ are mutually exclusive and $S \cup \theta = S$, hence (2.2.1.1) yields $P(S) + P(\theta) = P(S)$, and $P(\theta) = 0$.

2.2.3. Theorem.   For any two events A, B (disjoint or not) we have

(2.2.3.1) $P(A \cup B) = P(A) + P(B) - P(A \cap B)$

Proof. We have

$$A \cup B = A \cup (B - A \cap B)$$

Since A and $B - A \cap B$ are disjoint, one obtains by P_3

$$P(A \cup B) = P(A) + P(B - A \cap B)$$

Furthermore,

$$B = A \cap B \cup (B - A \cap B)$$

and $A \cap B$, $B - A \cap B$ being disjoint,

$$P(B) = P(A \cap B) + P(B - A \cap B)$$

hence

$$P(B - A \cap B) = P(B) - P(A \cap B)$$

so that

$$P(A \cup B) = P(A) + P(B) - P(A \cap B)$$

An immediate consequence is the useful inequality

(2.2.3.2) $P(A \cup B) \le P(A) + P(B)$

which clearly becomes an equality if and only if $P(A \cap B) = 0$. This inequality can be generalized to the following statement known as *Boole's inequality*.

For any finite sequence of events $A_1, A_2, \cdots, A_n$ one has

(2.2.3.3) $P(A_1 \cup A_2 \cup \cdots \cup A_n) \le P(A_1) + P(A_2) + \cdots + P(A_n)$

Proof. For $n = 2$, we have (2.2.3.2.) For proof by induction we assume (2.2.3.3) true and by using (2.2.3.2) we obtain

$$P(A_1 \cup A_2 \cup \cdots \cup A_n \cup A_{n+1}) = P([A_1 \cup A_2 \cup \cdots \cup A_n] \cup A_{n+1})$$

$$\le P(A_1 \cup A_2 \cup \cdots \cup A_n) + P(A_{n+1}) \le P(A_1) + P(A_2) + \cdots$$

$$+ P(A_n) + P(A_{n+1})$$

2.3 Probability Distributions

When a random experiment is studied, one would like to know the set of all its possible outcomes (outcome space), the subsets of this set to which probabilities are assigned (events) and, finally, the probabilities assigned to these subsets. In our formal presentation this may be stated as follows: A probability distribution is a triple $(S, \mathscr{B}, P)$, where S is an outcome space, $\mathscr{B}$ a Borel field on S, and P a probability measure on $\mathscr{B}$.

In order to know a probability distribution, each of its three components S, $\mathscr{B}$, and P must be given. This may clearly offer considerable difficulties, especially in cases where $\mathscr{B}$ is a family of infinitely many events and a complete listing of events and their probabilities is not possible. We shall see how this can be done in various special classes of probability distributions.

2.4   Discrete Probability Distributions

2.4.1. Definition. A probability distribution $(S,\mathscr{B},P)$ is called *discrete* when its outcome space S is a finite or countable set, and $\mathscr{B}$ contains all single outcome sets.

According to this definition, all outcomes in S for a discrete probability distribution can be arranged into a finite or countable sequence

$$x_1, x_2, x_3, \cdots, x_j, \cdots$$

The Borel field $\mathscr{B}$ must contain all sets $\{x_1\}, \{x_2\}, \{x_3\}, \cdots, \{x_i\}, \cdots$, each containing one outcome. By taking unions of any finite or countable sequence of these single outcome sets we obtain by axiom B_2 events in $\mathscr{B}$, and since this procedure yields all possible subsets of S, $\mathscr{B}$ contains all possible subsets of S.

To determine the probability measure P on $\mathscr{B}$, it is enough to give $P(\{x_1\})$, $P(\{x_2\})$, $P(\{x_3\})$, $\cdots$, $P(\{x_j\})$, that is, the probabilities of all single outcome events. For, as noted above, every event in $\mathscr{B}$ is of the form

$$A = \{x_{j_1}, x_{j_2}, \cdots, x_{j_i}, \cdots\} = \bigcup_{(1)} \{x_{j_i}\}$$

hence by axiom P_3 we have

(2.4.1.1)
$$P(A) = \sum_{(i)} P(\{x_{j_i}\})$$

We denote the probabilities of single outcome events by

(2.4.1.2)
$$P(\{x_j\}) = p_j, \quad j = 1, 2, 3, \cdots$$

so that (2.4.1.1) may be written

(2.4.1.3)
$$P(\{x_{j_1}, x_{j_2}, \cdots, x_{j_i}, \cdots\}) = \sum_{(i)} p_{j_i}$$

The probabilities p_j must have the two arithmetic properties:

(i) $p_j \geq 0$ for $j = 1 \ 2, \cdots$

(ii) $\sum_{(j)} p_j = 1$ (summation over all outcomes in S)

which are immediate consequences of axioms P_1 and P_2.

2.4.2. Laplace Distributions. We have seen that a discrete probability distribution is completely determined whenever the sequence of probabilities

(2.4.1.2) is given. The numbers p_j, for $j = 1, 2, \cdots$ need not be equal, since it is easy to design random experiments for which the different single outcomes are not equally probable, e.g., in rolling a die with one corner chipped off one would not expect all six faces to have the same probabilities. It is possible, however, and happens in many practical applications that in a discrete probability distribution all single outcomes have equal probabilities, that is,

(2.4.2.1) $$p_1 = p_2 = p_3 = \cdots = p_j = \cdots$$

Discrete distributions for which (2.4.2.1) holds are of great historical and practical importance. We will call them *Laplace distributions.*

It is easily seen that for a Laplace distribution the outcome space S must be finite. For, if the common value of all the p_j in (2.4.2.1) is denoted by p, we have, according to (ii) of the preceding section,

$$\sum_{(j)} p_j = \sum_{(j)} p = 1$$

This shows that $p > 0$ and that there are $1/p$, hence a finite number, of outcomes in S.

2.4.3. Theorem.   If there are m possible outcomes for a Laplace distribution, and if l of them are favorable to an event A, then $P(A) = l/m$.
   Proof.   From

$$p_1 = p_2 = \cdots = p_m = p \quad \text{and} \quad \sum_{j=1}^{m} p_j = mp = 1$$

follows

$$p_1 = p_2 = \cdots = p_m = 1/m$$

and from

$$A = \{x_{j_1}, x_{j_2}, \cdots, x_{j_l}\}$$

one obtains

$$P(A) = \sum_{i=1}^{l} P(\{x_{j_i}\}) = l \cdot \frac{1}{m}$$

Laplace* used the statement contained in Theorem 2.4.3 as the definition of probability and based on it his presentation of the theory of probabilities. His definition was: If a random experiment has m "equally likely elementary outcomes" and if l of them are favorable to an event, then the probability of this event is equal to l/m. This definition has been recognized as being too narrow, since it can be applied only to experiments for which either all outcomes may be reasonably assumed to be equally likely, or at least all outcomes can be decomposed into some "elementary outcomes" which are equally likely. This assumption is far from plausible for some quite simple random

---

* P. S. de Laplace, "*Essai Philosophique sur les Probabilités,*" 5th edition, Bachelier, Paris, 1825, p. 12.

experiments. Already in the case of a die with a chipped-off corner it would be difficult to indicate a decomposition of the outcomes into equally likely elementary outcomes. It may be still more difficult to perform this decomposition, even as an intellectual exercise, in the kind of random experiment performed by life insurance companies as part of their business which consists in, say, a man of age 43 surviving or not surviving until age 44. Nevertheless, if a discrete distribution can be assumed to be a Laplace distribution, Theorem 2.4.3 makes the computation of various probabilities very simple.

2.4.4. Example. Consider an urn containing w white, b black and r red balls which differ only in color and are practically undistinguishable by shape, weight, smoothness, etc. Let an experiment consist in drawing one ball at random. The outcome space contains as many different outcomes as there are individual balls, that is $k = w + b + r$. If we assume that all balls are equally probable then by Theorem 2.4.3 we immediately find for the probabilities P_w of the event "white ball drawn," P_b of "black ball drawn," and P_r of "red ball drawn" the values

$$P_w = \frac{w}{w + b + r}, \qquad P_b = \frac{b}{w + b + r}, \qquad P_r = \frac{r}{w + b + r}$$

It may be noted that these values are not justified if some of the balls are larger or heavier than the rest, since then it would be unrealistic to assume that we are dealing with a Laplace distribution.

2.4.5. Example. We wish to compute the probability that the total number of points obtained by rolling two dice is 7. If, as in 1.5.2, we consider the outcome space of this experiment consisting of 36 outcomes, and assume that all these outcomes are equally probable, then the event "total = 7," indicated in Fig. 1.5.2 by a broken line, consists of the six outcomes (1,6), (2,5), (3,4), (4,3), (5,2), (6,1), hence by Theorem 2.4.3 we obtain

$$P \text{ (total} = 7) = \tfrac{6}{36} = \tfrac{1}{6}$$

2.5 Continuous Probability Distributions

2.5.1. Some Preliminary Concepts and Notations. Let R_n denote the n-dimensional Euclidean space. A point in R_n is an n-tuple of coordinates $(x_1, x_2, \cdots, x_n)$, and we will use the abbreviated notation

$$(x_1, x_2, \cdots, x_n) = \mathbf{x}$$

In R_1 (line) any set defined by $a \leq x \leq b$ where a, b are finite real numbers is called a *closed interval*, a set defined by $a < x \leq b$ where a is finite or $-\infty$ and b is finite or by $a \leq x < b$ where a is finite and b finite or $+\infty$ a *half-open interval,* and a set defined by $a < x < b$ where a is finite or $-\infty$ and b finite or $+\infty$ an *open interval.* Similarly, in R_2 (plane) sets of the form $a \le x_1 \le b$, $c \le x_2 \le d$ are called *closed rectangles,* sets of the form $a < x_1 < b$, $c < x_2 < d$ *open rectangles,* and sets defined by $a \le x_1 < b, c \le x_2 \le d$ or $a \le x_1 < b, c \le x_2 \le d$, or $a \le x_1 < b, a \le x_2 < d$, or by any other such two inequalities with at least one equality sign and at least one strict inequality sign *half-open rectangles.* In general, for any number of dimensions $n \ge 1$, sets defined by $a_1 \le x_1 \le b_1, a_2 \le x_2 \le b_2, \cdots, a_n \le x_n \le b_n$ will be called *closed n-dimensional intervals,* sets defined by $a_1 < x_1 < b_1, a_2 < x_2 < b_2, \cdots,$ $a_n < x_n < b_n$ *open n-dimensional intervals,* and sets defined by similar inequalities containing at least one equality sign and at least one strict inequality *half-open n-dimensional intervals.*

In particular in R_1 the half-open intervals $a \le x < +\infty, -\infty < x \le b$, and the open intervals $a < x < +\infty, -\infty < x < b$ are often considered and are called *half lines.* In R_2 one considers *half planes* $a \le x < +\infty$, $-\infty < y < +\infty$; or $-\infty < x < +\infty, -\infty < y \le b$, etc.; quadrants $a < x < +\infty, b < y < +\infty$, etc. And in R_n are the many different *unbounded intervals* such as

$$a_1 \le x_1 < +\infty, \qquad a_2 \le x_2 < +\infty, \cdots, \qquad -\infty < x_n < b_n$$

2.5.2. Definition. A probability distribution $(S, \mathscr{B}, P)$ is called *continuous* when S is a Euclidean space R_n, $\mathscr{B}$ a Borel field containing all open and closed intervals in R_n, and P is defined as follows.

A function

$$f(x_1, x_2, \cdots, x_n) = f(\mathbf{x})$$

is given which has the properties:

C_1. $f(x) \ge 0$ for all $\mathbf{x} \in R_n$

C_2. $\displaystyle\int_A f(\mathbf{x})dx$ exists for every $A \in \mathscr{B}$

C_3. $\displaystyle\int_{R_n} f(\mathbf{x})dx = 1$

and the probability measure P is defined as

(2.5.2.1) $P(A) = \displaystyle\int_A f(\mathbf{x})dx$ for every $A \in \mathscr{B}$

A function f which satisfies C_1, C_2, C_3 is called a *probability density.* The integrals in C_2, C_3, (2.5.2.1), are *n*-dimensional integrals, and dx denotes the *n*-dimensional volume element.

By using known properties of the definite integral, one verifies that if f is a probability density, then $P(A)$ defined by (2.5.2.1) satisfies the axioms P_1, P_2,

P_3. For P_1 follows from C_1 and C_2, P_2 from C_3, and P_3 is equivalent with the property of the integral that for disjoint sets $A_1, A_2, \cdots A_j, \cdots$ one has

$$\int_{\underset{(j)}{\cup A_j}} f(\mathbf{x})d\mathbf{x} = \sum_{(j)} \int_{A_j} f(\mathbf{x})d\mathbf{x}$$

A continuous probability distribution is therefore completely determined when the number of dimensions n and the probability density $f(\mathbf{x})$ are given.

2.5.3. Remarks.   It can be shown, although we shall not attempt the proof, that the Borel field $\mathscr{B}$ in R_n which contains all open and closed intervals contains also all elementary geometric regions, such as interiors of closed polygons and curves in the plane and solids in R_3, with their boundaries included or excluded, so that (2.5.2.1) ascribes a probability to any such elementary geometric region. Furthermore, every bounded set $A \in \mathscr{B}$ has a volume $V(A)$ which for all elementary geometric regions is equal to the usual volume of those regions.

One can also show that (2.5.2.1) assigns probability 0 to any geometric region which has n-dimensional volume equal to zero. In particular, no matter what the probability density $f(\mathbf{x})$, probability zero will be assigned to single points or finite sets of points in R_1, to arcs of curves or polygons in R_2, to two-dimensional surfaces or pieces of such surfaces in R_3, etc.

Any function $g(\mathbf{x})$ on R_n which has the properties C_1 and C_2 and such that

(2.5.3.1)
$$I = \int_{R_n} g(\mathbf{x})d\mathbf{x} \neq 0$$

may be used to obtain a probability density in the form

$$f(\mathbf{x}) = Kg(\mathbf{x})$$

For it follows from C_1 and (2.5.3.1) that $I > 0$, hence writing $K = 1/I$ we have

$$f(\mathbf{x}) = (1/I)g(\mathbf{x}) = Kg(\mathbf{x}) \geq 0 \text{ for all } \mathbf{x}$$

From C_2 follows that

$$\int_A f(\mathbf{x})d\mathbf{x} = K \int_A g(\mathbf{x})d\mathbf{x} \text{ exists for all } A \in \mathscr{B}$$

and

$$\int_{R_n} f(\mathbf{x})d\mathbf{x} = \frac{1}{I} \int_{R_n} g(\mathbf{x})d\mathbf{x} = 1$$

so that $f(\mathbf{x})$ satisfies C_1, C_2, and C_3. The constant $K = 1/I$ is called the *normalizing constant*.

2.5.4. Example (Uniform Distributions). Let D be any region in R_n with finite positive volume

$$0 < V(D) = V < +\infty$$

The function

$$g(x) = \begin{cases} 1 & \text{for} \quad x \in D \\ 0 & \text{for} \quad x \in \bar{D} \end{cases}$$

clearly has property C_1. It also satisfies (2.5.3.1) since

$$\int_{R_n} g(x)dx = \int_D 1dx = V$$

and for any set $A \in \mathscr{B}$ we have

$$\int_A g(x)dx = \int_{A \cap D} g(x)dx + \int_{A \cap \bar{D}} g(x)dx = \int_{A \cap D} 1dx = V(A \cap D)$$

which is finite since it is $\leq V(D)$. By using the normalizing constant $K = 1/V$ we obtain the probability density

(2.5.4.1)
$$f(x) = \begin{cases} 1/V(D) & \text{for} \quad x \in D \\ 0 & \text{for} \quad x \in \bar{D} \end{cases}$$

The continuous probability distribution on R_n with the probability density (2.5.4.1) is known as the *uniform distribution on D.*

Let us consider simple one- and two-dimensional uniform distributions.

If $n = 1$ and D is the interval $[a, a + l]$ on the x line, then $V(D) = l$ and the uniform distribution on $[a, a + l]$ has the probability density

(2.5.4.2)
$$f(x) = \begin{cases} 1/l & \text{for} \quad a \leq x \leq a + l \\ 0 & \text{elsewhere} \end{cases}$$

If $n = 2$ and D is the square in the (x, y) plane defined by the conditions

$$D: |x| + |y| \leq 1$$

then $V(D) = 2$ and the uniform probability density on D is

(2.5.4.3)
$$f(x,y) = \begin{cases} \frac{1}{2} & \text{for} \quad |x| + |y| \leq 1 \\ 0 & \text{elsewhere} \end{cases}$$

2.5.4.4. Theorem. Let D be a region with finite positive volume in R_n and P the probability measure of the uniform probability distribution on D. Then for any set $A \in \mathscr{B}$ we have

(2.5.4.4.1)
$$P(A) = \frac{V(A \cap D)}{V(D)}$$

Proof. We have by (2.5.4.1)

$$P(A) = \int_A f(\mathbf{x})d\mathbf{x} = \int_{A \cap D} \frac{1}{V(D)} d\mathbf{x} + \int_{A \cap \bar{D}} 0 d\mathbf{x} = \frac{V(A \cap D)}{V(D)}$$

This theorem points out that the uniform probability distributions correspond, in the family of continuous distributions, to the Laplace distributions among discrete probability distributions.

2.5.5. Example   (Normal Probability Distribution).   We consider the function

(2.5.5.1)
$$g(x) = e^{-(x-a)^2/2\sigma^2}$$

of $x \in R_1$, where a is a given real number and σ^2 a given positive real number. Clearly

$$0 < g(x) < 1 \quad \text{for all real } x$$

hence $g(x)$ satisfies C_1, and

$$\int_A g(x)dx \leq \int_{-\infty}^{+\infty} g(x)dx \quad \text{for } A \in \mathscr{B}$$

so that C_2 is satisfied if we can show that $\int_{-\infty}^{+\infty} g(x)dx$ exists. To see this we first evaluate the special definite integral

$$I = \int_{-\infty}^{+\infty} e^{-u^2} du$$

We observe that

$$I^2 = \int_{-\infty}^{+\infty} e^{-u^2} du \int_{-\infty}^{+\infty} e^{-v^2} dv = \int_{-\infty}^{+\infty} \int_{-\infty}^{+\infty} e^{-(u^2+v^2)} du dv$$

and changing to polar coordinates obtain

$$I^2 = \int_{\theta=0}^{2\pi} \int_{r=0}^{\infty} e^{-r^2} r \, dr \, d\theta = \int_{\theta=0}^{2\pi} \left(-\tfrac{1}{2} e^{-r^2} \Big|_{r=0}^{\infty} \right) d\theta = \int_0^{2\pi} \tfrac{1}{2} d\theta = \pi$$

hence

(2.5.5.2)
$$\int_{-\infty}^{+\infty} e^{-u^2} du = \sqrt{\pi}$$

We compute the normalizing constant for $g(x)$

$$\int_{-\infty}^{+\infty} g(x)dx = \int_{-\infty}^{+\infty} e^{-(x-a)^2/2\sigma^2} \, dx = \sigma\sqrt{2} \int_{-\infty}^{+\infty} e^{-u^2} du = \sigma\sqrt{2\pi}$$

and obtain the probability density

(2.5.5.3)
$$\varphi(x) = \frac{1}{\sigma\sqrt{2\pi}} e^{-(x-a)^2/2\sigma^2}$$

The continuous probability distribution on R_1 with a probability density of the form (2.5.5.3) is called a *normal probability distribution* or, more specifically a one-dimensional normal, or a univariate normal distribution. The probability density depends on two constants, a and σ^2, and to reflect this dependence, we shall sometimes use the notation

(2.5.5.4)
$$\varphi(x;a,\sigma^2) = \frac{1}{\sigma\sqrt{2\pi}} e^{(x-a)^2/2\sigma^2}$$

2.5.6. Cumulative Distribution Functions.   Let X be a one-dimensional random variable, i.e., a random experiment whose outcomes are real numbers, so that its outcome space can be represented by a set S of points on the real line R_1.

2.5.6.1. Definition.   For a one-dimensional random variable X the function

(2.5.6.1)
$$F(s) = P(\{x: x \le s\}) = P(x \le s)$$

is called the cumulative distribution function of X, or more concisely the distribution function (d.f.) of X.

According to this definition, $F(s)$ is the probability of the event "the random variable X assumes a value less than or equal to s."

2.5.6.2. Theorem.   If X is a discrete one-dimensional random variable with the outcome space

$$S: x_1, x_2, \cdots, x_j, \cdots$$

and the corresponding probabilities $p_j = f(x_j), j = 1, 2, \cdots$, then:

(a) The d.f. is
$$F(s) = \sum_{x_j \le s} p_j, \quad \text{for all real } s$$

(b) $F(s)$ is a non-decreasing function of s, continuous from the right.
(c) The only points of discontinuity of $F(s)$ are the points $s = x_j, j = 1, 2, \cdots$, and at these points we have
$$F(x_j + 0) - F(x_j - 0) = F(x_j) - F(x_j - 0) = p_j$$

(d)
$$\lim_{s \to -\infty} F(s) = 0, \quad \lim_{s \to +\infty} F(s) = 1.$$

Proof.   (a) follows immediately from (2.5.6.1.1) and (2.4.1.1), and from (a) follows that $F(s)$ is non-decreasing.   We observe that for any $h > 0$
$$F(s + h) = P(x \le s + h)$$
$$= P(x \le s) + P(s < x \le s + h)$$
$$= F(s) + \sum_{s < x_j \le s+h} p_j$$

hence

(2.5.6.2.1) $F(s + 0) = \lim_{0 < h \to 0} F(s + h) = F(s) + \lim_{0 < h \to 0} \sum_{s < x_j \le s+h} p_j$

$\qquad\qquad = F(s),$

which shows that $F(s)$ is right-continuous. Similarly, for $h > 0$

$$F(s - h) = P(x \le s - h)$$
$$= P(x \le s) - P(s - h < x \le s)$$
$$= F(s) - \sum_{s-h < x_j \le s} p_j$$

hence

(2.5.6.2.2) $F(s - 0) = \lim_{0 < h \to 0} F(s - h) = F(s) - P(x = s)$

Subtracting (2.5.6.2.2) from (2.5.6.2.1) one obtains

$$F(s + 0) - F(s - 0) = P(x = s)$$

When s is one of the possible outcomes, $s = x_j$, then this becomes

$$F(x_j + 0) - F(x_j - 0) = P(x = x_j) = p_j$$

while for any other values of s we have $P(x = s) = 0$ and conclude that $F(s + 0) = F(s - 0)$, hence s is a point of continuity for F.

The limits in (d) follow directly from (a).

We observed in 2.4.1 that a discrete probability distribution is determined when the probabilities $p_1, p_2, \cdots, p_j, \cdots$ are given. We see now that the probability distribution of a discrete one-dimensional random variable is determined when the distribution function $F(s)$ is given since, by (c) of Theorem 2.5.6.2, this determines the outcome space (all points x_j of discontinuity of F) and the probabilities p_j (the jumps of F at the points of discontinuity x_j).

2.5.6.3. Example.   If $X =$ number of points appearing in a throw of a die, $F(s)$ has the following values:

$$F(s) = \begin{cases} 0 & \text{for} \quad x < 1 \\ \frac{1}{6} & \text{for} \quad 1 \le s < 2 \\ \frac{2}{6} & \text{for} \quad 2 \le s < 3 \\ \frac{3}{6} & \text{for} \quad 3 \le s < 4 \\ \frac{4}{6} & \text{for} \quad 4 \le s < 5 \\ \frac{5}{6} & \text{for} \quad 5 \le s < 6 \\ 1 & \text{for} \quad 6 \le s \end{cases}$$

The graph of $F(s)$ is plotted in Fig. 2.5.6.3. In plotting a d.f. it is difficult, without use of special conventions, to exhibit its right continuity at points of discontinuity. For example, the point $(2, \frac{2}{6})$ is on the graph, while $(2, \frac{1}{6})$ is not, but this is hard to indicate on a drawing. Nevertheless, the graph of $F(s)$ yields all information on the probability distribution, since it shows the points where F is discontinuous (possible outcomes x_j) and the height of the saltus (jump) of F at these points (probabilities p_j).

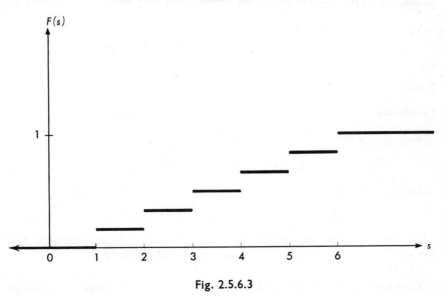

Fig. 2.5.6.3

2.5.6.4. Example. Let Y be the random variable determined as follows. A coin is thrown until heads appears for the first time. If this happens at the Nth throw, we set $Y = 1/N$. Clearly the possible values of Y are $1, \frac{1}{2}, \frac{1}{3}, \frac{1}{4}, \cdots$, and we shall see later on that

$$p_j = P(Y = 1/j) = 2^{-j}, \quad \text{for} \quad j = 1, 2, 3, \cdots$$

Since S is countably infinite, one can only indicate $F(s)$ on a graph, as in Fig. 2.5.6.4. The point 0 on the y axis is a limit point of the possible values, hence of points of discontinuity of F.

Whenever the set of possible values of a discrete one-dimensional random variable has no limit points, the graph of the d.f. consists only of horizontal line segments between any two adjacent possible values and has a saltus at each possible value. Functions of that kind are called *step functions*.

2.5.6.5. Theorem. For a one-dimensional continuous random variable X with the probability density $f(x)$:

(a) The d.f. is

(2.5.6.5.1)
$$F(s) = \int_{-\infty}^{s} f(x)dx$$

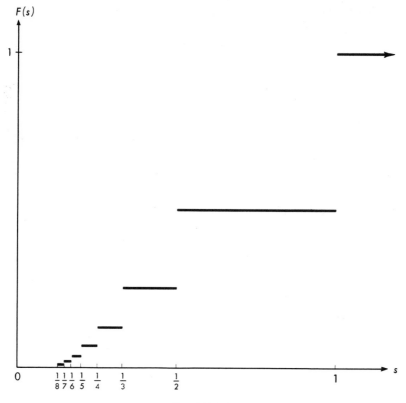

Fig. 2.5.6.4

(b) $F(s)$ is a non-decreasing and continuous function of s, its derivative exists at every point of continuity of f, and at every such point we have

(2.5.6.5.2)
$$\frac{dF(s)}{ds} = f(s)$$

(c) For every pair of real numbers $s_1 \le s_2$ the probability of the event $\{s_1 < x \le s_2\}$ is

(2.5.6.5.3)
$$P(s_1 < x \le s_2) = F(s_2) - F(s_1)$$

(d) Also

(2.5.6.5.4)
$$\lim_{s \to -\infty} F(s) = 0, \quad \lim_{s \to +\infty} = F(s) = 1$$

Proof. Consider (2.5.2.1) for one-dimensional x and the event $A = \{x \le s\}$. By definition (2.5.6.1) of the d.f. and by (2.5.2.1) we have

$$F(s) = P(x \le s) = \int_{x \le s} f(x)dx = \int_{-\infty}^{s} f(x)dx,$$

hence (2.5.6.5.1). Since $f(x) \geq 0$, we have for $s_1 < s_2$

$$F(s_2) = \int_{-\infty}^{s_2} f(x)dx$$

$$= \int_{-\infty}^{s_1} f(x)dx + \int_{s_1}^{s_2} f(x)dx$$

$$= F(s_1) + \int_{s_1}^{s_2} f(x)dx \geq F(s_1)$$

and $F(s_2) \geq F(s_1)$, F a non-decreasing function. The rest of (b) and equality (2.5.6.5.2) is a consequence of the well-known theorem that the derivative of a definite integral with regard to its upper limit of integration exists at points of continuity of the integrand, and is equal to the integrand. (c) is obtained directly:

$$P(s_1 < x \leq s_2) = \int_{s_1}^{s_2} f(x)dx$$

$$= \int_{-\infty}^{s_2} f(x)dx - \int_{-\infty}^{s_2} f(x)dx$$

$$= F(s_2) - F(s_1)$$

and so is (d)

$$\lim_{s \to +\infty} F(s) = \lim_{s \to +\infty} \int_{-\infty}^{s} f(x)dx = \int_{-\infty}^{+\infty} f(x)dx = 1$$

$$\lim_{s \to -\infty} F(s) = \lim_{s \to -\infty} \int_{-\infty}^{s} f(x)dx$$

$$= \lim_{s \to -\infty} \left[\int_{-\infty}^{+\infty} f(x)dx - \int_{s}^{+\infty} f(x)dx \right]$$

$$= 1 - \lim_{s \to -\infty} \int_{s}^{+\infty} f(x)dx$$

$$= 1 - 1 = 0$$

2.5.6.6.   Similarly, as in the case of one-dimensional discrete random variables, it may be noted that, for a one-dimensional continuous random variable, the probability distribution determines the distribution function and, conversely, the distribution function determines the probability distribution for all practical purposes. For the d.f. $F(s)$ is determined by (2.5.6.5.1) when $f(x)$ is given. The probability density $f(x)$ is determined at all its points of continuity by (2.5.6.5.2) when $F(s)$ is given. This leaves $f(x)$ undetermined at its points of discontinuity, but a theorem in the theory of functions of real variables asserts that the set of such points of discontinuity must be of "measure zero," that is, such that the values of $f(x)$ at points of that set have no effect on any integrals $\int_A f(x)dx$ for $A \in \mathcal{B}$. Since only these integrals are needed to compute probabilities of all events A, these probabilities are completely determined whenever the d.f. F is given.

The remark made in 2.5.3, that a continuous probability distribution assigns probability 0 to any geometric region which has n-dimensional volume equal to zero, has a consequence worth noting in the one-dimensional case. Let A be a set consisting of one point on the real line. Then

$$P(A) = \int_A f(x)dx = 0$$

for every probability density $f(x)$, so that events consisting of one point always have probability zero. It follows that

$$\begin{aligned}
P(s_1 \le x \le s_2) &= P(x = s_1) + P(s_1 < x \le x_2) \\
&= 0 + F(s_2) - F(s_1) \\
&= P(s_1 < x \le s_2)
\end{aligned}$$

and, in general, the probability is the same for any two intervals no matter whether either one or both end points are included.

EXERCISES

2.1. What is the probability of throwing at least one ace in rolling two dice?

2.2. There are three works, one consisting of 2 volumes, the other of 3 volumes, the third of 4 volumes. The nine volumes are placed on a shelf at random. What is the probability that the volumes of the same works are all together?

2.3. Four objects 1, 2, 3, 4 are distributed at random on four places numbered 1, 2, 3, 4. What is the probability that at least one of the objects will be in a place carrying the same number?

2.4. Two squares are selected at random on a chessboard. What is the probability that they are adjacent?

2.5. If the 26 letters of the alphabet are written in a row, in random order, what is the probability that a and b will be together?

2.6. What is the probability that three letters taken at random from the word abracadabra are all different?

2.7. If eight persons form a ring, what is the probability that two assigned persons are together?

2.8. Four cards are drawn at random from a pack. What is the probability that they are one from each suit?

2.9. There are 5 positive and 4 negative numbers. Six of those numbers are selected at random and multiplied out. What is the probability that the product is positive?

2.10. Six men and six women are invited for dinner. Among them are two men and two women who all dislike each other. The uninformed host arranges a seating order at a round table at random, alternating men and women. What is the probability that no two of the four persons who dislike each other will sit together?

2.11. Two of the integer numbers 1, 2, 3, 4, 5, 6, 7 are selected at random. Find the probability that their sum is even.

2.12. Two dice are used, each loaded so that the probabilities of throwing 1, 2, 3, 4, 5, 6 are

$$\frac{1-x}{6}, \frac{1+2x}{6}, \frac{1-x}{6}, \frac{1+x}{6}, \frac{1-2x}{6}, \frac{1+x}{6}$$

respectively. Compute the probability that, in one rolling of two such dice, one obtains a total (a) equal seven, (b) equal six.

2.13. The discrete random variable X has the possible values $1, 2, 3, \cdots, j, \cdots, n$, and the probabilities p_j are proportional to j. Find the general expression for p_j. In the special case $n = 10$, compute $P(X \leq 3)$.

2.14. The probability density of a random variable X is 0 for $x \leq -a$

$$f(x) = \frac{1}{a^2}(a + x) \quad \text{for } -a \leq x \leq 0$$

$$= \frac{1}{a^2}(a - x) \quad \text{for } 0 \leq x \leq a$$

$$= 0 \qquad\qquad \text{for } a \leq x$$

Verify that

$$\int_{-\infty}^{+\infty} f(x)dx = 1$$

Compute the cumulative distribution function $F(x)$. Plot $f(x)$ and $F(x)$ for $a = 1$.

2.15. Find the points of inflection of the normal probability density (2.5.5.1).

2.16. Verify that

$$g(x) = \frac{1}{\pi} \cdot \frac{b}{b^2 + x^2}$$

is a probability density, and find its points of inflection.

2.17. For the random variable of Exercise 2.14 with $a = 1$, compute the probabilities $P(|X| < 0.5)$, $P(|X| > 0.1)$, $P(-0.1 \leq X \leq 0.5)$. Find a number b such that $P(|X| < m) = P(|X| > m)$.

2.18. A stone is thrown and the distance thrown is measured. We assume that this distance X is a continuous random variable with a probability density $f(x)$ proportional to $1/(1 + x^2)$ for $x \geq 0$. Determine $f(x)$, the d.f. $F(x)$, and $P(X \geq 5)$.

2.19. Let $F(x)$ be the cumulative distribution function of a random variable X. Prove that for any $a > 0$ the integral

$$\int_{-\infty}^{+\infty} [F(x) - F(x - a)]dx$$

exists and equals a.

CHAPTER 3

Discrete *n*–Dimensional
Random Variables

3.1 An Example

Before developing a general theory, let us consider in detail the following definite example.

3.1.1. An urn contains 100 tags of equal shape and weight. On each tag three numbers n, x, y are written, n in black, x in red, and y in blue. The red numbers x and the blue numbers y are written on opposite sides of each tag. The numbers n run from 1 to 100 so that every value of n occurs on one and only one tag, x has the range of values 18, 19, 20, 21, and y the range 1, 2, 3, 4, 5. The different combinations of a value of x and a value of y occur in the urn the number of times shown in Table 3.1.1.

TABLE 3.1.1. Frequencies of (x, y)

y \ x	18	19	20	21	Totals
1	0	2	5	0	7
2	1	2	6	0	9
3	7	14	18	6	45
4	6	8	9	2	25
5	3	7	3	1	14
Totals	17	33	41	9	100

Several random experiments can be performed with such an urn. The game which consists in drawing one tag at random and reading n, x, y determines the three-dimensional discrete random variable (N, X, Y). This random variable has 100 different possible values, since any two tags differ at least in the n coordinate. In view of the physical similarity of the tags, we shall consider all of them equally probable and ascribe to each of them the probability 1/100. The random variable (N,X,Y) is, therefore, a Laplace variable. Another experiment consists in drawing a tag at random and reading x and y, regardless of n. This game defines a two-dimensional random variable (X,Y) with 20 possible values such as (18,3), (20,4), or (19,1). In order to determine the probabilites for each of these possible values of (X,Y), we may argue that each of them is an event for the random variable (N,X,Y). For example the value (18,3) of (X,Y) occurs if and only if (N,X,Y) assumes one of the values $(n,18,3)$. According to Table 3.1.1. the set of values (n,x,y) such that $x = 18$, $y = 3$, contains 7 different tags. Hence these 7 tags are favorable to the event $(x,y) = (18,3)$ and, according to Theorem 2.4.3, $P(18,3) = 7/100$. By a similar argument we find the probabilities $f(x,y)$ for all possible values of (x,y). These probabilities are shown in Table 3.1.2.

TABLE 3.1.2.   Joint probability $f(x, y)$
of the random variable (X, Y)

y \ x	18	19	20	21	$h(y)$
1	0.00	0.02	0.05	0.00	0.07
2	0.01	0.02	0.06	0.00	0.09
3	0.07	0.14	0.18	0.06	0.45
4	0.06	0.08	0.09	0.02	0.25
5	0.03	0.07	0.03	0.01	0.14
$g(x)$	0.17	0.33	0.41	0.09	1.00

One easily verifies that these probabilities fulfill (i) and (ii) of 2.4.1. The probability $f(x,y)$ is called the *joint probability of x and y*.

Still another random experiment consists in drawing one tag at random and reading x only, disregarding n and y. This game defines a one-dimensional discrete random variable X, with the possible values 18, 19, 20, 21. To determine its probabilities we observe that the occurrence of the value $x = 18$ is equivalent to the event "(x,y) takes one of the values (18,1) or (18,2) or (18,3) or (18,4) or (18,5)," for the two-dimensional random variable (X,Y). According to (2.4.1.3) we compute

$$P(E) = P(18,1) + P(18,2) + P(18,3) + P(18,4) + P(18,5)$$
$$= 0.00 + 0.01 + 0.07 + 0.06 + 0.03 = 0.17$$

and have

$$P(X = 18) = 0.17$$

Similarly, one computes the probability of X taking any other of its possible values, regardless of the value assumed by Y. These probabilities are listed in the lower marginal row of Table 3.1.2 and are labeled $g(x)$. Clearly $g(x)$ fulfills (i) and (ii). Rewriting the top row and the lower marginal row of Table 3.1.2 in the form of Table 3.1.3a, one obtains the probability distribu-

TABLE 3.1.3.a

x	18	19	20	21
$g(x)$	0.17	0.33	0.41	0.09

TABLE 3.1.3.b

y	1	2	3	4	5
$h(y)$	0.07	0.09	0.45	0.25	0.14

tion of the one-dimensional random variable X. In an analogous manner the values of Y, regardless of X, can be considered as a one-dimensional random variable with the set of possible values 1, 2, 3, 4, 5 with the probabilities listed in the right marginal column of Table 3.1.2 under the heading $h(y)$. The probability distribution of Y is completely presented in Table 3.1.3b. The probability distributions in Tables 3.1.3a and 3.1.3b are called the *marginal probability distribution of X* or *absolute probability distribution of X*, and the *marginal probability distribution of Y* or *absolute probability distribution of Y*, respectively. From the way they were obtained it is obvious that $g(x)$ and $h(y)$ are related to $f(x,y)$ by the equations

$$g(x) = \sum_{(y)} f(x,y), \qquad h(y) = \sum_{(x)} f(x,y)$$

Another game may be played with our tags by drawing one at random and putting it on the table with the red number x up and the blue number y hidden, reading the value of x, and considering the number y as our random variable. It may, for example, happen that on the tag drawn we read $x = 20$; we may then ask for the probability that $y = 4$. This probability $P(y = 4$ if $x = 20)$, that is, the probability that $y = 4$ if it is known that $x = 20$ can be found as follows. Since $x = 20$, we know from Table 3.1.1 that the tag drawn is one of the 41 tags with $x = 20$; out of these 41 tags, 9 have $y = 4$. Hence, among 41 equally probable values of the three-dimensional random variable (N,X,Y), 9 values are favorable to the event "$y = 4$ if it is known that $x = 20$," and we will write $P(y = 4$ if $x = 20) = 9/41$.

The probability of a value of y if a value of x is known will be denoted by $h(y \mid x)$ and called the *conditional probability of y for given x* or, in short, probability of y if x. By repeating the above argument we find the complete probability distribution of y, if $x = 20$:

$$h(1 \mid 20) = \ 5/41$$
$$h(2 \mid 20) = \ 6/41$$
$$h(3 \mid 20) = 18/41$$
$$h(4 \mid 20) = \ 9/41$$
$$h(5 \mid 20) = \ 3/41$$

One also may compute the conditional probability distributions of Y for other given values of X. All these conditional probability distributions are listed in Table 3.1.4a. It may be worth noting that each column of that table is a probability distribution of the one-dimensional random variable Y. The probability distributions in the different columns of Table 3.1.4a will generally (although not always) differ, according to which value of X is known to have occurred.

TABLE 3.1.4a. $h(y \mid x)$

y \ x	18	19	20	21
1	0	$\frac{2}{33}$	$\frac{5}{41}$	0
2	$\frac{1}{17}$	$\frac{2}{33}$	$\frac{6}{41}$	0
3	$\frac{7}{17}$	$\frac{14}{33}$	$\frac{18}{41}$	$\frac{6}{9}$
4	$\frac{6}{17}$	$\frac{8}{33}$	$\frac{9}{41}$	$\frac{2}{9}$
5	$\frac{3}{17}$	$\frac{7}{33}$	$\frac{3}{41}$	$\frac{1}{9}$
Total	1	1	1	1

TABLE 3.1.4b. $g(x \mid y)$

y \ x	18	19	20	21	Total
1	0	$\frac{2}{7}$	$\frac{5}{7}$	0	1
2	$\frac{1}{9}$	$\frac{2}{9}$	$\frac{6}{9}$	0	1
3	$\frac{7}{45}$	$\frac{14}{45}$	$\frac{18}{45}$	$\frac{6}{45}$	1
4	$\frac{6}{25}$	$\frac{8}{25}$	$\frac{9}{25}$	$\frac{2}{25}$	1
5	$\frac{3}{14}$	$\frac{7}{14}$	$\frac{3}{14}$	$\frac{1}{14}$	1

Clearly the values of $h(y \mid x)$ could also be obtained from Table 3.1.2 by writing

$$h(y \mid x) = \frac{f(x,y)}{g(x)}$$

In an analogous manner one may consider the probabilities $g(x \mid y) =$ *conditional probability of x for given y* or, in short, probability of x if y, and evaluate their values either directly from Table 3.1.1 or from Table 3.1.2 by setting

$$g(x \mid y) = \frac{f(x,y)}{h(y)}$$

The values so obtained are listed in Table 3.1.4b. Each row of that table contains a probability distribution of the one-dimensional random variable X, and these distributions may (but need not) be different for different given values of Y.

3.2   Absolute and Conditional Probabilities

The derivations of Example 3.1 were made possible only by the assumption that each tag had equal probability, i.e., that we were dealing with a Laplace distribution. Under that assumption we established certain relationships by which, the joint probability distribution $f(x,y)$ being given, it was possible to compute both marginal probability distributions and all conditional probability distributions.

In the general case, without the assumption of a Laplace distribution, such relationships cannot be proved and, for the general two-dimensional discrete random variable, we shall introduce them in the form of the definitions $D_2 4$ and $D_2 5$. It should be noted that these definitions will be formulated for the two-dimensional case only.

$D_2 4$.　For a discrete two-dimensional random variable (X, Y) with the possible values $x_1, x_2, \cdots$ for X and $y_1, y_2, \cdots$ for Y, and the probabilities $f(x_i, y_k)$ (called *joint probabilities of* x_i, y_k) the *absolute* (or *marginal*) *probability* that $X = x_i$ is

(3.2.1) $$g(x_i) = \sum_{(k)} f(x_i, y_k) \quad \text{for } i = 1, 2, \cdots$$

and the *absolute* (or *marginal*) *probability* of $Y = y_k$ is

(3.2.2) $$h(y_k) = \sum_{(i)} f(x_i, y_k) \quad \text{for } k = 1, 2, \cdots$$

$D_2 5$.　The *conditional probability of* $X = x_i$ *for given* $Y = y_k$ is defined for all y_k such that $h(y_k) > 0$, and is equal to

(3.2.3) $$g(x_i \mid y_k) = \frac{f(x_i, y_k)}{h(y_k)} \quad \text{for } i = 1, 2, \cdots, \quad k = 1, 2, \cdots$$

and the *conditional probability of* $Y = y_k$ *for given* $X = x_i$ is defined for all x_i such that $g(x_i) > 0$, and is equal to

(3.2.4) $$h(y_k \mid x_i) = \frac{f(x_i, y_k)}{g(x_i)} \quad \text{for } i = 1, 2, \cdots, \quad k = 1, 2, \cdots$$

The definitions $D_2 4$ and $D_2 5$ introduce the rules by which $g(x_i)$, $h(y_k)$, $g(x_i \mid y_k)$, $h(y_k \mid x_i)$ are to be derived from the joint probabilities $f(x_i, y_k)$ without reference to experience and without further assumptions (such as the Laplace character of the game).

All probabilities introduced in $D_2 4$ and $D_2 5$ obviously fulfill P_1 since $f(x_i, y_k)$ fulfills P_1. Since $f(x_i, y_k)$ fulfills P_2 we have

$$\sum_{(i)} \sum_{(k)} f(x_i, y_k) = 1$$

and hence

$$\sum_{(i)} g(x_i) = \sum_{(i)} \sum_{(k)} f(x_i, y_k) = 1$$

so that $g(x_i)$, too, fulfills P_2. Similarly, one verifies that $h(y_k)$ fulfills P_2. Axiom P_2 is also fulfilled by $g(x_i \mid y_k)$, for each fixed y_k, since

$$\sum_{(i)} g(x_i \mid y_k) = \sum_{(i)} \frac{f(x_i, y_k)}{h(y_k)} = \frac{1}{h(y_k)} \sum_{(i)} f(x_i, y_k) = 1$$

and an analogous argument shows that P_2 holds for $h(y_k \mid x_i)$ for every fixed value x_1. Whenever there is no danger of misunderstanding we shall omit the subscripts i, k, and write

$$f(x,y), \; g(x), \; h(y), \; g(x \mid y), \; h(y \mid x)$$

3.3 Independence. Multiplication Theorems

3.3.1.   Let (X, Y) be a two dimensional discrete random variable. The one-dimensional *random variable X is called independent of* the one-dimensional *random variable Y* if

(3.3.1.1) $g(x \mid y) = g(x)$

for all possible values of x and of y such that both probabilities are defined.
    For the example in 3.1.1 X is not independent of Y since $g(19 \mid 1) = 2/7 \neq g(19) = 0.33$.

3.3.2. Theorem.   If X is independent of Y then Y is independent of X.
    Proof.   Since X is independent of Y, we have,

$$g(x_i \mid y_k) = g(x_i)$$

for every pair of values x_i, y_k. From this, (3.2.4) and (3,2.3), we obtain

$$h(y_k \mid x_i) = \frac{f(x_i, y_k)}{g(x_i)} = \frac{f(x_i, y_k)}{g(x_i \mid y_k)} = \frac{f(x_i, y_k)}{f(x_i, y_k)/h(y_k)} = h(y_k)$$

for every pair of values x_i, y_k, and this completes the proof.
    In view of Theorem 3.3.1 there is no need to specify which variable is independent of the other, but one may say that X *and Y are independent* of each other.

3.3.3. Theorem. X and Y are independent if and only if, for all possible values of X and Y, the joint probability can be factored in the form

(3.3.3.1) $f(x,y) = \varphi(x) \cdot \psi(y)$

where $\varphi(x)$ depends only on x and $\psi(y)$ only on y.

Proof. If (3.3.3.1) holds, then we have

$$g(x_i) = \sum_{(k)} f(x_i, y_k) = \varphi(x_i) \sum_{(k)} \psi(y_k)$$

$$1 = \sum_{(i)} g(x_i) = \sum_{(i)} \varphi(x_i) \sum_{(k)} \psi(y_k)$$

$$h(y_k) = \sum_{(i)} f(x_i, y_k) = \psi(y_k) \cdot \sum_{(i)} \varphi(x_i) = \frac{\psi(y_k)}{\sum_{(k)} \psi(y_k)}$$

$$g(x_i \mid y_k) = \frac{f(x_i, y_k)}{h(y_k)}$$

$$= \frac{\varphi(x_i)\psi(y_k)}{\psi(y_k) / \sum_{(k)} \psi(y_k)}$$

$$= \varphi(x_i) \cdot \sum_{(k)} \psi(y_k)$$

$$= g(x_i)$$

for all pairs of values x_i, y_k. Hence (3.3.1.1) is true, and X is independent of Y. If X and Y are independent, then (3.3.1.1) holds and one obtains from (3.2.3)

$$f(x_i, y_k) = h(y_k) \cdot g(x_i \mid y_k) = h(y_k) \cdot g(x_i)$$

for all pairs of values x_i, y_k, hence $f(x, y)$ can be factored in the form (3.3.3.1)
The following corollary follows immediately from the preceding theorem.

Corollary. X and Y are independent if and only if

(3.3.3.2) $$f(x_i, y_k) = g(x_i) \cdot h(y_k)$$

for all possible values x_i, y_k.
The relations

(3.3.4) $$f(x_i, y_k) = g(x_i) \cdot h(y_k \mid x_i)$$

(3.3.5) $$f(x_i, y_k) = h(y_k) \cdot g(x_i \mid y_k)$$

which are an immediate consequence of (3.2.3) and (3.2.4) are often referred to as the *multiplication theorem for probabilities*. The relation (3.3.3.2), true for independent variables, is known as the *multiplication theorem for probabilities of independent random variables*.

The problem of deciding whether two random variables are independent or not is of a similar character to the problem of finding the probabilities of events for a random experiment; an answer to either one must be left in many cases to commonsense and experience, while in some other cases it may be derived from other assumptions by purely deductive arguments. If, for example, a two-dimensional random variable consists in rolling a white and black die and reading off the number X of points on the white die and the number Y of points on the black die, then it is known from experience that the knowledge of the outcome of X does not affect our estimates of the probabilities for Y, i.e., we know empirically that Y is independent of X. In the case of the bleeder disease* it is empirically known that the variable whose values are "male," "female," and the variable with the values "having the bleeder disease," "not having the bleeder disease" are dependent. In the later parts of this book we shall see how statistical methods are helpful in interpreting empirical material in order to decide whether there is independence between random variables. If, however, it is assumed that X and Z are independent and that Y and Z are independent, then it is possible to prove by purely mathematical argument, without further reference to experience, that $S = X + Y$ is a random variable independent of Z (see Theorem 5.1.4).

3.4 Bayes' Formula

3.4.1. Theorem.   For any discrete two-dimensional random variable (X, Y) we have

(3.4.1.1) $$g(x_i) = \sum_{(k)} h(y_k)\, g(x_i \mid y_k) \quad \text{for all values } x_i$$

(3.4.1.2) $$h(y_k) = \sum_{(i)} g(x_i)\, h(y_k \mid x_i) \quad \text{for all values } y_k$$

Proof.

$$\sum_{(k)} h(y_k)\, g(x_i \mid y_k) = \sum_{(k)} h(y_k) \frac{f(x_i, y_k)}{h(y_k)}$$
$$= \sum_{(k)} f(x_i, y_k) = g(x_i)$$

and similarly for (3.4.1.2)

3.4.2. Theorem (Bayes' Formula).   The equalities

(3.4.2.1) $$h(y_k \mid x_i) = \frac{h(y_k) g(x_i \mid y_k)}{\sum_{(k)} h(y_k) g(x_i \mid y_k)}$$

(3.4.2.2) $$g(x_i \mid y_k) = \frac{g(x_i) h(y_k \mid x_i)}{\sum_{(i)} g(x_i) h(y_k \mid x_i)}$$

hold for all values x_i and y_k.
   Proof.   From (3.4.1.1) and (3.3.5) we have

$$\frac{h(y_k) g(x_i \mid y_k)}{\sum_{(k)} h(y_k) g(x_i \mid y_k)} = \frac{f(x_i, y_k)}{g(x_i)} = h(y_k \mid x_i)$$

and similarly for (3.4.2.2).

---

   * The bleeder disease (hemophilia) is a condition in which the platelets in the blood, which cause the clotting of the blood in case of injuries, fail to function normally. As a result any slight cut leads to bleeding which is hard to stop and therefore dangerous. This condition is known to manifest itself only in men but it is genetically transmitted by women.

Theorem 3.4.2 is often quoted as the *theorem on the probability of causes*, a name due to the following interpretation. Let us consider an experiment in which two features X and Y are observed, each capable of assuming several values, say $x_1, x_2, \cdots, x_i, \cdots$ and $y_1, y_2, \cdots, y_k, \cdots$. Let us further suppose that the value assumed by Y has a determining effect on the value assumed by X, which we will also describe by saying that the value of Y is a "cause" of the value of X, or that the value of X is a "consequence" of the value of Y. Let the value of Y be only one of the factors which determine X so that the value of Y does not determine X completely but only influences the probabilities of X assuming its various possible values. Then it may happen that in an experiment a consequence x_i was observed while it is not known which of the possible causes $y_1, y_2, \cdots, y_k, \cdots$ has occurred. Is it possible, knowing that the consequence x_i has occurred, to evaluate the probabilities $h(y_k \mid x_i)$ for $k = 1, 2, 3, \cdots$, that is, the probabilities that any given cause has occurred? Bayes's formula (3.4.2.1) shows that this is possible if one knows $h(y_k)$ for all y_k (the absolute probability of every possible cause) and $g(x_i \mid y_k)$ for the x_i observed and for all y_k (the probabilities with which every possible cause y_k would "produce" the observed consequence x_i).

3.4.3 Example. Urn A contains one 5-dollar bill and two 10-dollar bills; urn B contains three 5-dollar bills and one 10-dollar bill. First one bill is drawn at random from urn A and thrown into urn B; the value of this bill is called Y. Then a bill is drawn at random from urn B; its value is called X. If $X = 10$, what is the probability that Y is 5? Here we have for Y the possible values 5 and 10 and, by assuming that the probability to be drawn is the same for each bill in an urn, the absolute probabilities $h(5) = 1/3$, $h(10) = 2/3$. The conditional probabilities needed are $g(10 \mid 5) = 1/5$, $g(10 \mid 10) = 2/5$. Hence from (3.4.2.1), we find

$$h(5 \mid 10) = \frac{\frac{1}{3} \cdot \frac{1}{5}}{\frac{1}{3} \cdot \frac{1}{5} + \frac{2}{3} \cdot \frac{2}{5}} = \frac{1}{1 + 4} = \frac{1}{5}$$

Bayes's formula has been often used in a special form which has caused much criticism. This special form is obtained if one accepts the principle that, if nothing is known about the absolute probabilities $h(y_1), h(y_2), \cdots$ of the possible causes, one is entitled to assume that they are all equally probable, i.e., that $h(y_1) = h(y_2) = \cdots$. That principle has been given various well-sounding names such as "principle of the equal distribution of ignorance" or "principle of insufficient reason." Clearly under that assumption (3.4.2.1) becomes

$$h(y_k \mid x_i) = \frac{g(x_i \mid y_k)}{\sum_{(k)} g(x_i \mid y_k)}$$

The denominator on the right side does not depend on y_k. The right side and, hence, $h(y_k \mid x_i)$ will therefore be largest for that value y_k for which $g(x_i \mid y_k)$ is largest. This has been stated frequently in a form known as "Bayes's principle": If the consequence x_i was observed and nothing is known about the absolute probabilities of the possible causes $y_1, y_2, \cdots$, then that cause y_k is most probable for which the probability $g(x_i \mid y_k)$ of producing the observed consequence x_i is greatest.

This particular manner of applying Bayes's formula has led to false conclusions and was the object of justified criticism. The source of the fallacies is not in Bayes's formula, which is a correct mathematical statement, but in the acceptance of the "principle of insufficient reason," which cannot be justified. For, if nothing is known about the absolute probabilities $h(y_k)$ those probabilities may quite well not all be equal, and the assumption that they are equal may be definitely wrong and lead to wrong conclusions.

3.5   The n-Dimensional Case

The concepts and theorems developed in 3.2–3.4 for two-dimensional discrete random variables may be generalized to any finite number of dimensions. If X is an n-dimensional random variable we shall, whenever needed, indicate this by writing $X = X_{(n)}$. Each possible value of a discrete random variable can be represented by a point

$$(x_{i_1}^{(1)}, x_{i_2}^{(2)}, \cdots, x_{i_n}^{(n)}) = x_{(n)}$$

in an n-dimensional space where $x_{i_1}^{(1)}$ is one of the possible values $x_1^{(1)}, x_2^{(1)}, x_3^{(1)}, \cdots$ of $X^{(1)}$, and $x_{i_2}^{(2)}$ one of the possible values $x_1^{(2)}, x_2^{(2)}, x_3^{(2)}, \cdots$ of $X^{(2)}$, etc. The probability $f(x_{(n)})$ which depends on each of the coordinates, and hence may be written as a function of these coordinates

$$f(x_{(n)}) = f(x_{i_1}^{(1)}, x_{i_2}^{(2)}, \cdots, x_{i_n}^{(n)})$$

for each possible value of $X_{(n)}$, is called the *joint probability* of $x_{i_1}^{(1)}, x_{i_2}^{(2)}, \cdots, x_{i_n}^{(n)}$; it must fulfill the axioms P_1, P_2, P_3. We shall again omit the subscripts wherever there is no danger of misunderstanding.

If m is an integer such that $1 \leq m \leq n - 1$, the coordinates $(X^{(1)}, X^{(2)}, \cdots, X^{(m)})$ of $X_{(n)} = (X^{(1)}, X^{(2)}, \cdots, X^{(m)}, X^{(m+1)}, \cdots, X^{(n)})$ define an m-dimensional random variable. Similarly, any m of the n coordinates of $X_{(n)}$, not necessarily the first m ones, define an m-dimensional random variable. If $X_{(m)}$ is an m-dimensional random variable consisting of some m coordinates of $X_{(n)}$ and $X_{(n-m)}$ is an $(n - m)$-dimensional random variable consisting of the remaining coordinates of $X_{(n)}$, then the random variables $X_{(m)}$ and $X_{(n-m)}$ shall be called *supplementary with respect to $X_{(n)}$*.

Besides the joint probability $f(x_{(n)}) = f(x^{(1)}, x^{(2)}, \cdots, x^{(n)})$, we shall consider the *absolute probabilities* $f(x_{(m)})$ for all m-dimensional random variables which can be obtained from $X_{(n)}$ by selecting m of its n coordinates, where m

is any integer such that $1 \leq m \leq n - 1$. We shall, furthermore, study all the *conditional probabilities* $f(x_{(m)} \mid x_{(n-m)})$ of $X_{(m)}$ for given $X_{(n-m)}$, where $X_{(m)}$ and $X_{(n-m)}$ are supplementary with respect to $X_{(n)}$. These various probabilities will be required to fulfill the relationships stated in the two definitions $D_n 4$ $D_n 5$ given below.

$D_n 4$.   The absolute (or marginal) probability of the event

$$X_{(m)} = (x_{k_1}^{(1)}, x_{k_2}^{(2)}, \cdots, x_{k_m}^{(m)})$$

where $1 \leq m \leq n - 1$, is

$$f_{(m)}(x_{(m)}) = f_{(m)}(x_{k_1}^{(1)}, x_{k_2}^{(2)}, \cdots, x_{k_m}^{(m)})$$
$$= \sum_{(k_{m+1})} \cdots \sum_{(k_n)} f(x_{k_1}^{(1)}, x_{k_2}^{(2)}, \cdots, x_{k_m}^{(m)}, x_{k_{(m+1)}}^{(m+1)}, \cdots, x_{k_n}^{(n)})$$

where the summation is extended over all possible values of $X_{(n)}$ such that the first m coordinates have the fixed values $x_{k_1}^{(1)}, \cdots, x_{k_m}^{(m)}$. The same holds if $X_{(m)}$ is defined by any m coordinates of $X_{(n)}$, not only the first m ones. Instead of $f_{(m)}(x_{(m)})$, the symbol $f(x_{(m)})$ will often be used to indicate the sum of the probabilities extended over all coordinates not included in $X_{(m)}$.

$D_n 5$.   The conditional probability of the event $X_{(m)} = (x_{k_1}^{(1)}, \cdots, x_{k_m}^{(m)})$ for given $x_{(n-m)} = (x_{k_{m+1}}^{(m+1)}, \cdots, x_{k_n}^{(n)})$ is defined for $x_{(n-m)}$ such that $f(x_{(n-m)}) > 0$ and is equal to

$$f(x_{(m)} \mid x_{(n-m)}) = \frac{f(x_{(n)})}{f(x_{(n-m)})}$$
$$= \frac{f(x_{k_1}^{(1)}, \cdots, x_{k_m}^{(m)}, x_{k_{m+1}}^{(m+1)}, \cdots, x_{k_n}^{(n)})}{f(x_{k_{m+1}}^{(m+1)}, \cdots, x_{k_n}^{(n)})}$$

The same holds if $X_{(m)}$ consists of any m coordinates of $X_{(n)}$ (not necessarily the first m) and $X_{(n-m)}$ is the supplementary variable.

It is easily seen that, given a random variable $X_{(n)}$ and any m such that $1 \leq m \leq n - 1$, one can define

$$\binom{n}{m} = \frac{n!}{m!(n-m)!}$$

different m-dimensional random variables $X_{(m)}$ by selecting m out of the n coordinates of $X_{(n)}$ in all different ways. Hence the joint probability distribution of $X_{(n)}$ leads to $\binom{n}{m}$ marginal probability distributions of m-dimensional random variables, and altogether to

$$\sum_{m=1}^{m=n-1} \binom{n}{m} = (1+1)^n - 1 - 1 = 2^n - 2 = 2(2^{n-1} - 1)$$

marginal probability distributions of all dimensions smaller than n. Each of these marginal probability distributions can be obtained from the joint probability distribution according to D_n4.

For each random variable $X_{(m)}$ there exists a supplementary random variable $X_{(n-m)}$, and the conditional probability distribution of $X_{(m)}$ for given $X_{(n-m)}$ can be obtained by D_n5. This leads again to $2(2^{n-1} - 1)$ conditional probability distributions of which $\binom{n}{m}$ are of dimension m for $\leq m \leq n - 1$.

Still more conditional probability distributions can be obtained from the original joint distribution $f(x_{(n)})$ by taking any $f(x_{(m)})$ as a joint distribution, splitting $X_{(m)}$ into l and $(m - l)$ coordinates $(1 \leq l \leq m - 1)$, defining $X_{(l)}$ and $X_{(m-l)}$ as random variables supplementary with respect to $X_{(m)}$, and computing

$$f(x_{(l)} \mid x_{(m-l)}) = \frac{f(x_{(m)})}{f(x_{(m-l)})}$$

in accordance with D_n5 in which n is replaced by m.

If $X_{(l)}$ and $X_{(m)}$ are supplementary variables (with respect to $X_{(l+m)}$), $X_{(m)}$ is called *independent* of $X_{(l)}$ if and only if $f(x_{(m)} \mid x_{(l)}) = f(x_{(m)})$ for all possible values $x_{(l)}$ and $x_{(m)}$.

By arguments quite analogous to those used to prove the statements of Sections 3.3 and 3.4, one obtains the following sequence of theorems.

3.5.1. Theorem. If $X_{(m)}$ is independent of $X_{(l)}$ then $X_{(l)}$ is independent of $X_{(m)}$.

3.5.2. Theorem. $X_{(l)}$ and $X_{(m)}$ are independent if and only if $f(x_{(l+m)})$ can be factored in the form

$$f(x_{(l+m)}) = \varphi(x_{(l)}) \cdot \psi(x_{(m)})$$

where $\varphi(x_{(l)})$ depends only on $x_{(l)}$ and $\psi(x_{(m)})$ only on $x_{(m)}$, for all possible values of $x_{(l)}$ and of $x_{(m)}$.

3.5.2.1. Corollary. $X_{(l)}$ and $X_{(m)}$ are independent if and only if

$$f(x_{(l+m)}) = f(x_{(l)}) \cdot f(x_{(m)})$$

for all possible values of $x_{(l)}$ and $x_{(m)}$.

3.5.3. Theorem.

$$f(x_{(m)}) = \sum f(x_{(l)}) \cdot f(x_{(m)} \mid x_{(l)})$$

where the summation is extended over all possible values of $x_{(l)}$.

3.5.4. Theorem.

$$f(x_{(l)} \mid x_{(m)}) = \frac{f(x_{(l)}) f(x_{(m)} \mid x_{(l)})}{\displaystyle\sum_{\text{(all values of } x_{(l)})} f(x_{(l)}) f(x_{(m)} \mid x_{(l)})}$$

Of particular importance is the following special case. Let $X_{(n)}$ be an *n*-dimensional random variable with the coordinates $X^{(1)}, X^{(2)}, \cdots, X^{(n)}$. The one-dimensional random variables $X^{(1)}, X^{(2)}, \cdots, X^{(n)}$ are called *totally independent* if each of them is independent of the supplementary $(n-1)$ dimensional random variable, i.e., if $X^{(1)}$ is independent of $(X^{(2)}, X^{(3)}, \cdots, X^{(n)})$, and $X^{(2)}$ of $(X^{(1)}, X^{(3)}, \cdots, X^{(n)})$, etc. In this special case 3.5.2 becomes:

3.5.5. Theorem.   The one-dimensional random variables $X^{(1)}, X^{(2)}, \cdots, X^{(n)}$ are totally independent if and only if their joint probability is equal to the product of the absolute probabilities

$$f(x^{(1)}, x^{(2)}, \cdots, x^{(n)}) = f_1(x^{(1)}) \cdot f_2(x^{(2)}) \cdots f_n(x^{(n)})$$

It should be pointed out that independence of all possible pairs $X^{(i)}$, $X^{(j)}$ for $i = 1, 2, \cdots, n, j = 1, 2, \cdots, n$, does not imply the total independence of $X^{(1)}, X^{(2)}, \cdots, X^{(n)}$.*

In discussing finite numbers of one-dimensional random variables, we shall use the term "independent" in the meaning of totally independent, unless something different will be explicitly stated.

Whether several random variables are totally independent or not may again be decided either from experience, or by mathematical argument from assumptions on the independence of some other variables. If, for example eight dice are rolled and their outcomes are denoted by $X^{(1)}, X^{(2)}, \cdots, X^{(8)}$, it is generally assumed that these eight random variables are totally independent, and this assumption is based on experience. Once total independence of $X^{(1)}, X^{(2)}, \cdots, X^{(8)}$ is assumed, it can be mathematically proved without reference to experience, that the random variables

$$U^{(1)} = X^{(1)} + X^{(2)}, \quad U^{(2)} = X^{(3)} + X^{(4)}, \quad U^{(3)} = X^{(5)} + X^{(6)} + X^{(7)} + X^{(8)}$$

are totally independent.

3.6   Examples of Discrete Random Variables

3.6.1. Example.   Two dice are rolled and their outcomes are denoted by $X^{(1)}$ and $X^{(2)}$. Find the probability distribution of the one-dimensional random variable $Y = X^{(1)} + X^{(2)}$.

---

* Examples of random variables independent by pairs but not totally independent may be found in J. V. Uspensky, *Introduction to Mathematical Probability*, McGraw-Hill Book Co., New York, 1937, p. 34, or in H. Cramér, *Mathematical Methods of Statistics*, Princeton University Press, Princeton, N.J., 1946, p. 162.

Solution. The two-dimensional random variable $(X^{(1)}, X^{(2)})$ has the 36 possible values shown in Fig. 1.5.2. From experience we assume that $X^{(1)}$ and $X^{(2)}$ are independent, and we then conclude by the corollary to 3.3.3 that $f(x^{(1)}, x^{(2)}) = g(x^{(1)}) \cdot h(x^{(2)})$ for all possible values of $(x^{(1)}, x^{(2)})$. Again from experience we assume that $g(1) = g(2) = \cdots = g(6)$ and $h(1) = h(2) = \cdots = h(6)$, hence, by axiom P_2 $g(1) = \cdots = g(6) = h(1) = \cdots = h(6) = \frac{1}{6}$ and $g(x^{(1)}, x^{(2)}) = 1/36$ for every possible value of $(x^{(1)}, x^{(2)})$. We now consider the following events and corresponding sets of values of $(x^{(1)}, x^{(2)})$:

Event	Set of Possible Values of $(x^{(1)}, x^{(2)})$
$y = 2$	(1,1)
$y = 3$	(1,2), (2,1)
$y = 4$	(1,3), (2,2), (3,1)
$y = 5$	(1,4), (2,3), (3,2), (4,1)
$y = 6$	(1,5), (2,4), (3,3), (4,2), (5,1)
$y = 7$	(1,6), (2,5), (3,4), (4,3), (5,2) (6,1)
etc.	etc.

According to axiom P_3 we compute:

$$P(Y = 2) = 1/36, \quad P(Y = 3) = 2/36, \quad P(Y = 4) = 3/36,$$
$$P(Y = 5) = 4/36, \quad P(Y = 6) = 5/36, \quad P(Y = 7) = 6/36, \text{ etc.,}$$

and tabulate the resulting probability distribution:

y:	2	3	4	5	6	7	8	9	10	11	12
$h(y)$:	1/36	2/36	3/36	4/36	5/36	6/36	5/36	4/36	3/36	2/36	1/36

As a final check we verify that $\sum_{(y)} h(y) = 1$.

3.6.2. Example. Three boxes, practically undistinguishable in appearance, have two drawers each. Box I contains a goldpiece in one and a silverpiece in the other drawer, box II contains a goldpiece in each drawer, box III contains a silver piece in each drawer. One box is chosen at random, one of its drawers is opened at random, and a goldpiece is found. What is the probability that the other drawer contains a piece of silver?

Solution. We consider a game which consists in choosing a box and opening one drawer at random, and denote by (X, Y) the two-dimensional random variable where X is the number of the chosen box and Y the metal found in the opened drawer. The possible values are 1, 2, 3 for X; and G (for gold), S (for silver) for Y. (One could code the metals in numbers if one insisted on complying strictly with the definition of a random variable.) The probability asked for is $g(1 \mid G)$. Assuming, for empirical reasons, that $g(1) = g(2) = g(3) = 1/3$ and that $h(G \mid 1) = 1/2, h(G \mid 2) = 1, h(G \mid 3) = 0,$

we find from Bayes's formula

$$g(1 \mid G) = \frac{g(1)h(G \mid 1)}{g(1) \, h(G \mid 1) + g(2) \, h(G \mid 2) + g(3) \, h(G \mid 3)}$$

$$= \frac{\frac{1}{3} \cdot \frac{1}{2}}{\frac{1}{3} \cdot \frac{1}{2} + \frac{1}{3} \cdot 1 + \frac{1}{3} \cdot 0} = \frac{1}{3}$$

3.6.3. Example (Problem of Chevalier de Méré).
A pair of dice is thrown n times in succession. What is the probability of obtaining double six at least once?

Solution. As a device frequently helpful in similar problems, we introduce n auxiliary random variables

$$Y^{(1)} = \begin{cases} 1 \text{ if a double six appears in the first throw} \\ 0 \text{ if a double six does not appear in the first throw} \end{cases}$$

$$Y^{(2)} = \begin{cases} 1 \text{ if a double six appears in the second throw} \\ 0 \text{ if a double six does not appear in the second throw} \end{cases}$$

$$Y^{(n)} = \begin{cases} 1 \text{ if a double six appears in the } n\text{th throw} \\ 0 \text{ if a double six does not appear in the } n\text{th throw} \end{cases}$$

We assume that each face on each die is equally probable and that the outcomes of the two dice in any single throw are independent. Then, as in Example 3.6.1, we conclude that the probability of a double six in one throw is $1/36$, and the probability of a non-double-six $35/36$. Each $Y^{(i)}$, for $i = 1, 2, \cdots, n$, then has the probability distribution

$$g(1) = 1/36, \qquad g(0) = 35/36$$

We also assume, by experience, that $Y^{(1)}, Y^{(2)}, \cdots Y^{(n)}$ are independent. According to 3.5.5 the joint probability of $(Y^{(1)}, Y^{(2)}, \cdots, Y^{(n)})$ is

$$f(Y^{(1)}, Y^{(2)}, \cdots, Y^{(n)}) = g(Y^{(1)}) \cdot g(Y^{(2)}) \cdots g(Y^{(n)})$$

In particular the probability of the event $\bar{E}$ "no double six in n throws" is

$$P(\bar{E}) = f(0,0,\cdots,0) = g(0) \cdot g(0) \cdots g(0) = (35/36)^n$$

The event E: "at least one double six in n throws" is complementary to $\bar{E}$, hence its probability is

(3.6.3.1) $$P(E) = 1 - P(\bar{E}) = 1 - (35/36)^n$$

which answers our problem.

This problem was described and solved by Pascal and Fermat, after an experienced gambler, Chevalier de Méré, had asked them the following more special question. If one bets even money that a six will appear at least once in 4 throws of one die, one wins in the long run. If one bets even money that a double six will appear at least once in 24 throws of two dice, one loses in the long run. Now 4 is two-thirds of the number of different possibilities of one die, and 24 is two-thirds of the number of different possibilities in rolling two dice. Hence, concluded de Méré, both bets should offer equal advantages. Instead, his experience taught him that in order to keep winning in the long run one has to bet even money that a double six will appear at least once in 25 throws of two dice. Why is that so? The answer follows from (3.6.3.1). In order to keep winning in the long run if one bets even money, one has to have a probability $> 1/2$ of winning in every single game, i.e., one must have

$$P(E) = 1 - (35/36)^n > 1/2$$

which is the case for

$$n > \log 2/(\log 36 - \log 35) = 24.6+$$

Hence 25 is the smallest integer which gives $P(E) > 1/2$, while 24 still gives $P(E) < 1/2$. To verify de Méré's statement on one die, one computes in a manner analogous to that used for two dice that the probability of having at least one six in n throws of one die is $P'(E) = 1 - (5/6)^n$. Hence, to have $P'(E) > 1/2$ one must have $n > \log 2/(\log 6 - \log 5) = 3.8+$, and the smallest integer fulfilling this condition is $n = 4$.

3.7 Binomial Probability Distribution. Repeated Drawings with Replacement

A random variable X, with two possible values 1 and 0 and the probabilities $g(1) = p$, $g(0) = 1 - p = q$, will be called a *simple alternative*. Such a random variable may be used to describe any random experiment with only two possible outcomes, such as tossing a coin or death or survival of an insured person within a given period of time. When speaking of a simple alternative, one often calls one of its values, say 1, a *success*, and the other value, say 0, a *failure*. The probability distribution of a simple alternative is completely determined if p, the probability of success, is given.

Let X be a simple alternative with probabilities p for success and q for failure, and let n be a fixed positive integer. We shall define a new random variable S, which will be called an *n-fold repetition of the simple alternative X*. The random experiment by which a value of S is determined consists in playing X independently n times and counting the number of successes obtained in those n games. Clearly the possible values of S are $0, 1, 2, \cdots, n$, since in n games of X it is possible to have $0, 1, 2, \cdots, n$ successes. Let $P(n,k)$ denote the probability that in an n-fold repetition we obtain $S = k$.

3.7.1. Theorem (Theorem of J. Bernoulli). If X is a simple alternative with probabilities $g(1) = p$, $g(0) = q$ and S is an n-fold repetition of X, then the probability that $S = k$ is

$$(3.7.1.1) \qquad P(n,k) = \frac{n!}{k!\,(n-k)!} \cdot p^k q^{n-k} \quad \text{for } k = 0, 1, \cdots, n$$

Proof. Let $X^{(1)}$, $X^{(2)}, \cdots$, $X^{(n)}$ denote the outcome of the 1st, 2nd, $\cdots$ _n_th playing of X. Each $X^{(i)}$ is a simple alternative with the same probabilities p for $X^{(i)} = 1$, q for $X^{(i)} = 0$. Our definition of an _n_-fold repetition assumes that the $X^{(i)}$, for $i = 1, 2, \cdots, n$, are independent. The joint probability of $(X^{(i)}, X^{(2)}, \cdots, X^{(n)})$ is, therefore, by Theorem 3.5.5

$$f(x^{(1)}, x^{(2)}, \cdots, x^{(n)}) = g(x^{(1)})g(x^{(2)}), \cdots, g(x^{(n)})$$

We have, for example,

$$f(\underbrace{1,1,\cdots,1,1,}_{k} \underbrace{0,0,\cdots,0,0}_{n-k}) = p^k q^{n-k}$$

and, similarly, the probability of any value of the _n_-dimensional random variable $X_{(n)} = (X^{(1)}, X^{(2)}, \cdots, X^{(n)})$ is $p^k q^{n-k}$ if k coordinates are 1 and the remaining $(n - k)$ are 0. Hence $P(n,k)$, which is the probability of the event "k coordinates of $X^{(n)}$ are 1 and the remaining $(n - k)$ are 0" is, by axiom P_3, the quantity $p^k q^{n-k}$ taken as many times as it is possible to choose k coordinates in different ways from the n coordinates available. The number of these different choices is the number of combinations of k out of n, which is $n!/k!\,(n-k)!$ hence,

$$P(n,k) = \frac{n!}{k!\,(n-k)!} \cdot p^k q^{n-k}$$

The probability distribution with possible values $0, 1, \cdots, n$ and probabilities given by (3.7.1) is known as the *binomial distribution* since $P(n,k)$ is exactly the $(k + 1)$st term in the expansion of $(p + q)^n$ according to the binomial theorem. It was first derived by Jacob Bernoulli in his classical treatise *Ars coniectandi* (1713) and is frequently also referred to as the *Bernoulli distribution*.

3.7.2. Example.   A typical application of Theorem 3.7.1 is the computation of probabilities for repeated *drawings with replacement*. From an urn containing w white and b black balls, one ball is drawn at random. Its color is recorded, then the ball is replaced in the urn and the urn is well shaken. Again a ball is drawn at random, its color recorded, the ball is replaced and the urn shaken. This procedure is repeated n times. The total number S of white balls drawn in those n drawings is our random variable. What is the probability distribution of S?

We assume that all $w + b$ balls are physically so similar that we may assume equal probability for the drawing of each of them. As in Example 2.4.4 we find that, under this assumption, the probability of drawing a white ball is $p = w/(w + b)$, and the probability of drawing a black ball is $q = b/(w + b)$. Since the ball drawn is replaced and the urn is well shaken after each drawing, one is justified in assuming that the single drawings are independent. If we call the drawing of a white ball a success and of a black ball a failure, each single drawing is a simple alternative, and the n independent drawings are an n-fold repetition which fulfills the assumptions of Theorem 3.7.1. Hence, the probability of drawing exactly s white balls in n drawings with replacement is

$$P(n,s) = \frac{n!}{s!\,(n-s)!} \left(\frac{w}{w+b}\right)^s \left(\frac{b}{w+b}\right)^{n-s}$$

3.7.3. Example. What is the probability of obtaining the total 11 exactly three times in eight throws of two dice?

Solution. We consider the simple alternative consisting of the events A: total $= 11$; $\bar{A}$: total $\neq 11$. From Example 3.6.1 we know that $P(A) = p = 2/36$, hence $q = 17/18$ and the required probability is

$$P(8,3) = \frac{8!}{3!\,5!} \left(\frac{1}{18}\right)^3 \left(\frac{17}{18}\right)^5 = 56(0.0001285) = 0.007216$$

to four significant digits.

3.7.4. Example. What is the probability that, throwing a coin ten times or, this being an equivalent experiment, ten coins simultaneously, one obtains at least six heads?

Solution. The events E_{10}, ten heads; E_9, nine heads; E_8, eight heads; E_7, seven heads; E_6, six heads, are mutually exclusive and the event E, at least six heads, is the union $E_{10} \cup E_9 \cup E_8 \cup E_7 \cup E_6$. Hence, by P_3, we have

$$P(E) = \sum_{i=6}^{10} P(E_i)$$

But

$$P(E_i) = \frac{10!}{i!\,(10-i)!} \left(\frac{1}{2}\right)^i \left(\frac{1}{2}\right)^{10-i} = \frac{10!}{i!\,(10-i)!} \cdot \frac{1}{2^{10}}$$

so that

$$P(E) = \frac{1}{2^{10}} \sum_{i=6}^{10} \frac{10}{i!\,(10-i)!}$$

$$= \frac{1}{2^{10}} (210 + 120 + 45 + 10 + 1)$$

$$= \frac{1}{2^{10}} \cdot 386 = 0.3770$$

to four significant digits.

3.7.5. Theorem. If a real number p such that $0 < p < 1$ and a positive integer n are given, the probability

$$P(n,s) = \frac{n!}{s!\,(n-s)!} p^s q^{n-s}$$

is greatest for that integer value s_m of s which fulfills the inequalities

(3.7.5.1) $$p(n + 1) - 1 < s_m \leq p(n + 1)$$

If $p(n + 1)$ is an integer, then $P(n, s_m - 1) = P(n,s_m)$ and both are greater than $P(n,s)$ for any other value of s.

Proof. We consider the ratio

(3.7.5.2) $$r(s) = \frac{P(n, s + 1)}{P(n,s)} = \frac{n - s}{s + 1} \cdot \frac{n}{q}$$

for $s = 0, 1, \cdots, n - 1$. Clearly $r(s)$ decreases as s increases.

We distinguish the following possibilities:

(a) $1 > r(0)$. Then we have, for all values $s = 0, 1, \cdots, n - 1$,

$$\frac{P(n, s + 1)}{P(n,s)} = r(s) \leq r(0) < 1$$

and $P(n, s + 1) < P(n,s)$ for $s = 0, 1, \cdots, n - 1$. In this case, therefore, $P(n,0)$ is largest. But $1 > r(0)$ is equivalent to $p(n + 1) - 1 < 0$, and since $p(n + 1) > 0$, the value $s_m = 0$ fulfills (3.7.5.1). The number $p(n + 1)$ cannot be an integer since $p(n + 1) - 1 < 0$.

(b) $r(n - 1) \geq 1$. Then we have

$$\frac{P(n, s + 1)}{P(n,s)} = r(s) > r(n - 1) \geq 1$$

hence

$$P(n,s + 1) > P(n,s) \quad \text{for } s = 0, 1, \cdots, n - 2$$

and

$$P(n,n) \geq P(n, n - 1)$$

In this case $P(n,n)$ is largest. Since $r(n - 1) \geq 1$ is equivalent to $n \leq p(n + 1)$, and since $p(n + 1) - 1 = pn - (1 - p) < pn < n$, the values $s_m = n$ fulfills (3.7.5.1). If $p(n + 1)$ is an integer, it must equal n, since we already know that $p(n + 1) \geq n$, and clearly $p(n + 1) = pn + p < n + 1$. Hence, we have $p = nq$, and $r(n - 1) = p/nq = 1$, so that $P(n,n) = P(n,n - 1)$.

(c) $r(0) \geq 1$ and $r(n - 1) < 1$. Since $r(s)$ is a decreasing function of s, there exists an integer s'_m such that

(3.7.5.3) $$r(s'_m - 1) \geq 1, \quad r(s'_m) < 1$$

It follows that $r(s) > 1$ for $s < s'_m - 1$ and $r(s) < 1$ for $s \geq s'_m$, hence also

$$P(n,0) < P(n,1) < \cdots < P(n, s'_m - 1) \leq P(n,s'_m)$$
$$> P(n, s'_m + 1) > \cdots > P(n,n)$$

so that $P(n,s'_m)$ has the largest value of all probabilities $P(n,s)$. But (3.7.5.3) is equivalent to

$$\frac{n - s'_m + 1}{s'_m} \cdot \frac{p}{q} \geq 1 > \frac{n - s'_m}{s'_m + 1} \cdot \frac{p}{q}$$

or $p(n + 1) - 1 < s'_m \leq p(n + 1)$, hence $s'_m = s_m$ where s_m is determined by (3.7.5.1). If $p(n + 1)$ is an integer, then $s_m = p(n + 1)$ and

$$\frac{P(n, s_m)}{P(n, s_m - 1)} = r(s_m - 1)$$

$$= r(pn + p - 1)$$

$$= \frac{n - pn - p + 1}{p(n + 1)} \cdot \frac{p}{q}$$

$$= \frac{n(1 - p) + 1 - p}{(n + 1)q} = 1$$

hence,

$$P(n, s_m - 1) = P(n, s_m)$$

Theorem 3.7.5 may also be stated by saying that, of the possible values $0, 1, \cdots, n$ of the random variable S with a binomial probability distribution, the most probable is the value s_m equal to the greatest integer contained in $p(n + 1)$. If $p(n + 1)$ is an integer, then s_m and $s_m - 1$ have equal probabilities, greater than the probability of any other possible value of S. The value s_m is called *the most probable value of S*.

3.7.6. Example.   What is the most probable number of throws with a total of 7 in 25 throws of a pair of dice? In 11 throws? In 5 throws?
   Solution.   According to Example 3.6.1 the probability of obtaining a total of 7 in one throw of two dice is 1/6. Hence by Theorem 3.7.5 we have for 25 throws $s_m = $ (greatest integer contained in $26 \cdot 1/6$) $= 4$. In 11 throws the most probable number of sevens is $s_m = $ (greatest integer in $12 \cdot 1/6$) $= 2$, but also $s_m - 1 = 1$ has the same probability; in view of the smallness of the numbers involved, this last statement may be easily verified:

$$P(11,1) = \frac{11!}{1! \, 10!} \cdot \frac{1}{6} \cdot \left(\frac{5}{6}\right)^{10} = \frac{11 \cdot 5^{10}}{6^{11}}$$

$$P(11,2) = \frac{11}{2! \, 9!} \cdot \frac{1}{6^2} \cdot \left(\frac{5}{6}\right)^{9} = \frac{5 \cdot 11 \cdot 5^9}{6^{11}} = \frac{11 \cdot 5^{10}}{6^{11}}$$

For 5 throws, $s_m = $ (greatest integer in $6 \cdot 1/6$) $= 1$ and $s = 0$ have the same probability.

3.8   Hypergeometric Probability Distribution. Repeated Drawings without Replacements

3.8.1.   The binomial probability distribution was derived under the assumption of n random experiments which are independent and each a simple alternative with the same probabilities. If these assumptions are not satisfied, the probability of having s successes in n experiments must be computed by some other, usually more cumbersome, method. A classical case is that of drawings without replacements. n balls are in an urn, each with the same probability of being drawn, and n_1 of them are labeled 1, n_2 labeled 0. Consecutive experiments are performed by drawing a ball, recording its label, then drawing another ball and recording its label, always leaving the balls drawn out of the urn (no replacements), and repeating this procedure m times. Let S be the number of balls labeled 1 among the m balls drawn.

One can see that an equivalent experiment would consist of drawing m balls from the urn all at once and recording the number S of them that are labeled 1. Clearly S is a random variable.

3.8.2. Theorem.   If an urn contains n_1 balls marked 1 and $n_2 = n - n_2$ balls marked 0, and if m of them are drawn at random without replacements, then the number of "1" balls among these m is a random variable with the probability distribution

$$(3.8.2.1) \quad f(s) = P\{s \text{ balls marked } 1\} = \frac{\binom{n_1}{s}\binom{n-n_1}{m-s}}{\binom{n}{m}} = \frac{\binom{m}{s}\binom{n-m}{n_1-s}}{\binom{n}{n_1}}$$

for $s = 0, 1, 2, \cdots, m$, known as the *hypergeometric distribution*.

Proof.   If s among the m balls drawn are 1 then $m - s$ are 0. From the total supply of n_1 balls of the 1 kind in the urn one can draw s in $\binom{n_1}{s}$ different ways and, from the $n_2 = n - n_1$ balls of kind 0, $m - s$ balls can be drawn in $\binom{n-n_1}{m-s}$ ways. There are therefore $\binom{n_1}{s}\binom{n-n_1}{m-s}$ different ways of obtaining exactly s balls of kind 1 in m balls drawn without replacement. Altogether m balls can be selected from the total supply of n balls in $\binom{n}{m}$ different ways. If one assumes that each ball is equally likely to be drawn, then each selection of m balls out of n has the same probability to be drawn, and by 2.4.3 the probability of obtaining exactly s balls of kind 1 is $\binom{n_1}{s}\binom{n-n_1}{m-s} / \binom{n}{m}$. The last expression of (3.8.2.1) is obtained by simple algebra.

EXERCISES

3.1.   There are seven urns, practically undistinguishable from the outside. Inside, two of them are marked A, and each of these contains 9 white balls and 1 black ball; the other five are marked B, and each of these contains 5 white and 5 black balls. One urn is chosen at random and its letter, A or B, is recorded, then a ball is drawn at random from this urn and its color, w (white) or b (black) is recorded. Let X denote the random variable with the possible values A, B, and Y the random variable with the possible values w, b. Find the absolute probability distribution $g(x)$, the conditional distributions $h(y \mid x)$, the joint distribution $f(x,y)$, the absolute distribution $h(y)$, the conditional distributions $g(x \mid y)$.

3.2. A nickel and a dime are tossed, and the number X of heads is recorded. Then the dime is picked up and tossed again, and the number Y of heads on the dime and on the (unchanged) nickel is recorded. Determine $f(x,y)$, $g(x)$, $h(y)$, $g(x \mid y)$, $h(y \mid x)$.

3.3. A two-dimensional discrete random variable has the joint probability distribution $f(x,y)$ given by the table

y \ x	-1	0	1
0	0.03	0.01	0.00
1	0.02	0.25	0.03
2	0.05	0.45	0.05
3	0.00	0.01	0.10

(a) Compute $g(x)$, $h(y)$, $g(x \mid y)$, $h(y \mid x)$.
(b) Decide whether x and y are independent.

3.4. From the seven urns of Exercise 3.1., one was chosen at random, its letter was not observed; a ball was drawn from it and was found to be white. What is the probability that the urn was of type A?

3.5. A New York firm receives three times as many letters from its correspondent in LONDON, England, as from the correspondent in CLIFTON, England, and has no other correspondents in England. A letter with a British poststamp arrives, and on the postmark only the two consecutive letters ON are legible. The postmarks are circular and the letters of the name of the city are arranged in a ring, with a larger space between the last and the first letter. Assuming that any two consecutive letters in such a ring have the same probability to remain legible, what is the probability that this letter came from Clifton? What is the answer to this question under the assumption that the New York firm receives 4 times as many letters from Clifton as from London?

3.6. One card is missing from a pack of 52 cards. From the remaining 51 cards, five are drawn at random, and all are clubs. What is the probability that the missing card is a club?

3.7. In rolling five dice, we say that a repetition occurred if not all five outcomes are different. How many times does one have to roll five dice to have a probability of at least 0.999 that at least one repetition will occur?

3.8. The faces of a coin are marked 3 and 4. This coin is tossed ten times. What is the probability that the total of the numbers thrown will not exceed 32?

3.9. A coin is tossed n times. What is the probability that heads will appear an even number of times?

3.10. From a deck of cards one card is drawn and recorded, then placed back in the deck and the cards are shuffled. This procedure is repeated ten times. What is the probability of having at least one ace in these ten drawings? What is the least number n of drawings such that the probability of having at least one ace in these n drawings is greater than $\frac{9}{10}$?

3.11. Cards are drawn from a deck, one at a time, without replacements. What is the least number n of such drawings for which the probability of having at least one ace is greater than $\frac{9}{10}$?

3.12. From a deck of 52 cards one card was removed at random. From the remaining 51 cards, five cards are drawn *with replacements*, i.e., each card drawn is recorded, replaced in the deck and all cards are shuffled before the next drawing. Of these five cards, three are diamonds. What is the probability that the one card removed was a diamond?

CHAPTER 4

Continuous *n*-Dimensional Random Variables

4.1 Absolute and Conditional Probability Densities: Two-Dimensional Case

Similarly as in the discrete case, marginal and conditional probability distributions are introduced for continuous two-dimensional random variables by the following definitions.

$D_2'4$. If (X, Y) has the joint probability density $f(x,y)$, then the *absolute (or marginal) probability density of X* is

$$g(x) = \int_{-\infty}^{+\infty} f(x,y)dy$$

and the *absolute (or marginal) probability density of Y* is

$$h(y) = \int_{-\infty}^{+\infty} f(x,y)dx$$

$D_2'5$. If (X, Y) has the joint probability density $f(x,y)$ then the *conditional probability density of X for given Y* is defined for any y such that $h(y) > 0$ and is equal to

For logical consistency use upper case letters for the μ pdf

$$g(x \mid y) = \frac{f(x,y)}{h(y)}$$

and the *conditional probability density of Y for given X* is defined for any x such that $g(x) > 0$ and is equal to

$$h(y \mid x) = \frac{f(x,y)}{g(x)}$$

One verifies easily that each of the functions $g(x)$, $g(x \mid y)$ as a function of x, and $h(y)$, $h(y \mid x)$ as a function of y, fulfills C_1 and C_2.

If (X, Y) is a continuous two-dimensional random variable with the joint probability density $f(x,y)$, and if the absolute and conditional densities are defined according to $D_2'4$ and $D_2'5$, the one-dimensional continuous random variable X is called *independent* of the one-dimensional continuous random variable Y, if

Poor Notation
g is used as the name of 2 different functions

$$g(x \mid y) = g(x)$$

for all values of x and y.

By arguments quite analogous to those of 3.3 one proves the following theorems.

4.1.1. Theorem. If X is independent of Y then Y is independent of X.

4.1.2. Theorem. X and Y are independent if and only if $f(x,y)$ can be factored in the form

$$f(x,y) = \varphi(x) \cdot \psi(y)$$

where $\varphi(x)$ depends only on x and $\psi(y)$ only on y.

Corollary. X and Y are independent if and only if

(4.1.2.1) $$f(x,y) = g(x) \cdot h(y)$$

Relationship (4.1.2.1) is known as the *multiplication theorem for probabilities of independent variables*. The relationships

(4.1.2.2) $$f(x,y) = g(x) h(y \mid x)$$

(4.1.2.3) $$f(x,y) = h(y) g(x \mid y)$$

are frequently referred to as the *multiplication theorem for probabilities*.

4.1.3. Theorem.

(4.1.3.1) $$g(x) = \int_{-\infty}^{+\infty} h(y) \cdot g(x \mid y) dy$$

(4.1.3.2) $$h(y) = \int_{-\infty}^{+\infty} g(x) \cdot h(y \mid x) dx$$

4.1.4. Theorem (Bayes' Formula).

(4.1.4.1) $$h(y \mid x) = \frac{h(y) \cdot g(x \mid y)}{\int_{-\infty}^{+\infty} h(y) \cdot g(x \mid y) dy} \, , \quad g(x \mid y) = \frac{g(x) \cdot h(y \mid x)}{\int_{-\infty}^{+\infty} g(x) \cdot h(y \mid x) dx}$$

4.1.5. Example. Random variable with uniform distribution. Let Q be the square with the vertices $(1,0)$, $(0,1)$, $(-1,0)$, $(0,-1)$ in the Cartesian (x,y) plane, and assume this plane is placed horizontally and exposed to raindrops falling from a great altitude. Every time a drop hits the area Q at a point (x,y), it determines a value of the random variable (X, Y). Drops hitting the plane outside of Q are disregarded. Since the drops come from great altitude, we shall be inclined to assume for empirical reasons that no part of Q is more likely to be hit than any other, and that the probability that a geometrical figure E contained in Q will be hit depends only on the area of E and not on its shape or its position within Q. The uniform distribution introduced in 2.5.4 is appropriate for this random variable (X, Y) in view of the following.

Generally, the uniform probability distribution of a two-dimensional continuous random variable (X, Y) may be described as follows. A part Q of the (x,y) plane is given, such that Q has a finite area $A(Q)$; the probability density $f(x,y)$ is equal to $1/A(Q)$ for (x,y) contained in Q, and equal to zero for (x,y) not contained in Q. Clearly, if any part E of Q with finite area $A(E)$ is considered, the probability of (X, Y) falling into E is

$$P(E) = \int\int_E f(x,y)dxdy = \frac{A(E)}{A(Q)}$$

and therefore depends on $A(E)$ but not on the shape or position of E.

If we return to our initial example where Q was a square with vertices on the positive and negative axes at unit distance from the origin, we have according to (2.5.4.3)

$$f(x,y) = \begin{cases} 1/2 & \text{for } |x| + |y| \leq 1 \\ 0 & \text{for } |x| + |y| > 1 \end{cases}$$

The marginal probability densities are

$$g(x) = \int_{-\infty}^{+\infty} f(x,y)dy = \int_{|x|+|y|\leq 1} \frac{1}{2} dy$$

$$= \int_{|x|-1}^{1-|x|} \frac{1}{2} dy = 1 - |x| \quad \text{for } |x| \leq 1$$

$$g(x) = \int_{-\infty}^{+\infty} f(x,y)dy = 0 \qquad \text{for } |x| > 1$$

and for reasons of symmetry

$$h(y) = 1 - |y| \quad \text{for } |y| \leq 1$$
$$h(y) = 0 \qquad \text{for } |y| > 1$$

The conditional probability densities are

$$g(x \mid y) = \begin{cases} \dfrac{1}{2(1 - |y|)} & \text{for } |x| \leq 1 - |y| \text{ if } |y| \leq 1 \\ 0 & \text{for } |x| > 1 - |y| \text{ if } |y| \leq 1 \end{cases}$$

$$g(x \mid y) \text{ not defined for all } x \text{ if } |y| > 1$$

and

$$h(y \mid x) = \begin{cases} \dfrac{1}{2(1 - |x|)} & \text{for } |y| \le 1 - |x| \text{ if } |x| \le 1 \\ 0 & \text{for } |y| > 1 - |x| \text{ if } |x| \le 1 \end{cases}$$

$h(y \mid x)$ not defined for all y if $|x| > 1$

Clearly X and Y are dependent since, for example, $g(\frac{1}{2} \mid \frac{1}{4}) = 1 \ne g(\frac{1}{2}) = \frac{1}{2}$.

4.2 Normal Bivariate Distribution

4.2.1. If the random variable (X, Y) has a probability density of the type

(4.2.1.1)

$$f(x,y) = \frac{1}{2\pi} \sqrt{A_{11}A_{22} - A_{12}{}^2}\; e^{-1/2[A_{11}(x-x_0)^2 + 2A_{12}(x-x_0)(y-y_0) + A_{22}(y-y_0)^2]}$$

where A_{11}, A_{22}, A_{12} are real constants such that

(4.2.1.2)
$$A_{11} > 0, \qquad A_{11}A_{22} - A_{12}{}^2 > 0$$

and x_0 and y_0 any two real constants, then we shall say that (X, Y) has a normal bivariate probability distribution.

For further discussion we introduce the abbreviations

$$K = (1/2\pi)\sqrt{A_{11}A_{22} - A_{12}{}^2}$$

$$Q(x,y) = A_{11}(x - x_0)^2 + 2A_{12}(x - x_0)(y - y_0) + A_{22}(y - y_0)^2$$

so that (4.2.1.1) becomes

(4.2.1.3)
$$f(x,y) = K \exp\left[-\tfrac{1}{2}Q(x,y)\right]$$

Obviously $f(X, Y)$ fulfills C_1. To verify that C_2 is also fulfilled we observe that after a change of origin, we have:

$$I = \int_{-\infty}^{+\infty} \int_{-\infty}^{+\infty} f(x,y)\,dx\,dy$$

$$= K \int_{-\infty}^{+\infty} \int_{-\infty}^{+\infty} \exp\left\{-\tfrac{1}{2}[A_{11}x^2 + 2A_{12}xy + A_{22}y^2]\right\}dx\,dy$$

$$= K \int_{-\infty}^{+\infty} \int_{-\infty}^{+\infty} \exp\left\{-\frac{A_{11}}{2}\left[x^2 + 2\frac{A_{12}}{A_{11}}xy + \left(\frac{A_{12}}{A_{11}}y\right)^2\right] - \frac{1}{2}\left[A_{22} - \frac{A_{12}{}^2}{A_{11}}\right]y^2\right\}dx\,dy$$

and this, after the change of variables

$$\xi = \left(x + \frac{A_{12}}{A_{11}}y\right)\left(\frac{A_{11}}{2}\right)^{1/2}, \qquad \eta = \left[\frac{1}{2}\left(A_{22} - \frac{A_{12}{}^2}{A_{11}}\right)\right]^{1/2}y$$

becomes

$$I = K \int_{-\infty}^{+\infty} \int_{-\infty}^{+\infty} e^{-\xi^2 - \eta^2} \frac{2}{(A_{11}A_{22} - A_{12}^2)^{1/2}} \, d\xi d\eta$$

$$= \frac{1}{\pi} \int_{-\infty}^{+\infty} e^{-\xi^2} d\xi \int_{-\infty}^{+\infty} e^{-\eta^2} d\eta = 1$$

We notice that

$$Q(x,y) = \left[\sqrt{A_{11}}(x - x_0) + \frac{A_{12}}{\sqrt{A_{11}}}(y - y_0) \right]^2 + \frac{A_{11}A_{22} - A_1^2}{A_{11}}(y - y_0)^2$$

and hence, in view of (4.2.1.2), we have $Q(x,y) > 0$ for all points different from (x_0,y_0). Since $Q(x_0,y_0) = 0$, the probability density $f(x,y)$ has a maximum at the point (x_0,y_0).

To find the marginal probability density $h(y)$ we write

$$h(y) = K \exp\left\{ -\frac{1}{2}\left(A_{22} - \frac{A_{12}^2}{A_{11}}\right)(y - y_0)^2 \right\}$$

$$\times \int_{-\infty}^{+\infty} \exp\left\{ -\frac{A_{11}}{2}\left[(x - x_0) + \frac{A_{12}}{A_{11}}(y - y_0)\right]^2 \right\} dx$$

and make the change of variables

$$\sqrt{\frac{A_{11}}{2}}\left[(x - x_0) + \frac{A_{12}}{A_{11}}(y - y_0)\right] = u$$

We then obtain

$$h(y) = K \exp\left[-\frac{1}{2}\left(A_{22} - \frac{A_{12}^2}{A_{11}}\right)(y - y_0)^2 \right] \int_{-\infty}^{+\infty} e^{-u^2} \sqrt{\frac{2}{A_{11}}} \, du$$

$$= \frac{1}{\sqrt{2\pi}}\left(\frac{A_{11}A_{22} - A_{12}^2}{A_{11}}\right)^{1/2} \exp\left[-\frac{1}{2}\frac{A_{11}A_{22} - A_{12}^2}{A_{11}}(y - y_0)^2 \right]$$

Comparing this with (2.5.5.1) we notice that $h(y)$ is a one-dimensional normal probability density with

$$\sigma = \left(\frac{A_{11}}{A_{11}A_{22} - A_{12}^2}\right)^{1/2}$$

and $a = y_0$. Similarly, we also obtain

$$g(x) = \frac{1}{\sqrt{2\pi}}\left(\frac{A_{11}A_{22} - A_{12}^2}{A_{22}}\right)^{1/2} \exp\left[-\frac{1}{2}\left(\frac{A_{11}A_{22} - A_{12}^2}{A_{22}}\right)(x - x_0)^2 \right]$$

which is a normal one-dimensional probability density with

$$\sigma = \left(\frac{A_{22}}{A_{11}A_{22} - A_{12}^2}\right)^{1/2} \quad \text{and} \quad a = x_0$$

The conditional probability density of X for given Y is

$$g(x \mid y) = \frac{f(x,y)}{h(y)} = \left(\frac{A_{11}}{2\pi}\right)^{1/2} \exp\left\{-\frac{A_{11}}{2}\left[x - \left(x_0 - A_{12}\frac{y-y_0}{A_{11}}\right)\right]^2\right\}$$

A symmetrical expression can be obtained for the conditional probability density $h(y \mid x)$:

$$h(y \mid x) = \left(\frac{A_{22}}{2\pi}\right)^{1/2} \exp\left\{-\frac{A_{22}}{2}\left[y - \left(y_0 - A_{12}\frac{x-x_0}{A_{22}}\right)\right]^2\right\}$$

All these properties of a bivariate normal probability distribution may be summarized as follows.

4.2.2. Theorem. If the random variable (X,Y) has the bivariate normal probability density (4.2.1.1), then the marginal and the conditional probability densities are all one-dimensional normal probability densities, namely

(4.2.2.1) $\quad g(x) = \dfrac{1}{\sqrt{2\pi}\sigma_x} \exp\left[-\dfrac{(x-x_0)^2}{2\sigma_x^2}\right] \quad$ with $\quad \sigma_x = \left(\dfrac{A_{22}}{A_{11}A_{22} - A_{12}^2}\right)^{1/2}$

(4.2.2.2) $\quad h(y) = \dfrac{1}{\sqrt{2\pi}\sigma_y} \exp\left[-\dfrac{(y-y_0)^2}{2\sigma_y^2}\right]$

$$\text{with } \sigma_y = \left(\frac{A_{11}}{A_{11}A_{22} - A_{12}^2}\right)^{1/2}$$

(4.2.2.3) $\quad g(x \mid y) = \dfrac{1}{\sqrt{2\pi}\sigma_x'} \exp\left\{-\dfrac{\left[x - \left[x_0 - \dfrac{A_{12}}{A_{11}}(y-y_0)\right]\right]^2}{2\sigma_x'^2}\right\}$

$$\text{with } \sigma_x' = \frac{1}{\sqrt{A_{11}}}$$

(4.2.2.4) $\quad h(y \mid x) = \dfrac{1}{\sqrt{2\pi}\sigma_y'} \exp\left\{-\dfrac{\left[y - \left[y_0 - \dfrac{A_{12}}{A_{22}}(x-x_0)\right]\right]^2}{2\sigma_y'^2}\right\}$

$$\text{with } \sigma_y' = \frac{1}{\sqrt{A_{22}}}.$$

By using the expressions for σ_x and σ_y in (4.2.2.1) and (4.2.2.2) and putting

(4.2.2.5) $$\rho = -\frac{A_{12}}{(A_{11}A_{22})^{1/2}}$$

we may rewrite (4.2.1.1) in the form

(4.2.2.6) $\quad f(x,y) = \dfrac{1}{2\pi\sigma_x\sigma_y\sqrt{1-\rho^2}}$

$$\times \exp\left\{-\frac{1}{2(1-\rho^2)}\left[\frac{(x-x_0)^2}{\sigma_x^2} - 2\rho\frac{x-x_0}{\sigma_x}\frac{y-y_0}{\sigma_y} + \frac{(y-y_0)^2}{\sigma_y^2}\right]\right\}$$

4.2.3. Theorem. If (X, Y) has a normal bivariate probability distribution then X and Y are independent if and only if $\rho = 0$.

Proof. If $\rho = 0$ then from (4.2.2.6) one immediately obtains $f(x,y) = \varphi(x) \cdot \psi(y)$, i.e., independence according to 4.1.2. If X and Y are independent then $g(x) = g(x \mid y)$ for all values of x and y, and in particular for $x = x_0$, $y = y_0$ so that (4.2.2.1) and (4.2.2.3) give

$$\frac{1}{\sqrt{2\pi}\sigma_x} = \frac{1}{\sqrt{2\pi}\sigma'_x}$$

hence $\sigma_x = \sigma'_x$, and $A_{12} = 0$. But in view of (4.2.2.5), this means $\rho = 0$.

Corollary. If (X, Y) has a normal bivariate probability distribution, then X and Y are independent if and only if $A_{12} = 0$.

Proof. In view of (4.2.2.5) and (4.2.1.2), one has $A_{12} = 0$ if and only if $\rho = 0$, that is, by Theorem 4.2.3, if and only if X and Y are independent.

4.3   The n-Dimensional Case

4.3.1. In a manner quite analogous to that in which the theory of two-dimensional discrete random variables was generalized to n dimensions, the theory of two-dimensional continuous random variables may be generalized to a theory of n-dimensional continuous random variables.

Let $(X^{(1)}, X^{(2)}, \cdots, X^{(n)}) = X_{(n)}$ be a continuous n-dimensional random variable. According to 2.5.2, the corresponding probability density $f(x_{(n)}) = f(x^{(1)}, x^{(2)}, \cdots, x^{(n)})$ satisfies C_1, C_2, and C_3, and the probability measure is defined by (2.5.2.1). In particular, the probability of $X_{(n)}$ falling into a prism r defined by the inequalities

(4.3.1.1) $$x'_j \leq x^{(j)} \leq x''_j, \quad j = 1, 2, \cdots, n$$

is given by the multiple integral

$$P(r) = \int_{x_1'}^{x_1''} \int_{x_2'}^{x_2''} \cdots \int_{x_n'}^{x_n''} f(x^{(1)}, x^{(2)}, \cdots, x^{(n)}) dx^{(n)} \cdots dx^{(2)} dx^{(1)}$$

As pointed out in 2.5.3, it follows from well-known properties of integrals that $P(r)$ will not change when some or all equality signs in (4.3.1.1.) are omitted so that $\leq$ is replaced by $<$, since, then, the region of integration is changed only by omitting some or all of the (less than n-dimensional) faces of the prism r.

The marginal and conditional probability distributions are defined by $D'_n 4$ and $D'_n 5$.

4. Any m coordinates of $X_{(n)}$, such as $X^{(1)}$, $X^{(2)}$, $\cdots$, $X^{(m)}$, with $m < n$, form an m-dimensional continuous random variable $X_{(m)}$, and its

probability density, called the marginal or absolute probability density of $X_{(m)}$, is

$$f(x_{(m)}) = \int_{-\infty}^{+\infty} \cdots \int_{-\infty}^{+\infty} f(x^{(1)}, x^{(2)}, \cdots, x^{(m)}, x^{(m+1)}, \cdots, x^{(n)}) dx^{(m+1)} \cdots dx^{(n)}$$

An analogous statement holds if $X_{(m)}$ consists of any m coordinates of $X_{(n)}$, not just the first m ones.

$D_n'5.$ The conditional probability density of the random variable $X_{(m)} = (X^{(1)}, \cdots, X^{(m)})$ for given value of $X_{(n-m)} = (X^{(m+1)}, \cdots, X^{(n)})$ is defined if $f(x_{(n-m)}) > 0$, and is equal to

$$f(x_{(m)} \mid x_{(n-m)}) = \frac{f(x_{(n)})}{f(x_{(n-m)})} = \frac{f(x^{(1)}, x^{(2)}, \cdots, x^{(n)})}{f(x^{(m+1)}, \cdots, x^{(n)})}$$

An analogous statement holds if $X_{(m)}$ consists of any m coordinates of $X_{(n)}$ and $X_{(n-m)}$ is the supplementary variable.

If $X_{(l)}$ and $X_{(m)}$ are supplementary random variables (with respect to $X_{(l+m)}$) then $X_{(m)}$ is called independent of $X_{(l)}$ if and only if

$$f(x_{(m)} \mid x_{(l)}) = f(x_{(m)})$$

for all values of $x_{(m)}$ and $x_{(l)}$.

The proofs of the following theorems may be left to the reader.

4.3.2. Theorem. If $X_{(m)}$ is independent of $X_{(l)}$ then $X_{(l)}$ is independent of $X_{(m)}$.

4.3.3. Theorem. $X_{(l)}$ and $X_{(m)}$ are independent if and only if

$$f(x_{(l+m)}) = f(x_{(l)}) f(x_{(m)})$$

4.3.4. Theorem. If $X_{(l)}$ and $X_{(m)}$ are supplementary random variables then the equality

$$f(x_{(l)}) = \int_{-\infty}^{+\infty} \cdots \int_{-\infty}^{+\infty} f(x_{(m)}) f(x_{(l)} \mid x_{(m)}) dx_{(m)}$$

holds with integration extended over all the coordinates of $x_{(m)}$.

4.3.5. Theorem (Bayes' Formula). If $X_{(l)}$ and $X_{(m)}$ are supplementary random variables, then the equality holds

$$f(x_{(l)} \mid x_{(m)}) = \frac{f(x_{(m)}) f(x_{(l)} \mid x_{(m)})}{\int_{-\infty}^{+\infty} \cdots \int_{-\infty}^{+\infty} f(x_{(m)}) f(x_{(l)} \mid x_{(m)}) dx_{(m)}}$$

The definition of total independence of continuous random variables is exactly the same as that given in 3.5 for discrete random variables.

4.3.6. Theorem. The one-dimensional random variables $X^{(1)}, X^{(2)}, \cdots, X^{(n)}$ are totally independent if and only if their joint probability density $f(x^{(1)}, \cdots,$

$x^{(n)})$ is the product of their absolute probability densities $f_1(x^{(1)}), f_2(x^{(2)}), \cdots$, $f_n(x^{(n)})$: $f(x^{(1)}, x^{(2)}, \cdots, x^{(n)}) = f_1(x^{(1)}) \cdot f_2(x^{(2)}) \cdots f_n(x^{(n)})$

EXERCISES

4.1. Let (X, Y) be the random variable with uniform probability distribution in the triangle with the vertices $(1,0)$, $(0,1)$, $(0,0)$. Compute $f(x,y)$, $g(x)$, $h(y)$, $g(x \mid y)$, $h(y \mid x)$. Evaluate numerically the probabilities

$$P(X + Y \leq \tfrac{1}{2}), \ P(X \leq \tfrac{1}{2}), \ P(Y \geq \tfrac{1}{4} \mid X = \tfrac{1}{2})$$

4.2. On a line segment of length a, two points A and B are chosen at random. Assuming that the choices are independent and that each choice has a uniform probability distribution, compute the probability density of the random variable $X = $ distance $\overline{AB}$.

4.3. Under the assumptions of Exercise 4.2., compute the probability that the three segments into which A and B divide the segment a form the sides of a possible triangle.

4.4. A line segment AB of length l is divided by a fixed point C into segments AC of length a such that $\tfrac{1}{3} < a < \tfrac{2}{3}$, and CB of length $b = 1 - a$. A point P is selected at random on AC, and a point Q at random on CB. Assuming that the choices of P and Q are independent and that each of them has a uniform probability distribution, find the probability that the distance PQ is not greater than $\tfrac{1}{3}$.

4.5. Let (X, Y) be a random variable with the joint probability density

$$f(x,y) = \begin{cases} \dfrac{(n-1)(n-2)}{(1+x+y)n} & \text{for } x > 0, \ y > 0 \\ 0 & \text{elsewhere} \end{cases}$$

where $n > 2$ is a given constant. Find the marginal probability density $g(x)$, and the conditional probability density $h(y \mid x)$.

4.6. The joint probability density of the two-dimensional random variable (X, Y) is of the form

$$f(x,y) = \begin{cases} ke^{-(x+y)} & \text{for } 0 \leq x \leq y \\ 0 & \text{elsewhere} \end{cases}$$

(a) Determine the constant k.
(b) Find the conditional probability density $g(x \mid y)$.
(c) Compute $P(Y \leq 3)$.

4.7. (X, Y) has the joint probability density

$$f(x,y) = \frac{1}{2\pi} \sqrt{3} \exp \{-[(x-7)^2 + (x-7)y + y^2]\}$$

Are X and Y dependent or independent? Why? Write down the marginal probability densities $g(x)$ and $h(y)$, and the conditional probability densities $g(x \mid y = 5)$, $g(x \mid y = 7)$.

CHAPTER 5

Transformation
of Random Variables

5.1 A General Principle

It was stated in Chapter 1 that the main object of the calculus of probabilities is to derive relationships between the probabilities of various events. A particularly important special case of this general problem presents itself when the probability distribution of a random variable X is given and the functional relationship of X with another variable Y is known, and it is required to determine the probability distribution of Y.

A principle which makes it possible to approach this problem is contained in the following postulate which we state as a further axiom on probabilities.

P_4. Let X be a random variable of any finite number of dimensions, and $Y = \lambda(X)$ a known single-valued function of X.* Then Y is a random variable. If E_y is an event for Y and $\lambda^{(-1)}(E_y)$ is the set of those values of X for which $\lambda(X) \subset E_y$, and if the probability $P[\lambda^{(-1)}(E_y)]$ of the event $\lambda^{(-1)}(E_y)$ for the variable X is determined, then the probability of E_y is determined and we have

$$P(E_y) = P[\lambda^{(-1)}(E_y)]$$

This applies to any continuous as well as any discrete random variable X. The random variable Y, too, may be continuous or discrete and the general principle of P_4 enables us in many specific cases to obtain its probability distribution. The following examples and theorems will illustrate the application of this principle.

---

* The single-valued function $\lambda(X)$ may be quite arbitrary, if X is a discrete random variable. If X is a continuous random variable, then $\lambda(X)$ must be restricted to a family known as Borel-measurable functions. No attempt will be made here to give a definition of this family of functions, but it can be safely said that it is so general that every $\lambda(X)$ ever considered in practical applications of probability theory is Borel-measurable.

5.1.1. Example. A game of dice is played for money according to the following rules. A player bets one dollar and rolls a pair of dice; he loses his dollar if the total X is 6, 7, or 8, and if X is any other number, he receives his dollar back and an additional payment of $2/5$ ($|X - 7| - 1$) dollars. Let Y denote the amount the player wins (-1 if he loses his dollar). We wish to find the probability distribution of Y.

   Solution. The possible values of Y are -1, $2/5$, $4/5$, $6/5$, $8/5$. Consider the events for the variable Y:

$$E_1: \{Y = 1\}; \ E_2: \{Y = 2/5\}; \ E_3: \{Y = 4/5\}; \ E_4: \{Y = 6/5\}; \ E_5: \{Y = 8/5\}.$$

The corresponding events $\lambda^{(-1)}(E_i)$ are:

$$\lambda^{(-1)}(E_1): \{X = 6, 7, \text{ or } 8\}; \ \lambda^{(-1)}(E_2): \{X = 5 \text{ or } 9\}; \ \lambda^{(-1)}(E_3): \{X = 4 \text{ or } 10\};$$
$$\lambda^{(-1)}(E_4): \{X = 3 \text{ or } 11\}; \ \lambda^{(-1)}(E_5): \{X = 2 \text{ or } 12\}$$

According to P_4 and to Example 3.6.1 we have:

$$P(Y = -1) = P(X = 6 \text{ or } 7 \text{ or } 8) = 5/36 + 6/36 + 5/36 = 8/18$$
$$P(Y = 2/5) = P(X = 5 \text{ or } 9) = 4/36 + 4/36 = 4/18$$
$$P(Y = 4/5) = P(X = 4 \text{ or } 10) = 3/36 + 3/36 = 3/18$$
$$P(Y = 6/5) = P(X = 3 \text{ or } 11) = 2/36 + 2/36 = 2/18$$
$$P(Y = 8/5) = P(X = 2 \text{ or } 12) = 1/36 + 1/36 = 1/18$$

We conclude that Y is a discrete random variable with the possible values -1, $2/5$, $4/5$, $6/5$, $8/5$, and the probabilities computed above.

5.1.2. Example (Cauchy's Distribution). A needle spins about the point $(0,b)$ of the (x,y) plane, with $b > 0$, and comes to a stop, thereby determining an angle Φ (see Fig. 5.1.2). The direction of the needle then intersects the x-axis at a point $(X,0)$. Assuming that Φ is a random variable with uniform probability distribution on the interval $(-\pi/2, \pi/2)$, what is the probability distribution of the random variable X?

   To answer this question we note that Φ is assumed to be a continuous random variable with the probability density

$$f(\varphi) = \begin{cases} 1/\pi & \text{for } |\varphi| < \pi/2 \\ 0 & \text{for } |\varphi| > \pi/2 \end{cases}$$

and that X is a known function of Φ

$$X = b \tan \Phi$$

By P_4 we have therefore for any $x_1 < x_2$

$$p\{x_1 < X \leq x_2\} = P\left\{\arctan \frac{x_1}{b} < \Phi \leq \arctan \frac{x_2}{b}\right\}$$
$$= \int_{\arctan x_1/b}^{\arctan x_2/b} f(\varphi)d\varphi = \frac{1}{\pi}\left\{\arctan \frac{x_2}{b} - \arctan \frac{x_1}{b}\right\}$$

In particular the d.f. of X is:

(5.1.2.1) $G(x) = P\{X \le x\} = \dfrac{1}{\pi} \left(\arctan \dfrac{x}{b} + \dfrac{\pi}{2} \right)$

and the differentiation yields the probability density

(5.1.2.2) $g(x) = \dfrac{1}{\pi} \cdot \dfrac{b}{b^2 + x^2}$

The probability distribution given by (5.1.2.1) or (5.1.2.2) is known as Cauchy's distribution. The graph of its probability density is very similar to that of the normal distribution, but its properties are very different.

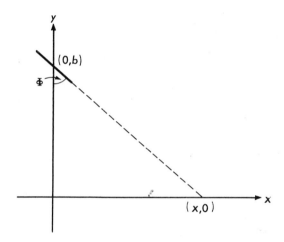

Fig. 5.1.2

5.1.3. Theorem. Let X be a one-dimensional continuous random variable with probability density $f(x)$, and let $y = \psi(x)$ be a strictly monotone function such that the derivative $dy/dx = \psi'(x)$ exists and is different from 0 except, possibly, at a finite number of points. Let, furthermore,

$$\lim_{x \to -\infty} \psi(x) = a, \qquad \lim_{x \to +\infty} \psi(x) = b$$

Then

$$Y = \psi(X)$$

is a continuous random variable with the probability density

(5.1.3.1)

$$g(y) = \begin{cases} f(x)\,|dx/dy| = f[\psi^{(-1)}(y)] / \,|\psi'[\psi^{(-1)}(y)]| & \text{for } a < y < b \\ 0 & \text{for } y < a \text{ and } y > b \end{cases}$$

Proof. Let us first assume $\psi(x)$ increasing. Then $\psi'(x) > 0$ and $g(y)$ defined by (5.1.3.1) is ≥ 0, so that $g(y)$ satisfies C_1. From

$$\int_{-\infty}^{+\infty} g(y)\,dy = \int_a^b g(y)\,dy = \int_{-\infty}^{+\infty} f(x)\,dx = 1$$

we see that $g(y)$ satisfies C_2. To see that $g(y)$ is the probability density for Y, we consider the d.f. for Y which is according to P_4:

For $y < a$:
$$G(y) = P(Y \leq y) = P(\text{empty set for } X) = 0$$

For $a \leq y < b$:
$$G(y) = P(X \leq \psi^{(-1)}(y)) = \int_{-\infty}^{\psi^{(-1)}(y)} f(x)\,dx$$

For $b \leq y$:
$$G(y) = P(Y \leq y) = P(Y \leq b) = P(X < +\infty) = 1$$

By differentiating $G(y)$ one obtains $g(y)$, and the derivatives of the right-hand sides in the three cases yield (5.1.3.1).

If $\psi(x)$ is a decreasing function, an analogous proof may be given, with the modification that instead of $\psi'[\psi^{(-1)}(y)]$ one has to consider $|\psi'[\psi^{(-1)}(y)]|$.

5.1.3.2. Example. Let X have the normal probability distribution with the probability density

$$f(x) = \frac{1}{\sqrt{2\pi}}\, e^{-x^2/2}$$

and let

$$Y = X^{1/3}$$

Find the probability density of Y.

Solution.

$$g(y) = \frac{1}{\sqrt{2\pi}}\, e^{-y^6/2} \cdot \frac{1}{\frac{1}{3}[y^3]^{-2/3}}$$

$$= \frac{3}{\sqrt{2\pi}}\, e^{-y^6/2}\, y^2$$

5.1.3.3. In practical applications, arguments often become formally easier if, instead of talking of the probability densities $f(x)$, $g(y)$, etc., one talks of the *probability elements* $f(x)dx$, $g(y)dy$, etc. In the language of probability elements the statement of Theorem 5.1.3. takes the form:

(5.1.3.3.1) $\quad g(y)dy = \pm f(x)dx$

$$= \pm f[\psi^{(-1)}(y)]\,\frac{dx}{dy}\,dy$$

$$= \pm f[\psi^{(-1)}(y)]\,\frac{1}{\psi'[\psi^{(-1)}(y)]}\,dy$$

for $a < y < b$, with the plus sign if $\psi(x)$ is increasing, the minus sign if $\psi(x)$ is decreasing, and

$$g(y)dy = 0 \quad \text{for } y < a \text{ and } y > b$$

An important particular case of (5.1.3.3.1) is that in which Y is a linear function of X. Then the following theorem holds.

5.1.3.4. Theorem. If X is a one-dimensional continuous random variable with the probability density $f(x)$ and if $Y = \alpha X + \beta$, with $\alpha \neq 0$, then Y is a continuous random variable with the probability density

$$g(y) = \frac{1}{|\alpha|} f\left(\frac{y - \beta}{\alpha}\right)$$

Proof. By (5.1.3.3.1)

$$g(y)dy = f(x)dx = f\left(\frac{y - \beta}{\alpha}\right)\frac{dy}{|\alpha|} \quad \text{for } -\infty < y < +\infty$$

It should be emphasized that Theorem 5.1.3 does not cover all cases of transformation of a one-dimensional continuous random variable, mainly in view of the restrictive assumptions of $\psi(X)$. If the assumptions of Theorem 5.1.3 are not fulfilled, it still is in many cases possible to find the probability distribution of the transformed variable by direct application of postulate P_4. This procedure is illustrated in the following example which has some useful applications.

5.1.3.5. Example. Let X have the normal distribution

$$f(x) = \frac{1}{\sigma\sqrt{2\pi}} e^{-(x-a)^2/2\sigma^2}$$

and let $Y = |X - a|$. What is the probability density of Y?
Solution. We consider the d.f. $G(y) = P(Y \leq y)$. The event $Y \leq y$ for the variable Y corresponds to the event $|X - a| \leq y$, i.e., to the event $a - y < X < a + y$ for the variable X. If $y < 0$, this event for X is the empty set, and

$$G(y) = 0$$

For $y \geq 0$ we have:

$$G(y) = P(a - y < X < a + y)$$

$$= \frac{1}{\sigma\sqrt{2\pi}} \int_{a-y}^{a+y} e^{-(x-a)^2/2\sigma^2} dx$$

$$= \frac{2}{\sigma\sqrt{2\pi}} \int_0^y e^{-u^2/2\sigma^2} du$$

By putting

$$g(y) = \begin{cases} 0 & \text{for } y < 0 \\ (2/\sigma\sqrt{2\pi})\, e^{-y/2\sigma^2} & \text{for } y \geq 0 \end{cases}$$

we have

$$G(y) = P(Y \leq y) = \int_{-\infty}^{y} g(y)dy$$

for all real values of y. Since $g(y)$ obviously satisfies P_1 and P_2, it is the probability density of Y.

5.1.4. Theorem. If the random variables $X_1, X_2, \cdots, X_{n-1}, X_n$ are totally independent, then X_n and $S_{n-1} = X_1 + X_2 + \cdots + X_{n-1}$ are independent.

Proof. We shall prove this theorem for $n = 3$. The general case follows by induction. Let the three variables be X_1, X_2, X_3. In the discrete case let X_1 have the possible values x_{1i}, $(i = 1,2,\cdots)$, X_2 the possible values x_{2j} $(j = 1,2,\cdots)$, and X_3 the possible values x_{3k} $(k = 1,2,\cdots)$. The assumption of total independence implies that the joint probability is the product of the three absolute probabilities

$$f(x_{1i},x_{2j},x_{3k}) = f_1(x_{1i}) \cdot f_2(x_{2j}) \cdot f_3(x_{3k})$$

Let $S_2 = X_1 + X_2$, and let its possible values be s_{2l}, $(l = 1,2,\cdots)$. Then the joint probability of S_2 and X_3 is, by virtue of postulate P_4, equal to

$$\begin{aligned} h(s_{2l},x_{3k}) &= P(X_1 + X_2 = s_{2l} \quad \text{and} \quad X_3 = x_{3k}) \\ &= \sum_{x_{1i}+x_{2j}=s_{2l}} f(x_{1i},x_{2j},x_{3k}) \\ &= \sum_{x_{1i}+x_{2j}=s_{2l}} f_1(x_{1i})f_2(x_{2j}) \cdot f_3(x_{3k}) \\ &= P(S_2 = s_{2l}) \cdot f_3(x_{3k}) \end{aligned}$$

which proves that S_2 and X_3 are independent. In the continuous case let $h(s_2,x_3)$ denote the joint probability density of S_2, X_3, and $g(s_2)$ the probability density of $S_2 = X_1 + X_2$. Then we have

$$\begin{aligned} P(S_2 \leq s_2, X_3 \leq x_3) &= \int_{-\infty}^{s_2} \int_{-\infty}^{x_3} h(u,v)dudv \\ &= P(X_1 + X_2 \leq s_2, X_3 \leq x_3) \\ &= \underset{\substack{t_1+t_2 \leq s_2 \\ t_3 \leq x_3}}{\int\int\int} f_1(t_1) f_2(t_2) f_3(t_3)dt_1dt_2dt_3 \\ &= \underset{t_1+t_2 \leq s_2}{\int\int} f_1(t_1) f_2(t_2)\, dt_1dt_2 \int_{-\infty}^{x_3} f_3(t_3)dt_3 \\ &= P(S_2 \leq s_2) \cdot P(X_3 \leq t_3) \end{aligned}$$

hence S_2 and X_3 independent.

The following theorem is a generalization of Theorem 5.1.3 to n dimensions:

5.1.5. Theorem. Let $X_{(n)} = (X^{(1)}, \cdots, X^{(n)})$ be an n-dimensional continuous random variable with a probability density $f(x^{(1)}, \cdots, x^{(n)})$ which is zero outside of a region Ω_x in the $(X_{(n)})$ space. Let

(5.1.5.1) $\qquad X^{(j)} = \psi_j(Y^{(1)}, \cdots, Y^{(n)}), \quad \text{for } j = 1, 2, \cdots, n$

be a transformation defined in a region Ω_y of the $(y_{(n)})$ space, such that to every point $(y^{(1)}, \cdots, y^{(n)}) = (y_{(n)})$ in Ω_y corresponds one and only one point of Ω_x, and that the Jacobian

$$J(y^{(1)}, \cdots, y^{(n)}) = \frac{\partial(x^{(1)}, \cdots, x^{(n)})}{\partial(y^{(1)}, \cdots, y^{(n)})}$$

exists, is continuous, and does not change signs in Ω_y. Then $(Y^{(1)}, \cdots, Y_{(n)})$ defined by (5.1.5.1) is a continuous random variable with a probability density $g(y^{(1)}, \cdots, y^{(n)})$ such that

(5.1.5.2) $\quad g(y^{(1)}, \cdots, y^{(n)}) = \begin{cases} f[\psi_1(y^{(1)}, \cdots, y^{(n)}), \cdots, \psi_n(y^{(1)}, \cdots, y^{(n)})] \times \\ \quad |J(y^{(1)}, \cdots, y^{(n)})| \quad \text{for } (y^{(1)}, \cdots, y^{(n)}) \text{ in } \Omega_y \\ 0 \qquad\qquad\qquad\qquad \text{for } (y^{(1)}, \cdots, y^{(n)}) \text{ outside } \Omega_y \end{cases}$

We shall only briefly indicate the proof of this theorem. Let

$$y'_j \leq y^{(j)} \leq y''_j, \quad j = 1, 2, \cdots, n$$

be a prism r in $(y_{(n)})$ space, contained in Ω_y. Transformation (5.1.5.1) maps it into a region R of the $(x_{(n)})$ space. According to P_4 we have

$$P(Y_{(n)} \in r) = P(X_{(n)} \in R)$$

But we have

$$P(X_{(n)} \in R) = \int \cdots \int_{(R)} f(x^{(1)}, \cdots, x^{(n)}) dx^{(1)} \cdots dx^{(n)}$$

and, according to a well-known theorem* on transformation of multiple integrals, this n-fold integral is equal to

(5.1.5.3) $\quad \displaystyle\int_{y'_n}^{y''_n} \cdots \int_{y'_1}^{y''_1} f[\psi_1(y^{(1)}, \cdots, y^{(n)}), \cdots, \psi_n(y^{(1)}, \cdots, y^{(n)})]$
$$\times |J(y^{(1)}, \cdots, y^{(n)})| \, dy^{(1)} \cdots dy^{(n)}$$

Thus $P(r)$ has the value (5.1.5.3) for any prism r contained in Ω_y. The set in $(x_{(n)})$ space which corresponds by (5.1.5.1) to any prism r located outside of Ω_y is the empty set, hence $P(r) = 0$ for r outside of Ω_y. From this one concludes that

$$P(Y_{(n)} \in r) = \int \cdots \int_{(r)} g(y^{(1)}, \cdots, y^{(n)}) dy^{(1)} \cdots dy^{(n)}$$

for any prism r in $(y_{(n)})$ space, located in Ω_y, outside Ω_y, or partly in and partly outside Ω_y. By verifying that $g(y^{(1)}, \cdots, y^{(n)})$ satisfies postulates $C_n 1$ and $C_n 2$, one completes the proof.

5.2   The Sum of Continuous Random Variables

5.2.1. Theorem.   If the two-dimensional continuous random variable (X, Y) has the joint probability density $f(x,y)$, then $Z = X + Y$ is a one-dimensional continuous random variable with the probability density

$$(5.2.1.1) \qquad h(z) = \int_{-\infty}^{+\infty} f(x, z - x)dx = \int_{-\infty}^{+\infty} f(z - y, y)dy$$

Proof.   The event $Z \leq z$ for Z corresponds to the set $X + Y \leq z$ in the (X, Y) space and, according to P_4, we have for the d.f. of Z

$$H(z) = P(Z \leq z)$$
$$= P(X + Y \leq z)$$
$$= \iint_{x+y \leq z} f(x,y)dxdy$$
$$= \int_{x=-\infty}^{+\infty} \left[\int_{y=-\infty}^{z-x} f(x,y)dy \right] dx$$
$$= \int_{x=-\infty}^{+\infty} \left[\int_{Z=-\infty}^{z} f(x, Z-x)dZ \right] dx$$
$$= \int_{Z=-\infty}^{z} \left[\int_{x=-\infty}^{+\infty} f(x, Z-x)dx \right] dZ$$
$$= \int_{-\infty}^{z} h(Z)dZ$$

where $h(Z)$ is defined by the first expression in (5.2.1.1). By differentiation we conclude that $h(z)$ is the probability density of Z. The change from a double integral to a repeated integral in this proof, as well as the change of the order of integration, are justified since $f(x,y)$ is absolutely integrable over the entire (x,y) plane according to C_1 and C_3. The second expression for $h(z)$ in (5.2.1.1) can be derived by a symmetrical argument.

5.2.2. Theorem.   If (X, Y) has a bivariate normal probability distribution then $Z = X + Y$ is a one-dimensional normal random variable.

Proof.   The joint probability density of (X, Y) is, by assumption,

$$(4.2.1.3) \qquad\qquad f(x,y) = Ke^{-1/2Q(x,y)}$$

where K, Q have been defined in section 4.2. By theorem 5.2.1 the probability density of Z is

$$g(z) = K \int_{-\infty}^{+\infty} e^{-1/2Q(z-y,y)} dy$$

By putting

(5.2.2.1) $x_0 + y_0 = z_0,$ $x + y = z$

we have

$$Q(x,y) = A_{11}(x - x_0)^2 + 2A_{12}(x - x_0)(y - y_0) + A_{22}(y - y_0)^2$$
$$= A_{11}[(z - z_0) - (y - y_0)]^2 + 2A_{12}[(z - z_0) - (y - y_0)](y - y_0)$$
$$+ A_{22}(y - y_0)^2$$
$$= A_{11}(z - z_0)^2 + (A_{11} - 2A_{12} + A_{22})(y - y_0)^2$$
$$+ 2(A_{12} - A_{11})(z - z_0)(y - y_0)$$
$$= \left(A_{11} - \frac{(A_{12} - A_{11})^2}{A_{11} - 2A_{12} + A_{22}} \right)(z - z_0)^2$$
$$+ \left[(A_{11} - 2A_{12} + A_{22})^{1/2}(y - y_0) + \frac{A_{12} - A_{11}}{(A_{11} - 2A_{12} + A_{22})^{1/2}}(z - z_0) \right]^2$$

In view of (4.2.1.2) we find

$$A_{11} - 2A_{12} + A_{22} > A_{11} - 2\sqrt{A_{11}A_{22}} + A_{22} = (\sqrt{A_{11}} - \sqrt{A_{22}})^2 \geq 0$$

hence

$$A_{11} - \frac{(A_{12} - A_{11})^2}{A_{11} - 2A_{12} + A_{22}} = \frac{A_{11}A_{22} - A_{12}^2}{A_{11} - 2A_{12} + A_{22}} > 0$$

With the abbreviations

$$b = \frac{A_{11}A_{22} - A_{12}^2}{A_{11} - 2A_{12} + A_{22}}, \qquad c = \sqrt{A_{11} - 2A_{12} + A_{22}}, \qquad d = \frac{A_{12} - A_{11}}{c}$$

we may write

$$g(z) = K \int_{-\infty}^{+\infty} e^{-1/2b(z-z_0)^2} \exp\left\{ -\tfrac{1}{2}[c(y - y_0) + d(z - z_0)]^2 \right\} dy$$
$$= K \exp\left[-\tfrac{1}{2}b(z - z_0)^2 \right] \int_{-\infty}^{+\infty} \exp\left\{ -\tfrac{1}{2}[c(y - y_0) + d(z - z_0)]^2 \right\} dy$$

By making the change of variables

$$\frac{1}{\sqrt{2}}[c(y - y_0) + d(z - z_0)] = u$$

we obtain

$$\int_{-\infty}^{+\infty} \exp\left\{ -\tfrac{1}{2}[c(y - y_0) + d(z - z_0)]^2 dy = \frac{\sqrt{2}}{c} \int_{-\infty}^{+\infty} e^{-u^2} du = \frac{\sqrt{2\pi}}{c}$$

We thus have for the probability density of Z the expression

(5.2.2.2) $g(z) = \dfrac{K\sqrt{2\pi}}{c} \exp\left[-\dfrac{b(z-z_0)^2}{2}\right] = \dfrac{(A_{11}A_{22} - A_{12}{}^2)^{1/2}}{(2\pi)^{1/2} \cdot (A_{11} - 2A_{12} + A_{22})^{1/2}}$

$$\times \exp\left[-\frac{A_{11}A_{22} - A_{12}{}^2}{2(A_{11} - 2A_{12} + A_{22})}(z - z_0)^2\right]$$

which is a one-dimensional normal probability density with

$$\sigma^2 = \frac{A_{11} - 2A_{12} + A_{22}}{A_{11}A_{22} - A_{12}{}^2}, \quad a = z_0$$

Theorem 5.2.2 is often referred to as the *reproductive property of normal variables*. It may be worth pointing out that independence is not assumed in this theorem: Under the additional assumption of independence one obtains as a special case the following very important statement:

5.2.3. Theorem. If X and Y are independent normally distributed random variables with the probability densities

$$f(x) = \frac{1}{\sqrt{2\pi}\sigma_x} \exp\left[-\frac{(x - x_0)^2}{2\sigma_x{}^2}\right]$$

$$g(y) = \frac{1}{\sqrt{2\pi}\sigma_y} \exp\left[-\frac{(y - y_0)^2}{2\sigma_y{}^2}\right]$$

then the random variable

$$Z = X + Y$$

has the normal probability density

$$h(z) = \frac{1}{\sqrt{2\pi}\sigma_z} \exp\left[-\frac{(z - z_0)^2}{2\sigma_z{}^2}\right]$$

where

$$z_0 = x_0 + y_0 \quad \text{and} \quad \sigma_z = \sqrt{\sigma_x{}^2 + \sigma_y{}^2}$$

Proof. Since X and Y are independent, their joint probability density is $f(x) \cdot g(y)$ and is, by the Corollary to 4.2.2, a bivariate normal probability density with $A_{12} = 0$. By substituting this in (5.2.2.2) we obtain

$$g(z) = \frac{(A_{11}A_{22})^{1/2}}{(2\pi)^{1/2}(A_{11} + A_{22})^{1/2}} \exp\left[-\frac{A_{11}A_{22}}{2(A_{11} + A_{22})}\right](z - z_0)^2$$

and according to (4.2.2.1), (4.2.2.2.), (5.2.2.1), this equals

$$\frac{1}{(2\pi)^{1/2}(\sigma_x{}^2 + \sigma_y{}^2)^{1/2}} \exp\left\{-\frac{[z - (x_0 + y_0)]^2}{2(\sigma_x{}^2 + \sigma_y{}^2)}\right\}$$

5.3. Theorem. Let X be a continuous random variable with the probability density $f(x)$. Then

$$U = X^2$$

is a continuous random variable with the probability density

$$h(u) = \begin{cases} \dfrac{1}{2\sqrt{u}} [f(\sqrt{u}) + f(-\sqrt{u})] & \text{for } u > 0 \\ 0 & \text{for } u \leq 0 \end{cases}$$

Proof. According to P_4 we have, with $U = X^2$,

$$P(U \leq u) = P(X^2 \leq u) = P(-\sqrt{u} \leq X \leq \sqrt{u})$$

$$= \int_{-\sqrt{u}}^{+\sqrt{u}} f(x)dx = \int_0^{\sqrt{u}} f(x)dx + \int_0^{\sqrt{u}} f(-x)dx$$

$$= \int_0^u h(s)ds = \int_{-\infty}^u h(s)ds \quad \text{for } u \geq 0$$

and

$$P(U \leq u) = P \text{ (empty set for the variable } X) = 0 \quad \text{for } u \leq 0.$$

Thus we have

$$P(U \leq u) = \int_{-\infty}^u h(s)ds$$

for all real values of u and $h(u)$ is the probability density of U.

EXERCISES

5.1. If X has the uniform probability density in $(-1,1)$, what is the probability distribution (a) of $Y = \sin(\pi/2)X$, (b) of $Z = \cos(\pi/2)X$?

5.2. Let X be the random variable with uniform probability distribution in the interval $0 \leq X \leq 1$. Find the probability distribution (a) of $Y = X^2$, (b) of $Y = 1/X$.

5.3. Let X have the probability density $f(x) = ke^{-|x|}$. Compute the constant k, then find the probability density of $U = X^2$.

5.4. The random variable X has the probability density

$$(X) = \begin{cases} 0 & \text{for } X \leq -a \\ \dfrac{1}{a^2}(a + X) & \text{for } -a \leq X \leq 0 \\ \dfrac{1}{a^2}(a - X) & \text{for } 0 \leq X \leq a \\ 0 & \text{for } a \leq X \end{cases}$$

Find the probability density of the random variable $Y = e^X$.

5.5. Let X and Y be independent random variables with the Cauchy distributions

$$\frac{1}{\pi} \cdot \frac{a}{a^2 + X^2} \quad \text{and} \quad \frac{1}{\pi} \cdot \frac{b}{b^2 + Y^2}$$

Find the probability distribution of $Z = X + Y$.

5.6. Let X_1 and X_2 be independent random variables, each with uniform probability distribution in the interval $(0,1)$. Find the probability distribution (a) of $S = X_1 + X_2$, (b) $\bar{X}_2 = (X_1 + X_2)/2$.

5.7. Let X_1, X_2, X_3 be independent random variables, each with uniform probability distribution in the interval $(0,1)$. Prove that the random variable $S = X_1 + X_2 + X_3$ has the probability density

$$f(s) = \begin{cases} \frac{1}{2}s^2 & \text{for } 0 < s \leq 1 \\ \frac{1}{2}[s^2 - 3(s-1)^2] & \text{for } 1 < s \leq 2 \\ \frac{1}{2}[s^2 - 3(s-1)^2 + 3(s-2)^2] & \text{for } 2 < s \leq 3 \\ 0 & \text{for } s \leq 0 \text{ and for } 3 < s \end{cases}$$

Plot $f(s)$; observe its close resemblance to a normal probability density.

5.8. Let X and Y be independent random variables, with the distribution functions $F(x)$ and $G(y)$.

(a) Consider the random variables $V = \min(X,Y)$, $W = \text{Max}(X,Y)$. What are their d.f.'s?

(b) Assume that X and Y each have the uniform distribution in $(0,1)$, and find the d.f.'s of V and W.

(c) Assume that X and Y have probability densities $f(x) = e^{-x}$ for $x \geq 0$ and 0 for $x < 0$, $g(y) = e^{-y}$ for $y \geq 0$, and 0 for $y < 0$, and find the d.f.'s of V and W.

5.9. Prove the statement: If the two-dimensional random variables (U_1, V_1) and (U_2, V_2) are independent, and if U_1 and V_1 are independent and U_2 and V_2 are independent, then the four one-dimensional random variables U_1, V_1, U_2, V_2 are independent and the random variables $U_1 + U_2$ and $V_1 + V_2$ are independent.

CHAPTER 6

Mathematical Expectation

6.1 Definitions and Examples

6.1.1. Let X be a discrete one-dimensional random variable with the possible values $x_1, x_2, \cdots, x_j, \cdots$ and the probabilities $f(x_1), f(x_2), \cdots f(x_j), \cdots$ and let $\varphi(x)$ be a single-valued real function of x, defined for all values $x = x_j$, $j = 1, 2, \cdots$. If the sum $\sum_{(j)} |\varphi(x_j)| f(x_j)$, extended over all possible values of X, is finite, we shall say that the *mathematical expectation of $\varphi(X)$*, in symbols $E[\varphi(X)]$, exists and is equal to

(6.1.1.1) $$E[\varphi(X)] = \sum_{(j)} \varphi(x_j) \cdot f(x_j)$$

In other words, the sum (6.1.1.1) will be called the mathematical expectation of $\varphi(X)$ if it converges absolutely. If $\sum_{(j)} |\varphi(x_j)| f(x_j)$ is divergent, we shall say that the mathematical expectation of $\varphi(x_j)$ does not exist. Clearly the mathematical expectation of any $\varphi(X)$ always exists if X is a discrete random variable with a finite number of possible values.

In particular, for $\varphi(x) = x$ the sum

(6.1.1.2) $$E(X) = \sum_{(j)} x_j f(x_j)$$

extended over all possible values of X will be called the mathematical expectation of the random variable X, provided that $\sum_{(j)} |x_j| f(x_j)$ converges.

For the mathematical expectation of X we shall also use the symbol x_0 so that

$$E(X) = x_0$$

6.1.1.3. Example. Let X be the number of points obtained in one throw of a die. Then

$$E(X) = 1 \cdot \tfrac{1}{6} + 2 \cdot \tfrac{1}{6} + 3 \cdot \tfrac{1}{6} + 4 \cdot \tfrac{1}{6} + 5 \cdot \tfrac{1}{6} + 6 \cdot \tfrac{1}{6}$$
$$= \frac{1}{6} \sum_{j=1}^{6} j = \frac{7}{2}$$

6.1.1.4. Example. Let X again be the outcome of one throw of a die, and $\varphi(x) = x^2$. Then

$$E[\varphi(X)] = E(X^2) = (1^2 + 2^2 + 3^2 + 4^2 + 5^2 + 6^2)\frac{1}{6} = \frac{91}{6}$$

6.1.1.5. Example. Let X be the number of throws of a pair of dice up to and including the throw which produces the first double six. The random variable X is discrete and has the infinitely many possible values $1, 2, 3, \cdots$, $j, \cdots$, with the corresponding probabilities

$$\frac{1}{36}, \frac{35}{36} \cdot \frac{1}{36}, \left(\frac{35}{36}\right)^2 \cdot \frac{1}{36}, \cdots, \left(\frac{35}{36}\right)^{j-1} \cdot \frac{1}{36}, \cdots$$

Since all possible values of X are positive, the series (6.1.1.2) is absolutely convergent if it converges at all. This is the case and we have

$$E(X) = \sum_{j=1}^{\infty} j \left(\frac{35}{36}\right)^{j-1} \cdot \frac{1}{36}$$

$$= \frac{1}{36} \left[\frac{d}{dx} \sum_{j=0}^{\infty} x^j \right]_{x=35/36}$$

$$= \frac{1}{36} \left[\frac{d}{dx} \frac{1}{1-x} \right]_{x=35/36}$$

$$= \frac{1}{36} \left[\frac{1}{(1-x)^2} \right]_{x=35/36} = 36$$

6.1.1.6. Example. Let X have the possible values $2, -2, \frac{8}{3}, -4, \cdots$, $(-1)^{j+1}(2^j/j), \cdots$, and the corresponding probabilities $\frac{1}{2}, \frac{1}{4}, \cdots, (\frac{1}{2})^j, \cdots$. Then

$$\sum_{(j)} |x_j| f(x_j) = \sum_{(j)} \frac{2^j}{j} \cdot \frac{1}{2^j} = \sum_{j=1}^{\infty} \frac{1}{j}$$

is a divergent series, and the expectation of X does not exist, although

$$\sum_{(j)} x_j f(x_j) = \sum_{j=1}^{\infty} (-1)^{j+1} \frac{1}{j}$$

converges.

6.1.1.7. In a game played for money in which X denotes the financial outcome of the game for one player and $x_1, x_2, \cdots, x_j, \cdots$ are the different possible financial outcomes, $E(X)$ represents an estimate of the prospects for this player. Later on it will be seen that, under certain conditions, if a gambler plays the same game independently many times, he may expect to average a financial outcome of about $E(X)$ per game, this being a gain if $E(X)$ is positive, a loss if it is negative. This property of $E(X)$ as well as more general properties stated in the different formulations of the law of large numbers (Theorems 6.5.3, 6.5.4, 6.5.5) explain why $E(X)$ is called "mathematical expectation" of X. If the rules of a game of chance played for money are such that they give a participant a mathematical expectation equal to zero then that game is called "fair" for this participant. If for a participant in a game the expectation $E(X)$ is positive, the game is called "favorable." and if $E(X)$ is negative it is called "unfavorable" for this participant.

6.1.1.8. Example. A game of roulette usually consists of the numbers $0, 1, 2, \cdots, 36.$* In view of the symmetrical construction of the roulette wheel, one assumes that each of those 37 numbers is equally probable, i.e., has the probability $1/37$ to appear in a single game. Eighteen of the numbers $1, \ldots, 36$ are red, the other eighteen are black, and 0 is "gray." Roulette may be played by many individual players against the house. Some of the different ways of playing are: (*a*) Betting on a color (red or black). If a number of this color comes out the player receives double his stake, if the other color or zero comes out he loses the stake. (*b*) Betting on a single number. If that number comes out, the player receives 36 times his stake, if it does not come out, he loses the stake. (*c*) Betting on a given dozen (first dozen: 1–12, second dozen: 13–24, third dozen: 25–36). If a number of that dozen comes out, the player receives three times his stake, otherwise he loses the stake. It is easily verified that in each of these variants of the game the mathematical expectation for the player is $-1/37$, and for the house $+1/37$, so that the game is unfavorable for the player and favorable for the house.

6.1.2. Let X be a continuous one-dimensional random variable with the probability density $f(x)$ and let $\varphi(x)$ be a single-valued, real function of x, defined for all real values of x. If the integral $\int_{-\infty}^{+\infty} |\varphi(x)| f(x) dx$ exists, we shall say that the *mathematical expectation of $\varphi(x)$* exists and is equal to

(**6.1.2.1**) $$E[\varphi(X)] = \int_{-\infty}^{+\infty} \varphi(x) f(x) dx$$

In particular, for $\varphi(x) = x$, we have

$$E(X) = \int_{-\infty}^{+\infty} x f(x) dx$$

and, as in the discrete case, we shall use the notation $E(X) = x_0$.

---

* There are other roulette wheels in use which have two zeros. The odds offered to the player are also not always the same as those described here.

6.1.2.2. Example. Let X be the random variable with a uniform probability density in the interval
$$a \leq x \leq a + l$$

According to (2.5.4.2) the probability density is $f(x) = 1/l$ for $a \leq x \leq a + l$, and $f(x) = 0$ for all other values of x. Hence,

$$\int_{-\infty}^{+\infty} |x| f(x)dx = \int_a^{a+l} |x| f(x)dx$$
$$= \frac{1}{l} \int_a^{a+l} |x| \, dx = \text{a finite number}$$

and the expectation of X exists and is equal to

$$E(X) = \frac{1}{l} \int_a^{a+l} x dx = \frac{1}{l}\left[\frac{(a+l)^2}{2} - \frac{a^2}{2}\right] = a + \frac{l}{2}$$

which is the midpoint of the range for X.

6.1.2.3. Example. If X has the normal probability distribution with the density

$$f(x) = \frac{1}{\sigma\sqrt{2\pi}} e^{-(x-x_0)^2/2\sigma^2}$$

then the integral

$$\int_{-\infty}^{+\infty} |x| \, f(x)dx$$

exists, as may be easily verified. Hence the mathematical expectation of X exists and is equal to

$$E(X) = \frac{1}{\sigma\sqrt{2\pi}} \int_{-+}^{+\infty} x e^{-(x-x_0)^2/2\sigma^2} dx$$
$$= \frac{1}{\sigma\sqrt{2\pi}} \int_{-\infty}^{+\infty} (u + x_0) e^{-u^2/2\sigma^2} du$$
$$= \frac{1}{\sigma\sqrt{2\pi}}\left[\int_{-\infty}^{+\infty} u e^{-u^2/2\sigma^2} du + x_0 \int_{-\infty}^{+\infty} e^{-u^2/2\sigma^2} du\right] = x_0$$

since the integrand $ue^{-u^2/2\sigma^2}$ of the first integral is an odd function, and

$$\int_{-\infty}^{+\infty} e^{-u^2/2\sigma^2} \, du = \sigma\sqrt{2\pi}$$

6.1.2.4. Example. Let X be a continuous random variable with Cauchy's distribution

(6.1.2.2) $$g(x) = \frac{1}{\pi} \frac{b}{b^2 + x^2} \quad \text{for } -\infty < x < +\infty$$

Since the integral

$$\int_{-\infty}^{+\infty} |x|\, g(x)\, dx = \frac{b}{\pi} \int_{-\infty}^{+\infty} \frac{|x|}{b^2 + x^2}\, dx$$

has no finite value, $E(X)$ does not exist.

6.1.3.   The definition of the mathematical expectation of a function $\varphi(X)$ of a one-dimensional random variable X is easily extended to the case when the random variable is n-dimensional, $n \geq 2$. For a two-dimensional discrete random variable (X, Y) with the possible values (x_j, y_k) and the probabilities $f(x_j, y_k), j = 1, 2, \cdots, k = 1, 2, \cdots$, the expectation of a function $\varphi(X, Y)$ is defined as the number

$$E[\varphi(X, Y)] = \sum_{(j)} \sum_{(k)} \varphi(x_j, y_k) f(x_j, y_k)$$

if the series on the right-hand side is absolutely convergent. Similarly, if (X, Y) is a continuous two-dimensional random variable with the probability density $f(x, y)$, the expectation of a function $\varphi(X, Y)$ is defined by

$$E[\varphi(X, Y)] = \int_{-\infty}^{+\infty} \int_{-\infty}^{+\infty} \varphi(x, y)\, f(x, y)\, dx\, dy$$

provided that

$$\int_{-\infty}^{+\infty} \int_{-\infty}^{+\infty} |\varphi(x, y)|\, f(x, y)\, dx\, dy$$

has a finite value.

The extension of these definitions to any number of dimensions is obvious.

6.2   Properties of Mathematical Expectations

6.2.1. Theorem.   If the expectation $E[\varphi(X)]$ exists for a random variable X and a function $\varphi(X)$ then, for any constant C, the expectation of $C\varphi(X)$ exists and is equal to

$$E[C\varphi(X)] = CE[\varphi(X)]$$

Proof.   If X is a discrete random variable then

$$E[C\varphi(X)] = \sum_{(j)} C\varphi(x_j) f(x_j) = C \sum_{(j)} \varphi(x_j) f(x_j) = CE[\varphi(X)]$$

and the sum $\sum_{(j)} C\varphi(x_j) f(x_j)$ is absolutely convergent together with $\sum_{(j)} \varphi(x_j) f(x_j)$.
Similarly, if X is a continuous random variable we have

$$E[C\varphi(X)] = \int_{-\infty}^{+\infty} C\varphi(x) f(x)\, dx = C \int_{-\infty}^{+\infty} \varphi(x) f(x)\, dx = CE[\varphi(x)]$$

and

$$\int_{-\infty}^{+\infty} |C\varphi(x)|\, f(x)\, dx = |C| \int_{-\infty}^{+\infty} |\varphi(x)|\, f(x)\, dx$$

is finite if $E[\varphi(X)]$ exists.

6.2.2. Theorem. For any random variable X and any constant c we have

$$E(c) = c$$

Proof. For discrete as well as for continuous X we have

$$E(1) = 1$$

for, in the discrete case,

$$E(1) = \sum_{(j)} 1 \cdot f(x_j) = 1$$

and in the continuous case

$$E(1) = \int_{-\infty}^{+\infty} 1 \cdot f(x)\, dx = 1$$

Hence, by 6.2.1, we find

$$E(c) = E(c \cdot 1) = cE(1) = c$$

6.2.3. Theorem (Addition Theorem for Mathematical Expectations).
Let (X, Y) be a two-dimensional random variable, discrete or continuous, and
let $\lambda(x)$ and $\psi(y)$ be two functions such that the expectations $E[\lambda(X)]$ and
$E[\psi(Y)]$, computed from the absolute distributions of X and of Y, exist. Then
the mathematical expectation of $\varphi(X, Y) = \lambda(X) + \psi(Y)$ also exists and we
have

(6.2.3.1) $E[\varphi(X, Y)] = E[\lambda(X) + \psi(Y)] = E[\lambda(X)] + E[\psi(Y)]$

Proof. If (X, Y) is a discrete random variable and (x_j, y_k) are its possible
values, $f(x_j, y_k)$ its probabilities, then

$$\sum_{(j)} \sum_{(k)} \varphi(x_j, y_k) f(x_j, y_k) = \sum_{(j)} \sum_{(k)} [\lambda(x_j) + \psi(y_k)] f(x_j, y_k)$$

$$= \sum_{(j)} \lambda(x_j) \sum_{(k)} f(x_j, y_k) + \sum_{(k)} \psi(y_k) \sum_{(j)} f(x_j, y_k)$$

$$= \sum_{(j)} \lambda(x_j) g(x_j) + \sum_{(k)} \psi(y_k) h(y_k)$$

$$= E[\lambda(X)] + E[\psi(Y)]$$

Since this equality also shows that

$$\sum_{(j)} \sum_{(k)} |\varphi(x_j, y_k)| f(x_j, y_k) \le \sum_{(j)} |\lambda(x_j)|\, g(x_j) + \sum_{(k)} |\psi(y_k)|\, h(y_k)$$

and the last two sums converge by assumption, and since

$$E[\varphi(X, Y)] = \sum_{(j)} \sum_{(k)} \varphi(x_j, y_k) f(x_j, y_k)$$

if that sum is absolutely convergent, the existence of $E[\varphi(X, Y)]$ and equality
(6.2.3.1) are proved.

If (X, Y) is a continuous random variable with probability density $f(x,y)$, we find, similarly,

$$\int_{-\infty}^{+\infty}\int_{-\infty}^{+\infty} \varphi(x,y) f(x,y) dx dy = \int_{-\infty}^{+\infty}\int_{-\infty}^{+\infty} [\lambda(x) + \psi(y)] f(x,y) dx dy$$

$$= \int_{-\infty}^{+\infty} \lambda(x) \left[\int_{-\infty}^{+\infty} f(x,y) dy \right] dx$$

$$+ \int_{-\infty}^{+\infty} \psi(y) \left[\int_{-\infty}^{+\infty} f(x,y) dx \right] dy$$

$$= \int_{-\infty}^{+\infty} \lambda(x) g(x) dx + \int_{-\infty}^{+\infty} \psi(y) h(y) dy$$

$$= E[\lambda(X)] + E[\psi(Y)]$$

That the changes from a double integral to a repeated integral and the change in the order of repeated integrations are justified, and that $E[\varphi(X, Y)]$ exists, follows from the inequality

$$\int_{-\infty}^{+\infty}\int_{-\infty}^{+\infty} |\varphi(x,y)| f(x,y) dx dy \leq \int_{-\infty}^{+\infty}\int_{-\infty}^{+\infty} [|\lambda(x)| + |\psi(y)|] f(x,y) dx dy$$

$$= \int_{-\infty}^{+\infty} |\lambda(x)| \left[\int_{-\infty}^{+\infty} f(x,y) dy \right] dx$$

$$+ \int_{-\infty}^{+\infty} |\psi(y)| \left[\int_{-\infty}^{+\infty} f(x,y) dx \right] dy$$

$$= \int_{-\infty}^{+\infty} |\lambda(x)| \, g(x) dx + \int_{-\infty}^{+\infty} |\psi(y)| \, h(y) dy$$

and from the assumption that $E[\lambda(X)]$ and $E[\psi(Y)]$ exist. Since

$$E[\varphi(X, Y)] = \int_{-\infty}^{+\infty}\int_{-\infty}^{+\infty} \varphi(x,y) f(x,y) dx dy$$

if this integral is absolutely convergent, we conclude that $E[\varphi(X, Y)]$ exists and is equal to $E[\lambda(X)] + E[\psi(Y)]$.

The importance of Theorem 6.2.3 is based on the fact that (6.2.3.1) has been shown to be true regardless of any assumptions on dependence or independence of X and Y, and that $E[\lambda(X) + \psi(Y)]$ can be computed from (6.2.3.1) even if none of the probability distributions $f(x, y)$, $g(x)$, $h(y)$ is known, as long as $E[\lambda(X)]$ and $E[\psi(Y)]$ are given.

By mathematical induction, Theorem 6.2.3 is easily extended to any finite number of random variables and may be stated in the following form. If $X_1, X_2, \cdots, X_n$ are random variables, discrete or continuous, dependent or not, and if $\psi_1(x_1), \psi_2(x_2), \cdots, \psi_n(x_n)$ are functions such that the expectations

$E[\psi_1(X_1)]$, $E[\psi_2(X_2)]$, $\cdots$, $E[\psi_n(X_n)]$, based on the absolute probability distributions, exist, then the expectation of $\psi_1(X_1) + \psi_2(X_2) + \cdots + \psi_n(X_n)$ exists and we have

(6.2.3.2) $E[\psi_1(X_1) + \psi_2(X_2) + \cdots + \psi_n(X_n)]$
$$= E[\psi_1(X_1)] + E[\psi_2(X_2)] + \cdots + E[\psi_n(X_n)]$$

6.2.4. Example. A gambler plays roulette according to the following system. He plays in sets of N games. In the first game he bets 1 on black; if he wins, he pockets his gain of 1 and does not bet in the remaining $N - 1$ games, but if he loses, he bets double his loss, i.e., 2, again on black. In the second game, if he bets and wins he pockets his total gain of 2 and does not bet in the remaining $N - 2$ games, but if he loses, he bets double his loss, i.e., 4, again on black in the next game. He continues that way, stopping for the rest of the set if he wins, but betting double his last loss if he loses. If he loses in all N games of the set—a very unlikely event in his opinion—he starts a new set. What is the expectation of his gain S_N in such a set?

Solution. Let X_j be the gain in the jth game, for $j = 1, 2, \cdots, N$, hence

$$S_N = \sum_{j=1}^{N} X_j$$

The absolute distributions of the X_j are:

X_1:   1 -1

$f_1(X_1)$: $\dfrac{18}{37}$ $\dfrac{19}{37}$

X_2:   0   2 -2

$f_2(X_2)$: $\dfrac{18}{37}$ $\dfrac{19}{37} \cdot \dfrac{18}{37}$ $\left(\dfrac{19}{37}\right)^2$

.
.
.

X_j: 0 2^{j-1} -2^{j-1}

$f_j(X_j)$: $\dfrac{18}{37} \displaystyle\sum_{r=0}^{j-2} \left(\dfrac{19}{37}\right)^r$ $\left(\dfrac{19}{37}\right)^{j-1} \dfrac{18}{37}$ $\left(\dfrac{19}{37}\right)^j$ for $j \leq N$

Clearly X_{j-1} and X_j are dependent, since

$$P\{X_j = 0 \mid X_{j-1} = 0\} = 1 \neq P\{X_j = 0\} = f_j(0) = \dfrac{18}{37} \sum_{r=0}^{j-2} \left(\dfrac{19}{37}\right)^r$$

We have

$$E(X_j) = 2^{j-1} \left(\dfrac{19}{37}\right)^{j-1} \dfrac{18}{37} - 2^{j-1} \left(\dfrac{19}{37}\right)^j = -\left(\dfrac{38}{37}\right)^{j-1} \dfrac{1}{37}$$

and according to the addition theorem for expectations

$$E(S_N) = \sum_{j=1}^{N} E(X_j) = -\frac{1}{37} \sum_{j=1}^{N} \left(\frac{38}{37}\right)^{j-1} = 1 - \left(\frac{38}{37}\right)^{N}$$

which is negative and tends to $-\infty$ as $N \to \infty$.

6.2.5. Theorem (Multiplication Theorem for Mathematical Expectations). If X and Y are independent one-dimensional random variables and $\lambda(x)$ and $\psi(y)$ functions such that $E[\lambda(X)]$ and $E[\psi(Y)]$ exist, then the expectation of $\varphi(X,Y) = \lambda(X) \cdot \psi(Y)$ exists and is equal to

$$(6.2.5.1) \qquad E[\lambda(X) \cdot \psi(Y)] = E[\lambda(X)] \cdot E[\psi(Y)]$$

In particular, for $\lambda(x) = x$, $\psi(y) = y$, we have

$$E(X,Y) = E(X) \cdot E(Y)$$

if X and Y are independent and $E(X)$ and $E(Y)$ exist.

Proof. In the discrete case, let the possible values of X be $x_j, j = 1, 2, \cdots$, and the possible values of Y be y_k, $k = 1, 2, \ldots$. The joint probabilities $f(x_j, y_k)$ can be factored as in (3.3.3.2)

$$f(x_j, y_k) = g(x_j) \cdot h(y_k)$$

where g and h are the absolute probabilities. Hence,

$$
\begin{aligned}
E[\lambda(X)\psi(Y)] &= \sum_{(j)} \sum_{(k)} \lambda(x_j)\psi(y_k) f(x_j, y_k) \\
&= \sum_{(j)} \sum_{(k)} \lambda(x_j)\psi(y_k) g(x_j) h(y_k) \\
&= \sum_{(j)} \lambda(x_j) g(x_j) \sum_{(k)} \psi(y_k) h(y_k) \\
&= E[\lambda(X)] \cdot E[\psi(Y)]
\end{aligned}
$$

and the absolute convergence of $\sum_{(j)} \sum_{(k)} \lambda(x_j)\psi(y_k) f(x_j, y_k)$ follows from the equality

$$\sum_{(j)} \sum_{(k)} |\lambda(x_j)\psi(y_k)| f(x_j, y_k) = \sum_{(j)} |\lambda(x_j)| g(x_j) \sum_{(k)} |\psi(y_k)| h(y_k)$$

and the assumption that $E[\lambda(X)]$ and $E[\psi(Y)]$ exist.

In the continuous case, the joint probability density of (X, Y) factors in the absolute probability densities

$$f(x,y) = g(x)h(y)$$

Hence,

$$
\begin{aligned}
E[\lambda(X)\psi(Y)] &= \int_{-\infty}^{+\infty} \int_{-\infty}^{+\infty} \lambda(x)\psi(y) f(x,y)\,dx\,dy \\
&= \int_{-\infty}^{+\infty} \lambda(x) f(x)\,dx \int_{-\infty}^{+\infty} \psi(y)h(y)\,dy \\
&= E[\lambda(X)] \cdot E[\psi(Y)]
\end{aligned}
$$

and the existence of $\int_{-\infty}^{+\infty}\int_{-\infty}^{+\infty}|\lambda(x)\psi(y)|\,f(x,y)dxdy$ follows from

$$\int_{-\infty}^{+\infty}\int_{-8}^{+\infty}|\lambda(x)\psi(y)|\,f(x,y)dxdy$$

$$\int_{-\infty}^{+\infty}|\lambda(x)|g(x)dx\int_{-\infty}^{+\infty}|\psi(y)|\,h(y)dy$$

6.3 Variance

6.3.1. Let X be a random variable, discrete or continuous, of any number of dimensions, and $\varphi(x)$ a single-valued real function of x such that the expectation $E[\varphi(X)] = \varphi_0$ exists. The expectation of the function $[\varphi(X) - \varphi_0]^2$ is called the *variance of* $\varphi(X)$ and is denoted by $\sigma^2_{\varphi(X)}$ or $\sigma^2[\varphi(X)]$

(6.3.1.1) $\sigma^2_{\varphi(X)} = \sigma^2[\varphi(X)] = E[\varphi(X) - \varphi_0]^2$

The non-negative value of the square root of the variance is called the *standard deviation of* $\varphi(X)$ and is denoted by $\sigma_{\varphi(X)}$ or $\sigma[\varphi(X)]$

(6.3.1.2) $\sigma[\varphi(X)] = \sigma_{\varphi(X)} = \sqrt{E\{[\varphi(X) - \varphi_0]^2\}}$

In particular, if X is a one-dimensional random variable and if $\varphi(x) = x$, the number
$$\sigma_X{}^2 = E[(X - x_0)^2]$$
is called the variance of X, and its non-negative square root
$$\sigma_X = \sqrt{E[(X - x_0)^2]}$$
is called the standard deviation of X.

6.3.2. Example. If X is the outcome of rolling one die then

$$\sigma_X{}^2 = \sum_{j=1}^{6}(j - 3.5)^2\,\frac{1}{6} = \frac{1}{6}(17.5) = \frac{35}{12}\,.$$

6.3.3. Example. If X has the normal probability density

(6.3.3.1) $f(x) = \dfrac{1}{\sigma\sqrt{2\pi}}\,e^{-(x-x_0)^2/2\sigma^2}$

then by 6.1.2.3 the expectation of X is $E(X) = x_0$ and we obtain

$$\sigma_X{}^2 = E[(X - x_0)^2] = \frac{1}{\sigma\sqrt{2\pi}}\int_{-\infty}^{+\infty}(x - x_0)^2\,e^{-(x-x_0)^2/2\sigma^2}dx$$

$$= \frac{1}{\sqrt{\pi}}\int_{-\infty}^{+\infty}2\sigma^2 u^2 e^{-u^2}du = \frac{\sigma^2}{\sqrt{\pi}}\int_{-\infty}^{+\infty}u\cdot 2ue^{-u^2}du$$

$$= \frac{\sigma^2}{\sqrt{\pi}}\left\{[-ue^{-u^2}]_{u=-\infty}^{+\infty} + \int_{-\infty}^{+\infty}e^{-u^2}du\right\} = \frac{\sigma^2}{\sqrt{\pi}}\{0 + \sqrt{\pi}\} = \sigma^2$$

The statements contained in Examples 6.1.2.3 and 6.3.3 together constitute the following theorem.

6.3.4. Theorem. If X has the normal probability density (6.3.3.1) then its expectation is $E(X) = x_0$ and its variance $\sigma_X{}^2 = \sigma^2$.

The variance need not always exist. In Example 6.3.6 a random variable will be constructed for which the expectation exists and the variance does not exist.

6.3.5. Theorem. For any one-dimensional random variable X and any constant we have

(6.3.5.1) $$E[(X - k)^2] = \sigma_X{}^2 + [E(X) - k]^2$$

and in particular, for $k = 0$,

(6.3.5.2) $$\sigma_X{}^2 = E(X^2) - [E(X)]^2$$

Proof. By virtue of the addition theorem for expectations (Theorem 6.2.3) we have, putting $E(X) = x_0$,

$$E[(X - k)^2] = E[(X - x_0)^2 + 2(X - x_0)(x_0 - k) + (x_0 - k)^2]$$
$$= \sigma_X{}^2 + E[2(X - x_0)(x_0 - k)] + E[(x_0 - k)^2]$$

and, by Theorems 6.2.1 and 6.2.2, this is equal to

$$\sigma_X{}^2 + 2(x_0 - k)E(X - x_0) + (x_0 - k)^2$$

and since, again by virtue of 6.2.3 we have $E(X - x_0) = E(X) - x_0 = 0$, (6.3.5.1) is proved. Equality (6.3.5.2) follows from (6.3.5.1) immediately.

6.3.6. Example. Let X be a discrete one-dimensional random variable with the possible values

$$x_k = k^{-1/2}2^{k/2}, \quad k = 1, 2, \cdots,$$

and the probabilities

$$f(x_k) = \frac{1}{2^k}, \quad k = 1, 2, \cdots$$

For the expectation we have the series

$$E(X) = \sum_{k=1}^{\infty} k^{-1/2}2^{-k/2} < \sum_{k=1}^{\infty} 2^{-k/2} = \sum_{k=1}^{\infty} (2^{-1/2})^k$$

and since that last series is a convergent geometrical progression, $E(X)$ exists.

For the variance, however, we find by (6.3.5.2)

$$\sigma_X{}^2 = E(X^2) - [E(X)]^2$$

$$= \sum_{k=1}^{\infty} k^{-1}2^k \frac{1}{2^k} - [E(X)]^2$$

$$= \sum_{k=1}^{\infty} \frac{1}{k} - [E(X)^2]$$

and this is the divergent harmonic series less a finite number, hence $\sigma_X{}^2$ does not exist.

If (X, Y) is a two-dimensional random variable, and $\varphi(x,y)$ a function such that the expectation $E[\varphi(X, Y)] = \varphi_0$ exists, then the expectation $E[\varphi(X, Y) - \varphi_0]^2$, if it exists, is called the variance of $\varphi(X, Y)$ and is denoted by $\sigma^2[\varphi(X, Y)]$ or $\sigma^2_{\varphi(X,Y)}$. The square root of the variance is again called the standard deviation of $\varphi(X, Y)$ and is denoted by $\sigma[\varphi(X, Y)]$ or $\sigma_{\varphi(X,Y)}$. These definitions can obviously be generalized to any number of dimensions.

6.3.7. Theorem. For any two-dimensional random variable (X, Y) and $\varphi(x,y) = x + y$, we have the equality

(6.3.7.1) $\sigma^2_{\varphi(X,Y)} = \sigma^2_{X+Y} = \sigma_X{}^2 + \sigma_Y{}^2 + 2E[(X - x_0)(Y - y_0)]$

where x_0 and $\sigma_X{}^2$ as well as y_0 and $\sigma_Y{}^2$ are computed from the absolute probability distributions.

Proof. We know that $E[\varphi(X, Y)] = E(X + Y) = x_0 + y_0$, hence,

$$\sigma^2_{X+Y} = E[(X + Y - x_0 - y_0)^2] = E[(X - x_0)^2 + 2(X - x_0)(Y - y_0)$$
$$+ (Y - y_0)^2]$$

and, by Theorems 6.2.3 and 6.2.1, this is equal to

$$\sigma_X{}^2 + 2E[(X - x_0)(Y - y_0)] + \sigma_Y{}^2$$

6.3.8. Theorem (Addition Theorem for Variances of Independent Variables). If X and Y are independent one-dimensional random variables then

(6.3.8.1) $$\sigma^2_{X+Y} = \sigma_X{}^2 + \sigma_Y{}^2$$

Proof. From Theorems 6.2.3, 6.2.5, 6.2.1, and 6.2.2 we obtain

(6.3.8.2) $E[(X - x_0)(Y - y_0)] = E[XY - x_0Y - y_0X + x_0y_0]$

$$= x_0y_0 - x_0y_0 - y_0x_0 + x_0y_0 = 0$$

This together with (6.3.7.1) proves our theorem.

A simple induction shows that the addition theorem for variances holds for any finite number of totally independent random variables, so that

(6.3.8.3) $\sigma^2(X_1 + X_2 + \cdots + X_n) = \sigma_{X_1}^2 + \sigma_{X_2}^2 + \cdots + \sigma_{X_n}^2$

if $X_1, X_2, \cdots, X_n$ are totally independent.

Several simple but useful properties of the variance are summarized in the next theorems.

6.3.9. Theorem. If, for a random variable X, the expectation $E(X^2)$ exists then also $E(X)$ exists, and hence, according to (6.3.5.2), also σ_X^2 exists.

Proof. In the discrete case we have, by virtue of Cauchy's inequality,

$$\sum_{(j)} |x_j| f(x_j) = \sum_{(j)} |x_j| \sqrt{f(x_j)} \cdot \sqrt{f(x_j)} \le \left[\sum_{(j)} x_j^2 \cdot f(x_j) \cdot \sum_{(j)} f(x_j)\right]^{1/2}$$
$$= \sqrt{E(X^2)}$$

and in the continuous case, by Schwarz's inequality,

$$\int_{-\infty}^{+\infty} |x| f(x)dx = \int_{-\infty}^{+\infty} |x| \sqrt{f(x)} \cdot \sqrt{f(x)}\, dx$$
$$\le \left[\int_{-\infty}^{+\infty} x^2 f(x)dx \cdot \int_{-\infty}^{+\infty} f(x)dx\right]^{1/2}$$
$$= \sqrt{E(X^2)}$$

so that in either case the existence of $E(X)$ follows from the existence of $E(X^2)$.

In the definition of the variance σ_X^2 the existence of $E(X)$ was assumed. Therefore, whenever we assume the existence of σ_X^2 we implicitly assume the existence of $E(X)$.

6.3.10. Theorem. If the variance σ_X^2 exists for a random variable X, then the variance exists also for KX and for $X + C$, for any constants K and C, and we have

(6.3.10.1) $\sigma^2(KX) = K^2\sigma_X^2$

(6.3.10.2) $\sigma^2(X + C) = \sigma_X^2$

In particular the variance exists for $[X - E(X)]/\sigma_X$ and we have

(6.3.10.3) $\sigma^2\left(\dfrac{X - x_0}{\sigma_X}\right) = 1, \quad E\left(\dfrac{X - x_0}{\sigma_X}\right) = 0$

Proof. From (6.3.1.1) and Theorem 6.2.1 we find

$$\sigma^2(KX) = E\{[KX - E(KX)]^2\}$$
$$= E\{[KX - E(X) \cdot K]^2\}$$
$$= E\{K^2[X - E(x)]^2\}$$
$$= K^2 E\{[x - E(x)]^2\}$$
$$= K^2\sigma_X^2$$

From (6.3.1.1) and Theorems 6.2.3 and 6.2.2

$$\sigma^2(X + C) = E\{[X + C - E(X + C)]^2\}$$
$$= E\{[X + C - E(X) - C]^2\}$$
$$= \sigma_X^2$$

To prove the first equality in (6.3.10.3) we use (6.3.10.2) with $C = -x_0/\sigma_X$ and (6.3.10.1) with $K = 1/\sigma_X$, and obtain

$$\sigma^2\left(\frac{X - x_0}{\sigma_X}\right) = \sigma^2\left(\frac{X}{\sigma_X} - \frac{x_0}{\sigma_X}\right)$$

$$= \sigma^2\left(\frac{X}{\sigma_X}\right) = \frac{1}{\sigma_X^2} \cdot \sigma^2(X) = 1$$

while the second equality in (6.3.10.3) is proved by

$$E\left(\frac{X - x_0}{\sigma_X}\right) = \frac{1}{\sigma_X} [E(X - x_0)]$$

$$= \frac{1}{\sigma_X} [E(X) - x_0] = 0$$

If the variance σ_X^2 exists, $(X - x_0)/\sigma_X$ is called the *normalized variable corresponding to X*.

6.4 Chebyshev's Inequality and Related Inequalities

6.4.1. Theorem. Let U be a random variable such that

(6.4.1.1) $P(U < 0) = 0$

If the expectation $E(U) = a$ exists, then

(6.4.1.2) $P(U < aT) \geq 1 - \dfrac{1}{T}$ for any $T \geq 1$

Proof. From (6.4.1.1) follows $a \geq 0$. In the discrete case (6.4.1.1) also implies that all possible values $u_1, u_2, \cdots, u_k, \cdots$ are ≥ 0, hence

$$a = E(U) = \sum_{(k)} u_k f(u_k)$$

$$= \sum_{u_k < aT} u_k f(u_k) + \sum_{u_k \geq aT} u_k f(u_k)$$

$$\geq \sum_{u_k \geq aT} u_k f(u_k) \geq \sum_{u_k \geq aT} aT f(u_k)$$

$$= aTP(U \geq aT) = aT[1 - P(U < aT)]$$

and (6.4.1.2) follows. In the continuous case (6.4.1.1) implies

$$\int_{-\infty}^{0} f(u)du = 0$$

hence also

$$\int_{-\infty}^{0} uf(u)du = 0$$

and again

$$a = E(U) = \int_{-\infty}^{+\infty} uf(u)du$$

$$= \int_{0}^{+\infty} uf(u)du \geq \int_{aT}^{+\infty} uf(u)du \geq aT \int_{aT}^{+\infty} f(u)du$$

$$= aTP(U \geq aT) = aT[1 - P(Y < aT)]$$

An immediate consequence is the following fundamental theorem.

6.4.2. Theorem (Chebyshev's Inequality). If the random variable X has the expectation x_0 and the variance σ_X^2 then, for any $t > 1$, we have the inequality

(6.4.2.1) $$P(|X - x_0| < t\sigma_X) \geq 1 - \frac{1}{t^2}$$

Proof. The random variable $U = (X - x_0)^2$ fulfills the assumptions of Theorem 6.4.1, and $E(U) = \sigma_X^2$. Hence, by substituting in (6.4.1.2) the values $a = \sigma_X^2$, $T = t^2$, we obtain

$$P(|X - x_0| < t\sigma_X) = P[(X - x_0)^2 < t^2\sigma_X^2]$$

$$= P(U < Ta) \geq 1 - \frac{1}{T}$$

$$= 1 - \frac{1}{t^2}$$

The importance of Chebyshev's inequality is due to the fact that it holds for any probability distribution, provided it has a finite variance. Under these general assumptions inequality (6.4.2.1) cannot be improved, as is shown by the following example.

6.4.2.2. Example. Let x_0 be any real number, and t and σ any real numbers such that $t > 1$, $\sigma > 0$. Then the discrete random variable X with the distribution:

Possible values:	$x_0 - t\sigma$,	x_0,	$x_0 + t\sigma$
Probabilities:	$\dfrac{1}{2t^2}$,	$1 - \dfrac{1}{t^2}$,	$\dfrac{1}{2t^2}$

has the expectation $E(X) = x_0$ and the variance $\sigma^2(X) = \sigma^2$ and we have

$$P(|X - x_0| < t\sigma_X) = P(X - x_0) = 1 - \frac{1}{t^2}$$

Inequality (6.4.2.1) gives a lower bound for the probability that X will fall into an interval of width $2t\sigma_x$, with the midpoint $E(X) = x_0$. The following theorem, due to Fréchet, is a generalization of Chebyshev's inequality to intervals containing x_0, but not necessarily as their midpoint.

6.4.3. Theorem. If the random variable X has the expectation x_0 and the standard deviation σ_X then, for any two positive numbers, t_1 and t_2, the inequality holds

(6.4.3.1) $P(x_0 - t_1\sigma_X < X < x_0 + t_2\sigma_X) \geq 1 - \dfrac{1 + [(t_2 - t_1)/2]^2}{[(t_2 + t_1)/2]^2}$

Proof.   We have

$$P(x_0 - t_1\sigma_X < X < x_0 + t_2\sigma_X)$$

$$= P\left(\left|X - x_0 - \frac{t_2 - t_1}{2}\sigma_X\right| < \frac{t_2 + t_1}{2}\sigma_X\right)$$

$$= P\left[\left(X - x_0 - \frac{t_2 - t_1}{2}\sigma_X\right)^2 < \left(\frac{t_2 + t_1}{2}\right)^2\sigma_X^2\right]$$

$$= P\left[U < \left(\frac{t_2 + t_1}{2}\right)^2\sigma_X^2\right]$$

where

$$U = \left(X - x_0 - \frac{t_2 - t_1}{2}\sigma_X\right)^2$$

We also have

$$E(U) = E\left[(X - x_0)^2 - 2(X - x_0)\frac{t_2 - t_1}{2}\sigma_X + \left(\frac{t_2 - t_1}{2}\right)^2\sigma_X^2\right]$$

$$= \sigma_X^2 + \left(\frac{t_2 - t_1}{2}\right)^2\sigma_X^2 = \sigma_X^2\left[1 + \left(\frac{t_2 - t_1}{2}\right)^2\right]$$

and since U fulfills the assumptions of Theorem 6.4.1, we obtain

$$P\left[U < \left(\frac{t_2 + t_1}{2}\right)^2\sigma_X^2\right] = P\left[U < E(U)\frac{[(t_2 + t_1)/2]^2}{1 + [(t_2 - t_1)/2]^2}\right]$$

$$\geq 1 - \frac{1 + [(t_2 - t_1)/2]^2}{[(t_2 + t_1)/2]^2}$$

6.4.4. Example. Let X be a continuous random variable with uniform probability distribution in the interval $(0,l)$. One easily computes

$$\sigma_X{}^2 = E(X^2) - E^2(X) = \frac{1}{l}\int_0^l X^2 dX - \frac{l^2}{4} = \frac{l^2}{12}$$

and inequality (6.4.2.1) yields

$$P\left(\frac{l}{2} - t\frac{l}{\sqrt{12}} < X < \frac{l}{2} + t\frac{l}{\sqrt{12}}\right) \geq 1 - \frac{1}{t^2}$$

for all $t > 1$, while the exact value of this probability is

$$\frac{2tl}{\sqrt{12}}\cdot\frac{1}{l} = \frac{t}{\sqrt{3}} \quad \text{for } t < \sqrt{3} \text{ and } 1 \text{ for } t \geq \sqrt{3}$$

It may be noted that Chebyshev's inequality has been considerably improved by various authors under additional assumptions on the probability distribution.

6.5 Law of Large Numbers

6.5.1. Let X be a simple alternative with the possible values 1 (also called "success") and 0 ("failure"), and the corresponding probabilities p and $q = 1 - p$. Then we clearly have

(6.5.1.1) $E(X) = 1 \cdot p + 0 \cdot q = p$

(6.5.1.2) $\sigma^2(X) = E(X^2) - E^2(X) = 1^2 \cdot p + 0^2 \cdot q - p^2 = pq$

According to 3.7.1 the probability that the number of successes S in an n-fold repetition of our simple alternative assumes the value k, is equal to

$$P(n,k) = \frac{n!}{k!(n-k)!}p^k q^{n-k}$$

Hence, for the random variable S, we have

$$E(S) = \sum_{k=0}^{n} k\,\frac{n!}{k!(n-k)!}p^k q^{n-k}$$

$$\sigma^2(S) = \sum_{k=0}^{n} (k - E(S))^2\,\frac{n!}{k!(n-k)!}p^k q^{n-k}$$

Each of these expressions may be evaluated by elementary but lengthy algebraic computation. In the proof of the following theorem we shall derive these values by a method which will be found useful in many similar problems.

6.5.2. Theorem. If S is the number of successes in an n-fold repetition of a simple alternative with the probability p for success and $q = 1 - p$ for failure, then the expectation and the variance of S are, respectively

(6.5.2.1) $$E(S) = np$$

(6.5.2.2) $$\sigma^2(S) = npq$$

Proof. Let X_j be a random variable determined by the jth repetition of the simple alternative, so that $X_j = 1$ if that repetition produces a success, and $X_j = 0$ if it produces a failure. By (6.5.1.1) and (6.5.1.2) we have

$$E(X_j) = p, \qquad \sigma^2(X_j) = pq \quad \text{for } j = 1, 2, \cdots, n$$

We obviously have the equality

$$S = X_1 + X_2 + \cdots + X_n$$

According to Theorem 6.2.3 we obtain

$$E(S) = E(X_1) + E(X_2) + \cdots + E(X_n) = np$$

Since the single repetitions in an n-fold repetition of a simple alternative are by assumption independent, we may also apply (6.3.8.3) and obtain

$$\sigma^2(S) = \sigma^2(X_1) + \sigma^2(X_2) + \cdots + \sigma^2(X_n) = npq$$

The ratio $S/n = f_n$ is called the *relative frequency* of successes in n repetitions. Clearly f_n is a random variable with the possible values $0, 1/n, 2/n, \cdots, (n-1)/n, 1$. From Theorems 6.2.1 and 6.3.10 we have

(6.5.2.3) $$E(f_n) = E\left(\frac{S}{n}\right) = \frac{1}{n} E(S) = p$$

(6.5.2.4) $$\sigma^2(f_n) = \sigma^2\left(\frac{S}{n}\right) = \frac{1}{n^2} \sigma^2(S) = \frac{pq}{n}$$

6.5.3. Theorem (Bernoulli's Form of the Law of Large Numbers).

Let S be the number of successes in an n-fold repetition of a simple alternative with the probability p for success and probability q for failure, and let $f_n = S/n$ be the relative frequency of successes. Then, for any number $\varepsilon > 0$, we have

(6.5.3.1) $$\lim_{n \to \infty} P(|f_n - p| < \varepsilon) = 1$$

More specifically, for any $\varepsilon > 0$ and any $\eta > 0$, we have

(6.5.3.2) $$P(|f_n - p| < \varepsilon) \geq 1 - \eta \quad \text{for any integer } n \geq pq/\varepsilon^2\eta$$

Proof. If $n \geq pq/\varepsilon^2\eta$, then $\varepsilon \geq \sqrt{pq/n\eta}$ and, from (6.5.2.3), (6.5.2.4), and Chebyshev's inequality applied to the random variable f_n, we obtain

$$P(|f_n - p| < \varepsilon) = P(|f_n - p| < \sqrt{pq/n\eta}) + P(\sqrt{pq/n\eta} \leq |f_n - p| < \varepsilon)$$

$$\geq P(|f_n - p| < \sqrt{pq/n\eta})$$

$$= P(|f_n - E(f_n)| < \sigma_{f_n}/\sqrt{\eta})$$

$$\geq 1 - \eta$$

This proves (6.5.3.2). For any positive integer m, we may give η in (6.5.3.2) the value $\eta = pq/\varepsilon^2 m$ and obtain

$$P(|f_n - p| < \varepsilon) \geq 1 - pq/\varepsilon^2 m \quad \text{for any integer } n \geq m$$

This inequality holds, in particular, for $n = m$, and we thus have

(6.5.3.3) $P(|f_m - p| < \varepsilon) \geq 1 - pq/\varepsilon^2 m$ for any positive integer m

From this and $P(|f_m - p| < \varepsilon) \leq 1$ we conclude

$$\lim_{m \to \infty} P(|f_m - p| < \varepsilon) = 1$$

which proves (6.5.3.1).

6.5.3.4. Example. How many times does one have to roll a perfectly symmetrical die to have a probability of at least 0.95 that the relative frequency of the outcome "five" will differ from $\frac{1}{6}$ by not more than 0.01?

Solution. Since rolling a die may be considered a simple alternative with the outcomes "five" and "non-five" and the corresponding probabilities $p = \frac{1}{6}$, $q = \frac{5}{6}$, we only have to set in (6.5.3.2) the values $\eta = 0.05$, $\varepsilon = 0.01$, $p = \frac{1}{6}$, $q = \frac{5}{6}$, to conclude that

$$P(|f_n - \tfrac{1}{6}| < 0.01) \geq 0.95 \quad \text{for } n \geq \frac{5}{36(0.01)^2(0.05)} = 27,777.7 \cdots$$

It will, therefore, be sufficient to roll the die 27,778 times. Later on (in 8.1.5) it will be shown that a substantially smaller number is already sufficient. The estimate (6.5.3.2) is necessarily crude since it is based on Chebyshev's inequality which makes no use of the properties of the particular probability distribution under consideration.

6.5.3.5. Example. A die has the usual 6 faces but is so crudely shaped and made of inhomogeneous material that there is no reason to accept the usual assumption of equal probability for each face. We still wish to know how many times one has to roll that die to have the inequality $P(|f_n - p| < 0.01) \geq 0.95$, where f_n again stands for the relative frequency of the outcome "five" in n throws, and p is the probability of "five."

Solution. If p is the probability of "five" and q the probability of "non-five," then certainly $pq = p(1 - p) \leq \frac{1}{4}$. The needed number of throws n will, according to (6.5.3.2), be not greater than the one obtained from the inequality $n \geq \frac{1}{4}/\varepsilon^2\eta$ which, for $\varepsilon = 0.01$ and $\eta = 0.05$, leads to $n \geq 50,000$. This estimate, too, can be considerably improved by a procedure analogous to that of 8.1.4.

6.5.4. Theorem (Poisson's Form of the Law of Large Numbers). Let
$X_1, X_2, \cdots, X_k, \cdots$ be a sequence of independent random variables such that the expectation and the variance of each variable exists and

$$E(X_k) = E_k, \quad \sigma^2(X_k) = \sigma_k^2$$

and that

(6.5.4.1)
$$\lim_{n \to \infty} \frac{1}{n} \left(\sum_{k=1}^{n} \sigma_k^2 \right)^{1/2} = 0$$

Then, for every pair of positive numbers ε, η, there exists a number $N(\varepsilon,\eta)$ such that, for any $n \geq N(\varepsilon,\eta)$, we have

$$P\left(\left| \frac{X_1 + X_2 + \cdots + X_n}{n} - \frac{E_1 + E_2 + \cdots + E_n}{n} \right| < \varepsilon \right) \geq 1 - \eta$$

Proof. Consider the random variable

$$\overline{X}_n = \frac{1}{n} \sum_{k=1}^{n} X_k$$

By Theorems 6.2.1 and 6.2.3,

$$E(\overline{X}_n) = \frac{1}{n} \sum_{k=1}^{n} E_k$$

and by Theorems 6.3.10 and 6.3.8,

$$\sigma^2(\overline{X}_n) = \frac{1}{n^2} \sum_{k=1}^{n} \sigma_k^2$$

Applying Chebyshev's inequality to the variable $\overline{X}_n$, we obtain

$$P\left[\left| \overline{X}_n - \frac{1}{n} \sum_{k=1}^{n} E_k \right| < t \cdot \frac{1}{n^2} \left(\sum_{k=1}^{n} \sigma_k^2 \right)^{1/2} \right] \geq 1 - \frac{1}{t^2}$$

for any positive t and any positive integer n.

By choosing $t = \eta^{-1/2}$, we find

$$P\left[\left| \overline{X}_n - \frac{1}{n} \sum_{k=1}^{n} E_k \right| < \eta^{-1/2} \cdot \frac{1}{n} \left(\sum_{k=1}^{n} \sigma_k^2 \right)^{1/2} \right] \geq 1 - \eta$$

for every positive integer n. Since, by assumption (6.5.4.1), there exists a number $N(\varepsilon,\eta)$ such that

$$\frac{1}{n} \left(\sum_{k=1}^{n} \sigma_k^2 \right)^{1/2} \leq \varepsilon \eta^{1/2}$$

for every integer $n \geq N(\varepsilon,\eta)$, we have, for $n \geq N(\varepsilon,\eta)$, the inequalities

$$P\left(\left| \bar{X}_n - \frac{1}{n} \sum_{k=1}^{n} E_k \right| < \varepsilon \right) = P\left[\left| \bar{X}_n - \frac{1}{n} \sum_{k=1}^{n} E_k \right| < \eta^{-1/2} \cdot \frac{1}{n} \left(\sum_{k=1}^{n} \sigma_k^2 \right)^{1/2} \right]$$

$$+ P\left[\eta^{-1/2} \cdot \frac{1}{n} \left(\sum_{k=1}^{n} \sigma_k^2 \right)^{1/2} \leq \left| \bar{X}_n - \frac{1}{n} \sum_{k=1}^{n} E_k \right| < \varepsilon \right]$$

$$\geq P\left[\left| \bar{X}_n - \frac{1}{n} \sum_{k=1}^{n} E_k \right| < \eta^{-1/2} \cdot \frac{1}{n} \left(\sum_{k=1}^{n} \sigma_k^2 \right)^{1/2} \right] \geq 1 - \eta$$

It may be useful to state Theorems 6.5.3 and 6.5.4 in a less rigorous and more intuitive way. The law of large numbers in Bernoulli's formulation tells us that, as the size n of an n-fold repetition of a simple alternative increases, the probability becomes very close to 1 that the relative frequency f_n of successes differs only by a small quantity from the probability p of a success in a single game. The law of large numbers in Poisson's formulation states that, when an increasing number n of the independent variables $X_1, X_2, \cdots, X_k, \cdots$ is played, the probability becomes very close to 1 that the arithmetic mean of the values obtained differs only by a small quantity from the arithmetic mean of the expectations, provided that condition (6.5.4.1) is fulfilled.

The condition (6.5.4.1) is certainly fulfilled if the variances $\sigma_1^2, \sigma_2^2, \cdots, \sigma_k^2, \cdots$ have a common upper bound, i.e., if there exists a number L such that $\sigma_k^2 \leq L$ for $k = 1, 2, \cdots$. For then

$$\frac{1}{n} \sqrt{\sum_{k=1}^{n} \sigma_k^2} \leq \frac{1}{n} \sqrt{nL} = \sqrt{L/n} \to 0 \quad \text{with } n \to \infty$$

In particular (6.5.4.1) is fulfilled if $X_1, X_2, \cdots, X_k, \cdots$ are independent repetitions of the same random variable X having a finite variance. In this case we have

$$E(X_1) = E(X_2) = \cdots = E(X_k) = \cdots = E(X) = x_0$$
$$\sigma^2(X_1) = \sigma^2(X_2) = \cdots = \sigma^2(X_k) = \cdots = \sigma^2(X) = \sigma_X^2$$

so that all variances have a common upper bound. From this and the proof of 6.5.4 one easily derives the following theorem.

6.5.5. Theorem. If X is a random variable with expectation $E(X) = x_0$ and variance σ_X^2, and if $X_1, X_2, \cdots, X_k, \cdots$ is a countable sequence of independent repetitions of X, then

$$P\left(\left| \frac{X_1 + X_2 + \cdots + X_n}{n} - x_0 \right| < \varepsilon \right) \geq 1 - \eta$$

for every pair of positive numbers ε, η and every integer n such that

$$n \geq \frac{\sigma_X^2}{\varepsilon^2 \eta}$$

A direct proof of Theorem 6.5.5 is obtained by setting

$$\bar{X} = \frac{X_1 + X_2 + \cdots + X_n}{n}$$

and observing that

$$E(\bar{X}) = x_0, \qquad \sigma^2(\bar{X}) = \frac{\sigma_X^2}{n}$$

From Chebyshev's inequality then follows:

$$P\left(\left| \frac{X_1 + X_2 + \cdots + X_n}{n} - x_0 \right| < \varepsilon \right)$$

$$= P\left(|\bar{X} - E(\bar{X})| < \sigma_{\bar{X}} \cdot \frac{\varepsilon}{\sigma_{\bar{X}}} \right) \geq 1 - \frac{\sigma^2(\bar{X})}{\varepsilon^2}$$

$$= 1 - \frac{\sigma_X^2}{n\varepsilon^2} \geq 1 - \eta \quad \text{for } n \geq \frac{\sigma_X^2}{\varepsilon^2 \eta}.$$

Theorem 6.5.3 is a special case of Theorem 6.5.5 from which it follows immediately if one takes for X a simple alternative with probabilities p for success and q for failure. Theorem 6.5.5 is much more general than Theorem 6.5.3, since it assumes nothing about the random variable X but the existence of a finite variance $\sigma^2(X)$; otherwise X may be any one-dimensional random variable, discrete or continuous.

EXERCISES

6.1. Compute the mathematical expectation of the total of points on two dice.

6.2. If all face cards and the aces are given the value 10, and one card is drawn at random from a complete deck, what is the mathematical expectation of its value?

6.3. A fair game is played by an individual player against a banker according to the following rules. The player deposits his stake, then a coin is tossed. If heads appear, the player receives double his stake; if tails appear he forfeits his stake. The player bets in sequences: he bets $1; if he loses he bets $3; if he loses again he bets $9, etc., tripling his stake after each loss; the first time he wins, he concludes the sequence. What is the mathematical expectation of the financial outcome of a sequence for this player? What is this expectation if the banker sets the additional rule that only bets up to 3^N are accepted, where N is a fixed positive integer?

6.4. A game is played by an individual player against a banker. The player deposits a lump sum M at the beginning of the game. Then a gambling device is operated which amounts to a simple alternative with probability p for outcome 1 and probability $q = 1 - p$ for outcome 0. This device is operated repeatedly and independently, until 1 appears for the first time. If this happens in the kth repetition, the banker must pay to the player the amount r^k and the game is concluded. For what values of q and of r is it possible to compute M so that the game is fair, and what is the amount M for those values? If the device consists in tossing a coin and $r = 2$, the rules of the game are still quite clear, but no such amount M can be computed; this special case is known as the *St. Petersburg paradox*.

6.5. Two white and three black dice are rolled, and the total is called X. Then the white dice are rolled again and their outcome is added to the total of the black dice (which were left unchanged from the first throw); this total is called Y. Compute the mathematical expectation of $Z = X + Y$.

6.6. Let X be a continuous one-dimensional random variable with the probability density

$$f(x) = \begin{cases} \dfrac{|x - a|}{b^2} & \text{for } |x - a| \le b \\ 0 & \text{for } |x - a| > b \end{cases}$$

where a and b are real constants, $b > 0$. Sketch this probability density. Compute $E(X)$ and $\sigma(X)$.

6.7. Compute $E(X)$ and $\sigma^2(X)$ for the continuous random variable with the probability density

$$f(X) = \begin{cases} k \cdot \cos \dfrac{x - a}{b} & \text{for } |x - a| \le \dfrac{b}{2} \\ 0 & \text{for } |x - a| > \dfrac{b}{2} \end{cases}$$

where a, b are real constants, $b > 0$, and k the normalizing constant.

6.8. The random variables X and Y in Exercise 6.5 are dependent. What is the variance of $Z = X + Y$?

6.9. Five coins are tossed simultaneously and the number of heads is called H. Find $P(H = 3)$. This game of throwing five coins and determining H is repeated n times. How large must n be according to Chebyshev's inequality, so that the probability is at least 9/10 that the relative frequency of $H = 3$ will differ from its expectation by less than 0.05?

6.10. A variable X with the probability density

$$f(x) = \frac{1}{x\sqrt{2\pi}} e^{-(\log x)^2/2} \quad (x > 0)$$

is said to have a log-normal distribution. Find the expectation and variance of this variable.

6.11. Let X have a probability density $f(x) = \frac{1}{2}e^{-|x|}$. Find the expectation and variance of x.

6.12. Prove the following generalization of Chebyshev's inequality. Let $\Phi(X)$ be a real function and X a random variable such that 1^0 $E[\Phi(X)] = M$ exists, 2^0 $\Phi(X) \geq 0$ for all X, 3^0 $\Phi(-X) = \Phi(X)$ for all X, 4^0 $\Phi(X)$ is non-decreasing for $X \geq 0$. Then $Pr\{|X| \leq t\} \geq 1 - [M/\Phi(t)]$.

Characteristic
Functions

7.1 Definitions and Elementary Properties.
The One-Dimensional Case

The fundamental problem of determining explicitly the probability distribution of some random variables from the given distributions of other random variables is often extremely difficult. This is, for example, already the case if one attempts to derive the probability density of $Z = X + Y$ by means of Theorem 5.2.1, for X and Y with moderately complicated probability densities. The theory of characteristic functions, outlined in this chapter, supplies methods which make it possible to solve this problem in many cases in which a direct approach, by use of the general principle of 5.1 or Theorem 5.2.1, would present prohibitive difficulties.

If X is a one-dimensional random variable and $\phi(X)$ a real function of X, the mathematical expectation $E[\phi(X)]$ is defined by (6.1.1.1) in the discrete and by (6.1.2.1) in the continuous case. If $\phi(X)$ is a function of X which assumes complex values, then it can be written in the form

$$\phi(X) = \mu(X) + i\nu(X)$$

where $\mu(X)$ and $\nu(X)$ are real functions of X. For such a complex function $\phi(X)$ the mathematical expectation shall be defined as the complex number

(7.1.1.1) $$E[\phi(X)] = E[\mu(X)] + iE[\nu(X)]$$

where $E[\mu(X)]$ and $E[\nu(X)]$ are defined by (6.1.1.1) or (6.1.2.1).

The reader will easily verify that Theorem 6.2.1 holds without changes for any complex constant C and any complex function $\phi(X)$, Theorem 6.2.2 for any complex constant c and Theorems 6.2.3 and 6.2.5 for any complex functions $\lambda(X)$ and $\psi(Y)$.

Let t be any real number and $\phi(X)$ the complex function of the random variable X

$$\phi(X) = e^{itX} = \cos(tX) + i\sin(tX)$$

The mathematical expectation $E[\phi(X)] = E(e^{itX})$ is a function of t. This function

(7.1.1.2) $$C_X(t) = E(e^{itX}) = E[\cos(tX)] + iE[\sin(tX)]$$

is called *the characteristic function corresponding to the random variable X*. Whenever there will be no danger of a misunderstanding, we shall omit the subscript X and write $C(t)$ instead of $C_X(t)$.

The characteristic function is defined for all values of the real variable t. For we have

$$|e^{itX}| = 1$$

and hence, in the discrete case, the series

$$C_X(t) = E(e^{itX}) = \sum_{(k)} e^{itx_k} \cdot f(x_k)$$

is absolutely convergent for all real values of t and

$$|C_X(t)| \leq \sum_{(k)} f(x_k) = 1$$

while in the continuous case the integral

$$C_X(t) = \int_{-\infty}^{+\infty} e^{itx} f(x) dx$$

is absolutely convergent for every real t, and we again have

$$|C_X(t)| = \left| \int_{-\infty}^{+\infty} e^{itx} f(x) dx \right| \leq \int_{-\infty}^{+\infty} f(x) dx = 1$$

In either case, for continuous as well as discrete X, we have proved the inequality

(7.1.1.3) $$|C_X(t)| \leq 1 \quad \text{for all real } t$$

7.1.2. Example.   Let X be the simple alternative with the possible values $1, 0$ and the probabilities p, q. Then the characteristic function is

$$C(t) = pe^{it} + qe^{it \cdot 0} = pe^{it} + q$$

7.1.3. Example.   For the random variable X which has a uniform probability density in the interval $(a, a + b)$, the characteristic function is

$$C(t) = \int_a^{a+b} e^{ixt} \cdot \frac{1}{b} dx = \frac{e^{iat}}{ibt} (e^{ibt} - 1)$$

7.1.4. Example.   If X has Cauchy's distribution (5.1.2.2)

$$g(x) = \frac{1}{\pi} \cdot \frac{b}{b^2 + x^2}$$

the characteristic function is

$$C(t) = \frac{b}{\pi} \left[\int_{-\infty}^{+\infty} \frac{\cos (tx)}{b^2 + x^2} \, dx + i \int_{-\infty}^{+\infty} \frac{\sin (tx)}{b^2 + x^2} \, dx \right]$$

In the second integral the integrand is an odd function of x for any fixed t, and the integral converges absolutely, so that

$$\int_{-\infty}^{+\infty} \frac{\sin (tx)}{b^2 + x^2} \, dx = 0$$

To evaluate the first integral, we refer to the known formula ✱

$$\int_0^\infty \frac{\cos (au)}{1 + u^2} \, du = \frac{\pi}{2} e^{-|a|}$$

for real a which, for $u = x/b$, $a = bt$, $b > 0$ leads to

$$\frac{1}{b} \int_0^\infty \frac{\cos (tx) dx}{1 + (x^2/b^2)} = b \int_0^\infty \frac{\cos (tx) dx}{b^2 + x^2} = \frac{\pi}{2} e^{-b|t|}$$

so that

$$\int_{-\infty}^{+\infty} \frac{\cos (tx) dx}{b^2 + x^2} = \frac{\pi}{b} e^{-b|t|}$$

and finally

$$C(t) = e^{-b|t|}$$

7.1.5. Example. If X is a normalized normal variable, it has the probability density

$$f(x) = (1/\sqrt{2\pi}) \cdot e^{-x^2/2}$$

The characteristic function then is

$$C(t) = \frac{1}{\sqrt{2\pi}} \left[\int_{-\infty}^{+\infty} \cos (tx) \, e^{-x^2/2} dx + i \int_{-\infty}^{+\infty} \sin (tx) \, e^{-x^2/2} \, dx \right]$$

To evaluate the second integral, we again notice that it is absolutely convergent and that its integrand is an odd function of x for any real t, so that we have

$$\int_{-\infty}^{+\infty} \sin (tx) \, e^{-x^2/2} dx = 0$$

By making use of the known integral formula

(7.1.5.1) $$\int_0^\infty e^{-a^2 x^2} \cos (bx) dx = \frac{\sqrt{\pi} e^{-b^2/4a^2}}{2a} \qquad \text{for } a > 0$$

we obtain upon writing $a = 1/\sqrt{2}$, $b = t$, the value

$$\int_0^\infty \cos (tx) \, e^{-x^2/2} dx = \tfrac{1}{2}\sqrt{2\pi} \, e^{-t^2/2}$$

and, considering that the integrand of the first integral is an even function of x,

$$\int_{-\infty}^{+\infty} \cos (tx) \, e^{-x^2/2} dx = \sqrt{2\pi} \, e^{-t^2/2}$$

✱ See R. V Churchhill Operational Math 1ˢᵗ ed McGraw Hill P94-95

The characteristic function corresponding to the normalized normal random variable is therefore $C(t) = e^{-t^2/2}$.

7.1.6. Theorem. If the random variable X has the characteristic function $C_X(t)$, then the random variable $U = aX + b$, where a and b are constants, has the characteristic function

(7.1.6.1) $C_U(t) = C_{aX+b}(t) = e^{bit}C_X(at)$

Proof.   The characteristic function corresponding to U is

$$C_U(t) = E(e^{itU}) = E(e^{it(aX+b)}) = E(e^{itb} \cdot e^{itaX})$$
$$= e^{itb} \cdot E(e^{itaX}) = e^{bit} \cdot C_X(at)$$

7.1.6.2. Example.   Let Y be a normal random variable with the probability density

$$f(y) = \frac{1}{\sigma\sqrt{2\pi}} e^{-(y-y_0)^2/2\sigma^2}$$

Then $X = (1/\sigma)(Y - y_0)$ is a normalized normal random variable, and the relationship holds

$$Y = \sigma X + y_0$$

According to Theorem 7.1.6 the characteristic functions $C_Y(t)$ and $C_X(t)$ are related by the equality

$$C_Y(t) = e^{y_0 it}\, C_X(\sigma t)$$

and since

$$C_X(t) = e^{-t^2/2}$$

as we know from Example 7.1.5, we have

$$C_Y(t) = e^{y_0 it} \cdot e^{-\sigma^2 t^2/2}$$

7.1.7. Theorem.   If the random variables X and Y are independent, and Z is the random variable defined by

$$Z = X + Y$$

then

$$C_Z(t) = C_{X+Y}(t) = C_X(t) \cdot C_Y(t)$$

Proof.   According to Theorem 6.2.5 for complex functions we have

$$C_Z(t) = E(e^{itZ}) = E(e^{itX} \cdot e^{itY})$$
$$= E(e^{itX}) \cdot E(e^{itY})$$
$$= C_X(t) \cdot C_Y(t)$$

This theorem clearly may be generalized to any finite number of variables so that for the independent random variables $X_1, X_2, \cdots, X_n$ we obtain

(7.1.7.1) $C_{X_1+X_2+\cdots+X_n}(t) = C_{X_1}(t) \cdot C_{X_2}(t) \cdots \cdots C_{X_n}(t)$

7.1.8. Example.   Let S be an n-fold repetition of a simple alternative with the probabilites p for success and q for failure.   With the notations introduced in the proof of Theorem 6.5.2, we have

$$S = X_1 + X_2 + \cdots + X_n$$

where the X_j, $j = 1, 2, \cdots, n$, are independent simple alternatives with the probabilities p for $X_j = 1$ and q for $X_j = 0$.   From (7.1.7.1) and Example 7.1.2, we conclude that

$$C_S(t) = (pe^{it} + q)^n$$

7.2   Moments

7.2.1.   For a random variable X, a real constant a, and a non-negative integer k, the expectation

$$E[(X - a)^k]$$

if it exists, is called the kth moment of X about a.   In particular, the numbers

(7.2.1.1) $\mu'_k(X) = E(X^k)$ for $k = 0, 1, 2, \cdots$

are called the 0th, 1st, 2nd, $\cdots$, *moment of X about the origin*, and the numbers

(7.2.1.2) $\mu_k(X) = E[(X - E(X))^k]$ for $k = 0, 1, 2, \cdots$

are known as the 0th, 1st, 2nd, $\cdots$, *moment of X about the expected value*.
   We have already encountered some of the moments, such as

$$\mu'_1(X) = E(X) = \text{expectation of } X$$
$$\mu_2(X) = \sigma^2(X) = \text{variance of } X$$

and we easily see that

$$\mu'_0(X) = \mu_0(X) = 1, \qquad \mu_1(X) = E[X - E(X)] = 0$$

According to (6.3.5.1) we may write the relationship

(7.2.2) $\mu_2(X) = \mu'_2(X) - [\mu'_1(X)]^2$

   This relationship may be easily generalized, as shown by the following theorems.

7.2.2.1. Theorem.   Any μ_k can be expressed in terms of $\mu'_0, \mu'_1, \cdots, \mu'_k$ by the relationship

$$\mu_k = \sum_{l=0}^{k} \frac{k!}{l!\,(k-l)!} (-\mu'_1)^l \mu'_{k-l}$$

Proof

$$\mu_k = E[(X - \mu'_1)^k]$$
$$= E\left[\sum_{l=0}^{k} \frac{k!}{l!\,(k-l)!} (-\mu'_1)^l X^{k-l}\right]$$
$$= \sum_{l=0}^{k} \frac{k!}{l!\,(k-l)!} (-\mu'_1)^l E(X^{k-l})$$

7.2.2.2. Theorem. Any μ'_k can be expressed in terms of $\mu'_1 = E(X)$ and $\mu_0, \mu_1, \cdots, \mu_k$ by the relationship

$$\mu'_k = \sum_{l=0}^{k} \frac{k!}{l! \, (k-l)!} \, (\mu'_1)^l \cdot \mu_{k-l}$$

Proof

$$\mu'_k = E[(X - \mu'_1 + \mu'_1)^k]$$

$$= E\left[\sum_{l=0}^{k} \frac{k!}{l! \, (l-k)!} \, (\mu'_1)^l (X - \mu'_1)^{k-l} \right]$$

$$= \sum_{l=0}^{k} \frac{k!}{l! \, (k-l)!} \, (\mu'_1) \mu_{k-l}$$

We have already seen examples of random variables for which certain moments such as $E(X)$ of $\sigma^2(X)$, do not exist, but we know (Theorem 6.3.9) that the existence of $E(X^2)$ implies the existence of $E(X)$. This statement is a special case of the following theorem.

7.2.2.3. Theorem. If a moment μ'_n exists then all moments μ'_k with $k \leq n$ exist.

Proof. In the discrete case, for a random variable X with the possible values x_j and probabilities $f(x_j), j = 1, 2, \cdots$, we have

$$\sum_{j=1}^{\infty} |x_j|^n f(x_j) = \sum_{|x_j| \leq 1} |x_j|^n f(x_j) + \sum_{|x_j| > 1} |x_j|^n f(x_j)$$

$$\geq \sum_{|x_j| \leq 1} |x_j|^n f(x_j) + \sum_{|x_j| > 1} |x_j|^k f(x_j)$$

hence

$$\sum_{|x_j| > 1} |x_j|^k f(x_j) \leq \sum_{j=1}^{\infty} |x_j|^n f(x_j)$$

and

$$\sum_{j=1}^{\infty} |x_j|^k f(x_j) = \sum_{|x_j| \leq 1} |x_j|^k f(x_j) + \sum_{|x_j| > 1} |x_j|^k f(x_j)$$

$$\leq \sum_{|x_j| \leq 1} f(x_j) + \sum_{j=1}^{\infty} |x_j|^n f(x_j) \leq 1 + \sum_{j=1}^{\infty} |x_j|^n f(x_j)$$

This shows that, if $\sum_{j=1}^{\infty} |x_j|^n f(x_j)$ converges, the series $\sum_{j=1}^{\infty} |x_j|^k f(x_j)$ also converges, which proves our theorem.

In the continuous case, for a random variable X with the probability density $f(x)$, we have

$$\int_{-\infty}^{+\infty} |x|^n f(x) dx = \int_{|x| \leq 1} |x|^n f(x) dx + \int_{|x| > 1} |x|^n f(x) dx$$

$$\geq \int_{|x| > 1} |x|^k f(x) dx$$

and

$$\int_{-\infty}^{+\infty} |x|^k f(x)dx = \int_{|x|\leq 1} |x|^k f(x)dx + \int_{|x|>1} |x|^k f(x)dx$$

$$\leq 1 + \int_{-\infty}^{+\infty} |x|^n f(x)dx$$

so that $\int_{-\infty}^{+\infty} |x|^k f(x)dx$ is finite if $\int_{-\infty}^{+\infty} |x|^n f(x)dx$ is finite, and this again proves that $E(X^k)$ exists if $E(X^n)$ exists.

7.2.3. Theorem. If $C_X(t)$ is the characteristic function corresponding to a random variable X for which the moment μ'_n exists, then the following relationships hold between $C_X(t)$ and the moments

$$\frac{d[C_X(t)]}{dt}\bigg|_{t=0} = i\mu'_1, \quad \frac{d^2[C_X(t)]}{dt^2}\bigg|_{t=0} = i^2\mu'_2, \cdots, \quad \frac{d^n[C_X(t)]}{dt^n}\bigg|_{t=0} = i^n\mu'_n$$

Proof. According to Maclaurin's theorem we have for any positive integer n and any real value u:

$$\cos u = 1 - \frac{u^2}{2!} + \frac{u^4}{4!} - \cdots + \frac{u^n}{n!}\left[\frac{d^n \cos v}{dv^n}\right]_{v=\theta_1 u}$$

$$\sin u = u - \frac{u^3}{3!} + \frac{u^5}{5!} - \cdots + \frac{u^n}{n!}\left[\frac{d^n \sin v}{dv^n}\right]_{v=\theta_2 u}$$

where θ_1 and θ_2 are functions of u such that

$$0 \leq \theta_1 \leq 1 \quad \text{and} \quad 0 \leq \theta_2 \leq 1$$

From Euler's identity

$$e^{iu} = \cos u + i \sin u$$

we thus obtain

(7.2.3.1) $\qquad e^{iu} = 1 + iu + \frac{(iu)^2}{2!} + \frac{(iu)^3}{3!} + \cdots + \frac{(iu)^{n-1}}{(n-1)!}$

$$+ \frac{u^n}{n!}\left\{\left[\frac{d^n \cos v}{dv^n}\right]_{v=\theta_1 u} + i\left[\frac{d^n \sin v}{dv^n}\right]_{v=\theta_2 u}\right\}$$

If X is a continuous random variable, we substitute $u = tx$ in (7.2.3.1), multiply both sides by the probability density $f(x)$, integrate from $-\infty$ to $+\infty$, and obtain

(7.2.3.2) $\quad C_X(t) = 1 + it\mu'_1 + \frac{(it)^2}{2!}\mu'_2 + \frac{(it)^3}{3!}\mu'_3 + \cdots$

$$+ \frac{(it)^{n-1}}{(n-1)!} \cdot \mu'_{n-1} + \frac{t^n}{n!}\int_{-\infty}^{+\infty} x^n f(x)\left\{\left[\frac{d^n \cos v}{dv^n}\right]_{v=\theta_1 tx}\right.$$

$$\left. + i\left[\frac{d^n \sin v}{dv^n}\right]_{v=\theta_2 tx}\right\}dx$$

The existence of $\mu'_n, \cdots, \mu'_{n-1}$ is assured by the assumption that μ'_n exists, according to Theorem 7.2.2.3. By differentiating (7.2.3.2) once, twice, $\cdots$, n and substituting $t = 0$, one obtains the theorem.

If X is a discrete random variable one substitutes $u = tx_j$ in (7.2.3.1) and multiplies by the probability $f(x_j)$ for $j = 1, 2, \cdots$, then sums over j and obtains

$$(7.2.3.3) \quad C_X(t) = 1 + it\mu'_1 + \frac{(it)^2}{2!}\mu'_2 + \cdots + \frac{(it)^{n-1}}{(n-1)!}\mu'_{n-1}$$

$$+ \frac{t^n}{n!} \sum_{(j)} x_j^n f(x_j) \left\{ \left[\frac{d^n \cos v}{dv^n} \right]_{v=\theta_1 tx_j} + i\left[\frac{d^n \sin v}{dv^n} \right]_{v=\theta_2 tx_j} \right.$$

From here on one concludes as in the continuous case.

7.2.3.4. Corollary. If all moments $\mu'_1, \mu'_2, \cdots$ exist and the series $\sum_{n=0}^{\infty} \frac{(it)^n}{n!} \mu'_n$ converges for an interval $|t| < T$, we have

$$C_X(t) = \sum_{n=0}^{\infty} \frac{(it)^n}{n!} \mu'_n$$

in that interval.

The computation of moments of a given probability distribution is in many instances greatly facilitated by the application of Theorem 7.2.3 or Corollary 7.2.3.4, as will be illustrated by the following examples.

7.2.3.5. Example. For a simple alternative we have

$$C(t) = pe^{it} + q = q + p\left(1 + \sum_{n=1}^{\infty} \frac{(it)^n}{n!}\right) = 1 + \sum_{n=1}^{\infty} \frac{(it)^n}{n!} p$$

hence

$$\mu'_0 = 1, \qquad \mu'_n = p \quad \text{for } n = 1, 2, \cdots$$

This could also have been obtained by direct application of the definition of μ'_n.

7.2.3.6. Example. The moments of a uniform distribution for the interval. $(a, a + b)$ are obtained from the characteristic function (Example 7.1.3)

$$C(t) = \frac{1}{ibt}(e^{i(a+b)t} - e^{iat})$$

$$= \frac{1}{ibt} \sum_{n=0}^{\infty} \frac{(it)^n}{n!} [(a+b)^n - a^n]$$

$$= \sum_{n=1}^{\infty} \frac{(it)^{n-1}}{n!} \cdot \frac{(a+b)^n - a^n}{b}$$

$$= \sum_{n=0}^{\infty} \frac{(it)^n}{n!} \cdot \frac{(a+b)^{n+1} - a^{n+1}}{b(n+1)}$$

and have the values

$$\mu_n' = \frac{(a+b)^{n+1} - a^{n+1}}{b(n+1)}$$

Again it would have been simple to compute these moments directly from (7.2.1.1.)

7.2.3.7. Example. For an n-fold repetition of a simple alternative the characteristic function was obtained in 7.1.8.

By applying Theorem 7.2.3 we obtain

$$\mu_1' = \frac{1}{i} \cdot \frac{d[C(t)]}{dt}\Big|_{t=0}$$

$$= \frac{1}{i} n(pe^{it} + q)^{n-1} \cdot pie^{it}\Big|_{t=0} = np$$

$$\mu_2' = \frac{1}{i^2} \frac{d^2[C(t)]}{dt^2}\Big|_{t=0}$$

$$= np(pe^{it} + q)^{n-2} \cdot e^{it}[(n-1)pe^{it} + (pe^{it} + q)]_{t=0}$$

$$= np[(n-1)p + 1]$$

This and (7.2.2) lead to

$$\mu_2 = \sigma^2 = np[(n-1)p+1] - n^2p^2 = npq$$

a result already known from Theorem 6.5.2.

7.2.3.8. Example. According to 7.1.5 the characteristic function for a normalized normal random variable is

$$C(t) = e^{-t^2/2}$$

$$= \sum_{k=0}^{\infty} \frac{(-1)^k t^{2k}}{2^k \cdot k!}$$

$$= \sum_{k=0}^{\infty} \frac{(it)^{2k}}{(2k)!} \cdot \frac{(2k)!}{2^k k!}$$

By Corollary 7.2.3.4 we therefore conclude that all the moments of odd order are zero, $\mu_{2k+1}' = 0$ for $k = 0, 1, 2, \cdots$, and the moments of even order have the values

$$\mu_{2k}' = \frac{(2k)!}{2^k k!} \quad \text{for } k = 0, 1, 2, \cdots$$

The first few moments have the values

$$\mu_2' = 1, \qquad \mu_4' = 3, \qquad \mu_6' = 15, \qquad \mu_8' = 105$$

7.2.3.9. Example. If X is a normal random variable with expectation x_0 and variance σ^2, then $Y = (1/\sigma)(X - x_0)$ is a normalized normal variable and its moments about the origin have the values computed in the preceding example. The moments about the expected value for X and the moments about the origin for Y are related by the equalities

$$\mu_n'(y) = E(y^n) = E\left[\frac{1}{\sigma^n}(X - x_0)^n\right] = \frac{1}{\sigma^n}\mu_n(X)$$

We thus obtain the values

$$\mu_{2k+1}(X) = \sigma^{2k+1}\mu_{2k+1}'(y) = 0$$

$$\mu_{2k}(X) = \sigma^{2k}\mu_{2k}'(y) = \sigma^{2k}\frac{(2k)!}{2^k \cdot k!}$$

for $k = 0, 1, 2, \cdots$.

7.3   Determination of a Probability Distribution by the Characteristic Function. The One-Dimensional Case

Whenever a probability distribution of a continuous or discrete one-dimensional random variable is known, the corresponding characteristic function is uniquely determined by the defining equality (7.1.2). It is the purpose of the present section to show that the converse also is true. If a function $C(t)$, defined for all real values of t, is given and is known to be the characteristic function of some random variable, then the probability distribution of that random variable is uniquely determined. It may be useful to observe in this connection that not every complex-valued function $C(t)$ is the characteristic function of some random variable. From (7.1.3) we already know that a necessary condition for $C(t)$ being a characteristic function is the inequality $|C(t)| \leq 1$ for all real values of t. This condition, however, is not sufficient. No necessary and sufficient conditions are known, simple enough to enable us to decide for any given function $C(t)$ whether it is a characteristic function of some random variable or not.

In the following discussion of the relationships between the characteristic function and the probability distribution of a random variable, we shall make use of a classical theorem, the Fourier integral formula, which is stated below without proof.*

---

* For a proof and a detailed presentation of this and related theorems the reader is referred to E. C. Titchmarsh, *Introduction to the Theory of Fourier Integrals*, 2nd edition, Oxford, 1948, particularly Section 1.14.

7.3.1. Theorem (Fourier Integral Formula). Let $G(x)$ be a real function defined for all real x and such that

(7.3.1.1)
$$\int_{-\infty}^{+\infty} \frac{|G(x)|}{1 + |x|} dx$$

exists. Then, for every value x such that the limits

$$\lim_{0 < t \to 0} G(x + t) = G(x + 0)$$

$$\lim_{0 < t \to 0} G(x - t) = G(x - 0)$$

exist, we have

$$\lim_{r \to +\infty} \frac{1}{\pi} \int_{-\infty}^{+\infty} G(\xi) \frac{\sin r(\xi - x)}{\xi - x} d\xi = \frac{G(x + 0) + G(x - 0)}{2}$$

7.3.1.2. Corollary. Under the assumptions of Theorem 7.3.1 one has

$$\lim_{r \to +\infty} \frac{1}{\pi} \int_{-\infty}^{+\infty} G(\xi) \frac{\sin r(\xi - x)}{\xi - x} d\xi = G(x)$$

if x is a point of continuity for $G(x)$.

The proof is immediate if one notes that we have $G(x + 0) = G(x - 0) = G(x)$ for a point of continuity.

7.3.2. Theorem. Let X be a continuous random variable with the probability density $f(x)$ and the characteristic function $C(t)$. Then the relationship

(7.3.2.1)
$$f(x) = \lim_{k \to +\infty} \frac{1}{2\pi} \int_{-k}^{+k} C(t) e^{-ixt} dt$$

holds for every x which is a point of continuity of $f(x)$.

Proof. In view of the definition of $C(t)$ we may write

$$J_k = \frac{1}{2\pi} \int_{-k}^{+k} C(t) e^{-ixt} dt$$

$$= \frac{1}{2\pi} \int_{-k}^{+k} \left[\int_{-\infty}^{+\infty} e^{ist} f(s) ds \right] e^{-ixt} dt$$

$$= \frac{1}{2\pi} \int_{-\infty}^{+\infty} f(s) \int_{-k}^{+k} e^{it(s-x)} dt ds$$

The change of the order of integrations is legitimate since $e^{it(s-x)} f(s)$ is absolutely integrable in the strip

$$-k \leq t \leq +k, \qquad -\infty < s < +\infty$$

We compute

$$\int_{-k}^{+k} e^{it(s-x)} dt = \frac{2 \sin k(s - x)}{s - x}$$

and obtain

$$J_k = \frac{1}{\pi} \int_{-\infty}^{+\infty} f(s) \frac{\sin k(s - x)}{s - x} ds$$

Since $f(s)$ clearly fulfills the assumption (7.3.1.1) (according to C_3 already $\int_{-\infty}^{+\infty} |f(x)|\, dx$ exists), the Fourier integral gives

$$\lim_{k \to +\infty} J_k = \tfrac{1}{2}[f(x+0) + f(x-0)]$$

for every x such that $f(x + 0)$ and $f(x - 0)$ exist, and

$$\lim_{k \to +\infty} J_k = f(x)$$

for every point of continuity of $f(x)$.

Theorem 7.3.2 tells us that if the probability densities of two continuous random variables have the same characteristic function, they may differ only in their points of discontinuity. In particular, if two continuous random variables have the same characteristic function, and if it is known that their probability densities have at most a finite number of points of discontinuity, then differences at these points have no effect on integrals of the probability densities, and both random variables have the same probability distribution. A more general statement is contained in the next theorem.

7.3.3. Theorem.   If a continuous random variable X has the characteristic function $C(t)$, then its d.f. satisfies the relationship

$$(7.3.3.1) \qquad F(x) - F(0) = \frac{1}{2\pi} \lim_{k \to \infty} \int_{-k}^{+k} C(t) \frac{1 - e^{-ixt}}{it}\, dt$$

Proof.   The integral

$$(7.3.3.2) \qquad I_k = \int_{-k}^{+k} C(t) \int_0^x e^{-it\xi} d\xi\, dt = \int_{-k}^{+k} C(t) \frac{1 - e^{-ixt}}{it}\, dt$$

may also be written in the form

$$(7.3.3.3) \qquad I_k = \int_{-k}^{k} \left[\int_{-\infty}^{+\infty} e^{its} f(s)\, ds \int_0^x e^{-it\xi} d\xi \right] dt$$

where f is the probability density of X. The product of the integrals in the brackets may be interpreted as a double integral and transformed as follows:

$$\int_{-\infty}^{+\infty} e^{its} f(s)\, ds \int_0^x e^{-it\xi} d\xi = \int_{\xi=0}^{x} \int_{s=-\infty}^{+\infty} e^{it(s-\xi)} f(s)\, ds\, d\xi$$

$$= \int_{\xi=0}^{x} \int_{u=-\infty}^{+\infty} e^{itu} f(u+\xi)\, du\, d\xi$$

$$= \int_{u=-\infty}^{+\infty} e^{itu} \int_{\xi=0}^{x} f(u+\xi)\, d\xi\, du$$

$$= \int_{u=-\infty}^{+\infty} e^{itu} \int_{s=u}^{u+x} f(s)\, ds\, du$$

$$= \int_{u=-\infty}^{+\infty} e^{itu} [F(u+x) - F(u)]\, du$$

This integral converges absolutely and uniformly with respect to t, since we have for any two numbers, $U < U'$, the estimate

$$\int_U^{U'} |F(u+x) - F(u)|\, du = \int_{u=U}^{U'} \left| \int_{x=u}^{u+x} f(s)\,ds \right| du$$

$$= \int_{u=U}^{U'} \left| \int_{\xi=0}^{x} f(\xi + u)\,d\xi \right| du$$

$$= \left| \int_{u=U}^{U'} \int_{\xi=0}^{x} f(\xi + u)\,d\xi du \right|$$

$$= \left| \int_{\xi=0}^{x} \int_{v=U+\xi}^{U'+\xi} f(v)\,dvd\xi \right|$$

$$= \left| \int_{\xi=0}^{x} [F(U' + \xi) - F(U + \xi)]d\xi \right| \le |x|$$

The integration for t in (7.3.3.3) therefore may be performed under the integral for u, and we obtain

$$I_K = \int_{u=-\infty}^{+\infty} [F(u+x) - F(u)] \int_{t=-k}^{k} e^{itu}dt$$

$$= \int_{u=-\infty}^{+\infty} \frac{2 \sin ku}{u} [F(u+x) - F(u)]du$$

$$= \int_{\xi=-\infty}^{+\infty} \frac{2 \sin k(\xi - x)}{\xi - x} [F(\xi) - F(\xi - x)]d\xi$$

This being a Fourier integral, we obtain from Corollary 7.3.1.2

$$\lim_{k \to \infty} I_K = 2\pi[F(x) - F(0)]$$

which proves (7.3.3.1).

From Theorem 7.3.3 one concludes that if two continuous random variables have the same characteristic function, they also have the same d.f. and hence the same probability distribution. To see this one observes that, according to (7.3.3.1), the cumulative distribution functions corresponding to two random variables with the same characteristic function can differ only by a constant, and this constant must be zero in view of 2.5.6.2(d).

7.3.4. Theorem. Let X be a discrete random variable, $x_l, l = 1, 2, \cdots$, all possible values of X, $f(x_l)$ the corresponding probabilities ($l = 1, 2, \cdots$), and $C(t)$ the characteristic function. Then the relationships hold

(7.3.4.1) $\quad \lim_{k \to \infty} \dfrac{1}{2k} \displaystyle\int_{-k}^{+k} C(t)e^{-ixt}dt \begin{cases} = f(x_l) & \text{for } x = x_l, l = 1, 2, \cdots \\ = 0 & \text{for } x \text{ different from all } x_l \end{cases}$

Proof. By using the notation

$$J_k = \int_{-k}^{+k} C(t)e^{-ixt}dt$$

and the expression

$$C(t) = \sum_{(l)} e^{ix_l t} f(x_l)$$

we may write

(7.3.4.2)
$$\frac{1}{2k} J_k = \frac{1}{2k} \int_{-k}^{k} \sum_{(l)} f(x_l) e^{it(x_l - x)} dt$$

We have

$$\sum_{(l)} |f(x_l) e^{it(x_l - x)}| \le \sum_{(l)} f(x_l) = 1$$

hence the series under the integral in (7.3.4.2) converges absolutely and uniformly with respect to t and may be integrated term by term:

(7.3.4.3)
$$\frac{1}{2k} J_k = \sum_{(l)} \frac{f(x_l)}{2k} \int_{-\infty}^{+\infty} e^{it(x_l - x)} dt = \sum_{(l)} f(x_l) \frac{\sin [k(x_l - x)]}{k(x_l - x)}$$

If x is one of the possible values, say $x = x_{l_0}$, we may write

(7.3.4.4)
$$\frac{1}{2k} J_k = f(x_{l_0}) + \sum_{l \ne l_0} f(x_l) \frac{\sin [k(x_l - x_{l_0})]}{k(x_l - x_{l_0})}$$

For given $\varepsilon > 0$, we choose N such that $\sum_{l-N+1}^{\infty} f(x_l) < \varepsilon$ and set

$$\inf_{\substack{l \le N \\ l \ne l_0}} (x_l - x_{l_0}) = \delta > 0$$

Then

$$\left| \sum_{l \ne l_0} f(x_l) \frac{\sin [k(x_l - x_{l_0})]}{k(x_l - x_{l_0})} \right| \le \sum_{\substack{l \le N \\ l \ne l_0}} f(x_l) \frac{1}{k\delta} + \sum_{l=N+1}^{\infty} f(x_l)$$

$$< \frac{1}{k\delta} + \varepsilon \xrightarrow[k \to \infty]{} \varepsilon$$

and, since this is true for any $\varepsilon > 0$, we have

$$\lim_{k \to \infty} \frac{1}{2k} J_k = f(x_{l_0})$$

If x is different from all x_l, $l = 1, 2, \cdots$, we apply to the right side of (7.3.4.3) the same argument which showed us that the sum in (7.3.4.4) tends to zero as $k \to \infty$, and obtain

$$\lim_{k \to \infty} \frac{1}{2k} J_k = 0$$

From Theorem 7.3.4 we conclude that if two one-dimensional discrete random variables have the same characteristic functions, their sets of different possible values and the corresponding probabilities are the same, i.e., both random variables have the same probability distribution.

The theorems 7.3.3 and 7.3.4 leave the possibility open that a continuous random variable and a discrete random variable have the same characteristic function. It can be proved that this is impossible. In fact, it can be proved that, for a given characteristic function, there exists only one random variable having this characteristic function, among all possible random variables, continuous, discrete, and those not belonging to either kind. The proof of this theorem is beyond the scope of this presentation.

We shall frequently make use of the preceding theorems in the following manner. A random variable X will be studied whose probability distribution is not known; it will be possible, however, to determine explicitly its characteristic function $C_X(t)$ which will be of a form known to correspond to a certain probability distribution of a continuous (discrete) random variable. We shall then conclude from Theorem 7.3.3 (Theorem 7.3.4) that X has that probability distribution. The following examples will illustrate this procedure.

7.3.5. Example (The Reproductive Law for Independent Normal Variables).

Let X and Y be independent random variables, each with a normal probability distribution. Then, according to Example 7.1.6.2, the corresponding characteristic functions are

$$C_X(t) = e^{x_0 it} e^{-\sigma_x^2 t^2/2}$$

$$C_Y(t) = e^{y_0 it} e^{-\sigma_y^2 t^2/2}$$

For the random variable

$$Z = X + Y$$

the characteristic function according to Theorem 7.1.7 is

$$C_Z(t) = C_X(t) \cdot C_Y(t) = e^{(x_0+y_0)it} e^{-\frac{(\sigma_x^2 + \sigma_y^2)t^2}{2}}$$

This is the characteristic function of a normal random variable with expectation $x_0 + y_0$ and variance $\sigma_x^2 + \sigma_y^2$. We conclude from Theorem 7.3.2 that Z has the normal probability density with $E(Z) = x_0 + y_0$, $\sigma^2(Z) = \sigma_x^2 + \sigma_y^2$. Thus we have again shown by a concise argument that the sum of independent normal random variables is a normal random variable. This argument does not yield, however, the result of 5.2.2 which includes the case of dependent X, Y.

7.3.6. Example.

We say that the discrete random variable X has a *Poisson distribution* if the set S of possible values consists of all non-negative integers, and the corresponding probabilities are

(7.3.6.1) $$f(x) = \frac{e^{-a} a^x}{x!} \quad \text{for } x = 0, 1, 2, \cdots$$

where a is a positive constant. The characteristic function corresponding to this distribution is

(7.3.6.2)
$$C_X(t) = \sum_{x=0}^{\infty} e^{ixt} \frac{e^{-a} a^x}{x!}$$

$$= e^{-a} \sum_{x=0}^{\infty} \frac{(e^{it} \cdot a)^x}{x!}$$

$$= e^{-a} \cdot e^{ae^{it}} = e^{a(e^{it}-1)}$$

If X has the probability distribution (7.3.6.1), and Y also has a Poisson distribution

$$g(y) = \frac{e^{-b} b^y}{y!} \quad \text{for } y = 0, 1, 2, \cdots$$

and hence the characteristic function $C_Y(t) = e^{b(e^{it}-1)}$, and if X and Y are independent, then the random variable $Z = X + Y$ has the characteristic function

$$C_Z(t) = C_X(t) C_Y(t) = e^{(a+b)(e^{it}-1)}$$

This is the characteristic function corresponding to the Poisson distribution

(7.3.6.3) $$f(z) = \frac{e^{-(a+b)}(a + b)^z}{z!} \quad \text{for } z = 0, 1, 2, \cdots$$

and we conclude from Theorem 7.3.4 that (7.3.6.3) is the probability distribution of Z. Thus the sum of two independent Poisson variables is again a Poisson variable, a statement known as the *reproductive law of Poisson distributions*. From (7.3.6.1) one easily computes the expectation and the variance of a Poisson variable:

$$E(X) = \frac{1}{i} \cdot \frac{dC_X(t)}{dt} \bigg|_{t=0} = \frac{1}{i} e^{a(e^{it}-1)} a e^{it} i \bigg|_{t=0} = a$$

$$E(X^2) = \mu_2' = - \frac{d^2 C_X(t)}{dt^2} \bigg|_{t=0} = -ae^{-a} e^{it+ae^{it}}(1 + ae^{it}) \bigg|_{t=0} = a(1 + a)$$

We have, therefore, for the Poisson distribution (7.3.6.1)

$$E(X) = a, \qquad \sigma^2(X) = a$$

7.3.7. Example. Let S be an m-fold repetition of a simple alternative with the probabilities p for success and $q = 1 - p$ for failure, and let S' be an n-fold repetition of the simple alternative with probabilities r for success and s for failure. If S and S' are independent, then their sum $Z = S + S'$ has the characteristic function $C_Z(t) = C_S(t) \cdot C_{S'}(t)$ which, according to 7.1.8, is equal to

$$C_Z(t) = (pe^{it} + q)^m (re^{it} + s)^n$$

This is the characteristic function of some $(m + n)$-fold repetition if and only if $p = r$ (and hence $q = s$). Since Z is a discrete random variable, it follows from Theorem 7.3.4 that the sum of two independent variables, each having a binomial probability distribution, is a variable with a binomial distribution if and only if both variables are repetitions of the same simple alternative.

7.4 The n-Dimensional Case

7.4.1. If $X_{(n)} = (X^{(1)}, X^{(2)}, \cdots, X^{(n)})$ is an n-dimensional random variable, then the function of n real variables $t_1, t_2, \cdots, t_n$ defined by

$$(7.4.1.1) \quad C_{X_{(n)}}(t_1, t_2, \cdots, t_n) = E[\exp(it_1 X^{(1)} + it_2 X^{(2)} + \cdots + it_n X^{(n)})]$$

is called the *characteristic function corresponding to the probability* distribution of $X_{(n)}$. Again, as in the one-dimensional case, we shall omit the subscript and write $C(t_1, \cdots, t_n)$, whenever there is no danger of a misunderstanding. As in the one-dimensional case one concludes that the characteristic function corresponding to a discrete or a continuous random variable is defined for all real values of $(t_1, t_2, \cdots, t_n)$.

7.4.2. Example. Let (X, Y) be the random variable with a uniform probability distribution in the rectangle (r) defined by

$$a \leq x \leq a + k, \qquad b \leq y \leq b + l$$

The probability density is

$$f(x, y) = \begin{cases} 1/kl & \text{for points in } (r) \\ 0 & \text{for points outside of } (r) \end{cases}$$

and the characteristic function is

$$C_{(X,Y)}(t_1, t_2) = \int_a^{a+k} \int_b^{b+l} \exp(it_1 x + it_2 y) \frac{1}{kl} \, dy \, dx$$

$$= -\frac{\exp[i(t_1 a + t_2 b)]}{kl t_1 t_2} \cdot (e^{it_1 k} - 1)(e^{it_2 l} - 1)$$

7.4.3. Example. Let (X, Y) be a discrete random variable with the possible values 0 and 1 for X, and also 0 and 1 for Y, and with the joint probabilities given in the following *two-by-two table* of probabilities

Y \ X	0	1
0	p_{00}	p_{10}
1	p_{01}	p_{11}

From these joint probabilities we compute the absolute probabilities for X

$$g(0) = p_{00} + p_{01}, \qquad g(1) = p_{10} + p_{11}$$

and for Y

$$h(0) = p_{00} + p_{10}, \qquad h(1) = p_{01} + p_{11}$$

According to Example 7.1.2 the characteristic functions for the one-dimensional random variables X and Y are

$$C_X(t) = (p_{10} + p_{11})e^{it} + (p_{00} + p_{01})$$

and

$$C_Y(t) = (p_{01} + p_{11})e^{it} + (p_{00} + p_{10})$$

The characteristic function for the two-dimensional random variable (X, Y) is

$$C_{(X,Y)}(t_1, t_2) = p_{00} + p_{01}e^{it_2} + p_{10}e^{it_1} + p_{11}e^{i(t_1+t_2)}$$

and a simple computation transforms this into

$$
\begin{aligned}
\textbf{(7.4.3.1)} \quad C_{(X,Y)}(t_1, t_2) &= [(p_{10} + p_{11})e^{it_1} + (p_{00} + p_{01})] \\
&\quad \times [(p_{01} + p_{11})e^{it_2} + (p_{00} + p_{10})] \\
&\quad + (p_{00}p_{11} - p_{01}p_{10})[1 - e^{it_1} - e^{it_2} + e^{i(t_1+t_2)}] \\
&= C_X(t_1)C_Y(t_2) + (p_{00}p_{11} - p_{01}p_{10}) \\
&\quad \times [1 - e^{it_1} - e^{it_2} + e^{i(t_1+t_2)}]
\end{aligned}
$$

This shows that the identity $C_{(X,Y)}(t_1, t_2) = C_X(t_1) \cdot C_Y(t_2)$ holds if and only if

$$p_{00}p_{11} - p_{01}p_{10} = 0$$

7.4.4. As in the case of one-dimensional random variables, not only does a continuous or a discrete probability distribution determine the characteristic function but, conversely, the characteristic function corresponding to a continuous random variable determines the probability density of that variable in all its points of continuity, and the characteristic function corresponding to a discrete random variable determines the set of all its different possible values and the corresponding probabilities. We shall not attempt to prove these statements here.

7.5 Limit Theorem

7.5.1. For large n, or s, or both, the expression

$$\textbf{(3.7.1.1)} \qquad P(n,s) = \frac{n!}{s! \, (n - s)!} p^s q^{n-s}$$

for the binomial distribution of the random variable S contains factorials of large numbers and thus does not lend itself easily to numerical computation.

A convenient approximation of (3.7.1.1) is obtained by making use of the expression

(7.5.1.1) $n! = \sqrt{2\pi} n^{n+(1/2)} \exp[-n + (\theta/12n)]$ where $0 < \theta < 1$

known as *Stirling's formula*. By substituting this expression for $n!$, $s!$, and $(n-s)!$ in (3.7.1.1), one obtains

$$P(n,s) = (2\pi)^{1/2} n^{n+(1/2)} \exp[-n + (\theta/12n)] p^s q^{n-s}$$
$$\times (2\pi)^{-1/2} s^{-s-(1/2)} \exp[s - (\theta'/12s)]$$
$$\times (2\pi)^{-1/2}(n - s)^{-n+s-(1/2)} \exp\{n - s - [\theta''/12(n - s)]\}$$
$$= \frac{n^{n+(1/2)} p^s q^{n-s}}{\sqrt{2\pi}\, s^{s+(1/2)}(n-s)^{n-s+(1/2)}} \exp[(\theta/12n) - (\theta'/12s) - (\theta''/12(n-s))]$$

We know that

$$E(S) = np, \qquad \sigma^2(S) = npq$$

and hence $X = (S - np)/\sqrt{npq}$ is a normalized random variable. Introducing $x = (s - np)/\sqrt{npq}$ in the expression for $P(n,s)$ we write

(7.5.1.2)

$$P(n,s) = \frac{1}{\sqrt{2\pi}} \cdot \frac{1}{\sqrt{npq}} \left[\frac{1}{1 + (s - np)/(np)}\right]^{s+(1/2)} \left[\frac{1}{1 - (s - np)/(nq)}\right]^{n-s+(1/2)}$$
$$\cdot \exp\left[\frac{\theta}{12n} - \frac{\theta'}{12s} - \frac{\theta''}{12(n - s)}\right]$$
$$= \frac{1}{\sqrt{2\pi}} \cdot \frac{1}{\sqrt{npq}} \left(\frac{1}{1 + x\sqrt{q/np}}\right)^{np + x\sqrt{npq} + (1/2)}$$
$$\times \left(\frac{1}{1 - x\sqrt{p/nq}}\right)^{nq - x\sqrt{npq} + (1/2)} \cdot \exp\left[\frac{\theta}{12n} - \frac{\theta'}{12s} - \frac{\theta''}{12(n - s)}\right]$$
$$= \frac{1}{\sqrt{2\pi}} \cdot \frac{1}{\sqrt{npq}} \exp[-(np + x\sqrt{npq} + \tfrac{1}{2}) \log(1 + x\sqrt{q/np})$$
$$- (nq - x\sqrt{npq} + \tfrac{1}{2}) \log(1 - x\sqrt{p/nq})]$$
$$\cdot \exp\left[\frac{\theta}{12n} - \frac{\theta'}{12s} - \frac{\theta''}{12(n - s)}\right]$$
$$= \frac{1}{\sqrt{2\pi}} \cdot \frac{1}{\sqrt{npq}} e^G$$

where G denotes the entire exponent.

For any t such that $|t| < 1$, we have the Taylor expansion

$$\log(1 + t) = t - \tfrac{1}{2}t^2 + \tfrac{1}{3}t^3 - \tfrac{1}{4}t^4 + \cdots$$
$$= t - \tfrac{1}{2}t^2 + t^3(\tfrac{1}{3} - \tfrac{1}{4}t + \tfrac{1}{5}t^2 - \cdots)$$
$$= t - \tfrac{1}{2}t^2 + t^3 r(t)$$

and for $|t| \leq \frac{1}{2}$,

$$|r(t)| \leq \tfrac{1}{3} + \tfrac{1}{4} \cdot \tfrac{1}{2} + \tfrac{1}{5}(\tfrac{1}{2})^2 + \cdots < \tfrac{1}{2} + (\tfrac{1}{2})^2 + (\tfrac{1}{2})^3 + \cdots = 1$$

We thus have

(7.5.1.3.1) $\log(1+t) = t - \tfrac{1}{2}t^2 + t^3 \cdot r(t)$

with

(7.5.1.3.2) $|r(t)| < 1 \quad \text{for } |t| \leq \tfrac{1}{2}$

By using (7.5.1.3.1), we may write the exponent G in (7.5.1.2)

$$G = -(np + x\sqrt{npq} + \tfrac{1}{2})[x\sqrt{q/np} - \tfrac{1}{2}x^2(q/np) + x^3(q/np)^{3/2}r(x\sqrt{q/np})]$$

$$- (nq - x\sqrt{npq} + \tfrac{1}{2})[-x\sqrt{p/nq} - \tfrac{1}{2}x^2(p/nq) - x^3(p/nq)^{3/2}r(-x\sqrt{p/nq})]$$

$$+ \frac{\theta}{12n} - \frac{\theta'}{12s} - \frac{\theta''}{12(n-s)}$$

$$= x \cdot \tfrac{1}{2}(\sqrt{p/nq} - \sqrt{q/np}) + x^2\left(-\frac{q}{2} - \frac{p}{2} + \frac{1}{4}\frac{q}{np} + \frac{1}{4}\frac{p}{nq}\right)$$

$$+ x^3[-q^{3/2}(np)^{-1/2}r(x\sqrt{q/np}) + \tfrac{1}{2}q^{3/2}(np)^{-1/2} - \tfrac{1}{2}q^{3/2}(np)^{-3/2}r(x\sqrt{q/np})$$

$$+ p^{3/2}(nq)^{-1/2}r(-x\sqrt{p/nq}) - \tfrac{1}{2}p^{3/2}(nq)^{-1/2} + \tfrac{1}{2}p^{3/2}(nq)^{-3/2}r(-x\sqrt{p/nq})]$$

$$+ x^4[-q^2(np)^{-1}r(x\sqrt{q/np}) - p^2(nq)^{-1}r(-x\sqrt{p/nq})]$$

$$+ \frac{\theta}{12n} - \frac{\theta'}{12(x\sqrt{npq} + np)} - \frac{\theta''}{12(np - x\sqrt{npq})}$$

In this expression, the only term independent of n is

$$x^2\left(-\frac{q}{2} - \frac{p}{2}\right) = -\frac{x^2}{2}$$

while all other terms contain negative powers of n. Hence G may be written in the form

(7.5.1.4) $G = -\dfrac{x^2}{2} + R_n(p,q,x)$

where, in view of (7.5.1.3.2),

(7.5.1.5)

$$|R_n(p,q,x)| < |x| \cdot \tfrac{1}{2}(\sqrt{p/nq} + \sqrt{q/np}) + x^2 \cdot \frac{1}{4}\left(\frac{p}{nq} + \frac{q}{np}\right)$$

$$+ |x|^3[\tfrac{3}{2}q^{3/2}(np)^{-1/2} + \tfrac{1}{2}q^{3/2}(np)^{-3/2} + \tfrac{3}{2}p^{3/2}(nq)^{-1/2} + \tfrac{1}{2}p^{3/2}(nq)^{-3/2}]$$

$$+ x^4[q^2(np)^{-1} + p^2(nq)^{-1}] + \frac{1}{12}\left[\frac{1}{n} + \frac{1}{np - |x|\sqrt{npq}} + \frac{1}{nq - |x|\sqrt{npq}}\right]$$

for x such that

$$|x|\sqrt{q/np} \le \tfrac{1}{2} \quad \text{and} \quad |x|\sqrt{p/nq} \le \tfrac{1}{2}$$

From (7.5.1.2) and (7.5.1.4) we obtain

$$P(n,s) = \frac{1}{\sqrt{2\pi}} \cdot \frac{1}{\sqrt{npq}} \, e^{-x^2/2} \cdot e^{R_n(p,q,x)}$$

Hence, if x, n, p, q, are such that the right-hand side of (7.5.1.5) is sufficiently small, we have the approximate equality

(7.5.1.6)
$$P(n,s) = \frac{1}{\sqrt{2\pi}} \cdot \frac{1}{\sqrt{npq}} \, e^{-x^2/2}$$

$$= \frac{1}{\sqrt{2\pi}} \cdot \frac{1}{\sigma_S} \, e^{-[s-E(S)]^2/2\sigma_S^2}$$

$$= \frac{1}{\sqrt{2\pi}} \cdot \frac{1}{\sqrt{npq}} \, e^{-(s-np)^2/2npq}$$

Clearly, a sufficient condition for the smallness of the right-hand side of (7.5.1.5), and hence for the goodness of the approximation (7.5.1.6), is that the quantities np and nq are both large with respect to $|x|$. In particular, a better approximation is assured for values of s close to np, than for values close to either 0 or to n.

The approximate formula (7.5.1.6) is often referred to as the *De Moivre-Laplace* approximation to the binomial probability.

Frequently one is interested in the probability that the random variable S will take a value contained between two given limits, s_1 and s_2:

$$P_n(s_1 \le S \le s_2) = \sum_{s=s_1}^{s_2} P(n,s) = \sum_{s=s_1}^{s_2} \frac{n!}{s!\,(n-s)!} \, p^s q^{n-s}$$

For large n and large $s_2 - s_1$, the exact computation of this expression becomes quite prohibitive. However, by carrying further the estimates which led us to (7.5.1.6), one obtains the approximate equation

(7.5.1.7)
$$P_n(s_1 \le S \le s_2) = \frac{1}{\sqrt{2\pi}} \int_{x_1}^{x_2} e^{-x^2/2} dx$$

where

$$x_1 = \frac{s_1 - np}{\sqrt{npq}}, \qquad x_2 = \frac{s_2 - np}{\sqrt{npq}}$$

This approximation is known as the *Laplace-Gauss* theorem.

The Laplace-Gauss theorem is a special case of a very general theorem known as the *central limit theorem of calculus of probabilities*. The rest of this section will be devoted to this general theorem.

Consider a countable sequence of random variables: $X_1, X_2, \cdots, X_n, \cdots$ with the cumulative distribution functions $F_1(s), F_2(s), \cdots, F_n(s), \cdots$. We shall say that the random variables X_n, $n = 1, 2, \cdots$ *converge in distribution* to the random variable X, if the random variable X has a d.f. $F(s)$ such that

$$F(s) = \lim_{n \to \infty} F_n(s)$$

at all points of continuity of F.

The following theorems on distribution functions and their relationship to characteristic functions will be stated here without proof.*

7.5.2. Theorem. If the distribution functions $F_n(s)$, $n = 1, 2, \cdots$, converge to a continuous d.f. $F(s)$, then the convergence is uniform in every finite interval.

7.5.3. Theorem. If the sequence of distribution functions $F_n(s)$, $n = 1, 2, \cdots$ converges to a d.f. $F(s)$ at all its points of continuity, and if the characteristic function $C_n(t)$ corresponds to the random variable with the d.f. $F_n(s)$ for $n = 1, 2, \cdots$, and the characteristic function $C(t)$ corresponds to the random variable with the d.f. $F(s)$, then

$$\lim_{n \to \infty} C_n(t) = C(t)$$

for all real values of t, and the convergence is uniform in every finite interval for t.

7.5.4. Theorem. If $C_n(t)$ are the characteristic functions corresponding to the random variables X_n for $n = 1, 2, \cdots$, and if the functions $C_n(t)$ converge for all t to a function $C(t)$ which is the characteristic function corresponding to a random variable X, then the random variables X_n converge in distribution to the random variable X.

The preceding theorems make it possible to give a concise proof of the central limit theorem in the following formulation.

7.5.5. Theorem. Let X be a one-dimensional random variable, either continuous or discrete, with a finite variance $\sigma^2(X) = \sigma^2$, and let its expectation be $E(X) = x_0$. Let $X_1, X_2, \cdots, X_n$ be n independent observations of X, and

$$\bar{X} = \frac{1}{n} \sum_{j=1}^{n} X_j$$

their arithmetic mean. Then the random variable

$$Z_n = (\sqrt{n}/\sigma)(\bar{X} - x_0)$$

---

* For proofs the reader is referred to Cramér, *Mathematical Methods of Statistics*, Princeton University Press, Princeton, N.J., 1946.

has a cumulative distribution function

$$F_n(z) = P(Z_n \leq z)$$

which, for $n \to \infty$, converges uniformly in every finite interval to the cumulative probability function

$$\Phi(z) = \frac{1}{\sqrt{2\pi}} \int_{-\infty}^{z} e^{-s^2/2} ds$$

of the normalized normal variable.

Proof. We denote by Y the normalized random variable corresponding to X

$$Y = \frac{X - x_0}{\sigma}$$

From (7.2.3.2) or (7.2.3.3), according to whether X (and hence Y) is continuous or discrete, we obtain

$$C_Y(t) = 1 + it\mu_1'(Y) + \frac{t^2}{2} \int_{-\infty}^{+\infty} y^2 f(y)\{-\cos\theta_1 ty - i\sin\theta_2 ty\} dy$$

or

$$C_Y(t) = 1 + it\mu_1'(Y) + \frac{t^2}{2} \sum_{(j)} y_j^2 f(y_j)(-\cos\theta_{1_j} ty_j - i\sin\theta_{2_j} ty_j)$$

and since

$$\mu_1'(Y) = E(Y) = 0$$

we have

(7.5.5.1) $$C_Y(t) = 1 - \frac{t^2}{2} \int_{-\infty}^{+\infty} y^2 f(y)(\cos\theta_1 ty + i\sin\theta_2 ty) dy$$

or

(7.5.5.2) $$C_Y(t) = 1 - \frac{t^2}{2} \sum_{(j)} y_j^2 f(y_j)(\cos\theta_{1_j} ty_j + i\sin\theta_{2_j} ty_j)$$

In view of the independence of $X_1, X_2, \cdots, X_n$ and the identity

$$Z_n = \sum_{j=1}^{n} \frac{X_j - x_0}{\sqrt{n}\sigma}$$

we have for the characteristic function of Z_n the expression

$$C_{Z_n}(t) = E(e^{itZ_n})$$

$$= E\left(\prod_{j=1}^{n} e^{it(X_j - x_0)/\sqrt{n}\sigma} \right)$$

$$= \prod_{j=1}^{n} E(e^{i(t/\sqrt{n})(X_j - x_0)/\sigma})$$

$$= \left[C_Y\left(\frac{t}{\sqrt{n}}\right) \right]^n$$

From this and (7.5.5.1) or (7.5.5.2), we obtain

$$C_{Z_n}(t) = \left[1 - \frac{t^2}{2n}\int_{-\infty}^{+\infty} y^2 f(y)\left(\cos\theta_1 \frac{ty}{\sqrt{n}} + i\sin\theta_2 \frac{ty}{\sqrt{n}}\right)dy\right]^n$$

or

$$C_{Z_n}(t) = \left[1 - \frac{t^2}{2n}\sum_{(j)} y_j^2 f(y_j)\left(\cos\theta_{1_j} \frac{ty_j}{\sqrt{n}} + i\sin\theta_{2_j} \frac{ty_j}{\sqrt{n}}\right)\right]^n$$

In either case we have for

$$C_{Z_n}(t) = \left[1 - \frac{t^2}{2n} g(n,t)\right]^n$$

where $g(n,t) \xrightarrow[n\to\infty]{} 1$ for every real t, and from this we conclude

$$\lim_{n\to\infty} C_{Z_n}(t) = e^{-t^2/2}$$

for any real value of t. Since this limit is the characteristic function of the normalized normal variable, Theorem 7.5.4 tells us that the distribution functions $F_n(z)$ converge to the d.f. of the normalized normal distribution at all points of continuity, that is, everywhere. Since $\Phi(z)$ is continuous, the convergence is uniform in every finite interval according to Theorem 7.5.2.

In view of the relationships $E(\bar{X}) = x_0$, $\sigma_{\bar{X}} = \sigma/\sqrt{n}$, one easily verifies that Z_n is the normalized variable $\bar{X}$. Theorem 7.5.5 may therefore also be stated by saying that, under its assumptions, the distribution functions of the normalized arithmetic means of $X_1, X_2, \cdots, X_n$ converge uniformly in every finite interval to the d.f. of the normalized normal variable.

It must be pointed out that Theorem 7.5.5 is only a special case of a much more general central limit theorem. Already Laplace was convinced that the following statement is true. Let $X_1, X_2, \cdots, X_n$ be independent random variables with expectations $E(X_j) = E_j$ and variances $\sigma^2(X_j) = \sigma_j^2$. Then, for n large, the distribution of the normalized arithmetic mean of $X_1, X_2, \cdots, X_n$, that is, of

$$T_n = \frac{\bar{X}_n - E(\bar{X}_n)}{\sigma(\bar{X}_n)} = \frac{\sum\limits_{j=1}^{n} X_j - \sum\limits_{j=1}^{n} E_j}{\sqrt{\sum\limits_{j=1}^{n} \sigma_j^2}}$$

is nearly normal. The argument by which Laplace attempted to prove this theorem was not a valid proof. In fact, this statement is only true under certain additional assumptions which, however, are of a very general character. Rigorous proofs were supplied, under various additional assumptions, by Lindeberg, Lévy, Cramér, Feller, and others.

Together with the reproductive property of normal variables, the central limit theorem presents a plausible explanation of the frequent occurrence in the empirical world of random variables with apparently normal distributions. In non-rigorous language this theorem tells us that any quantity which is the arithmetic mean of many random variables, has an approximately normal distribution. As examples of such quantities one may consider the arithmetic mean of a number of measurements of a physical quantity, errors of observation (if one assumes that the observable errors are the results of a super-imposition of many small independent errors), or the velocity of a gas particle which is the result of a large number of impacts by other particles.

EXERCISES

7.1. Let X be the random variable with uniform probability density in the interval $(-a, +a)$, and let X_1 and X_2 be two independent determinations of X. Find the characteristic function corresponding to $X_2 = \frac{1}{2}(X_1 + X_2)$.

7.2. Find the characteristic function corresponding to the total S of points on two dice.

7.3. What is the characteristic function corresponding to the random variable X of Exercise 2.14?

7.4. Find the general formula for μ_n for the random variable of Exercise 2.14.

7.5. Determine the characteristic function and the moments μ'_n for the continuous random variable with the probability density $f(x) = \frac{1}{2}e^{-|x|}$. Then find the characteristic function and the moments μ_n for the random variable with the more general probability density

$$g(x) = \frac{1}{2m} e^{-(|x-a|)/m}$$

7.6. Find the characteristic function corresponding to the probability density

$$f(x) = \begin{cases} 0 & \text{for } x < -1 \\ \frac{1}{2}ke^{-x}(1 + x)^2 & \text{for } -1 \le x \end{cases}$$

By using this characteristic function obtain the first four moments about the expectation.

7.7. Let X_1, X_2, X_3 be three independent observations of the random variable X with the probability density $f(x) = \frac{1}{2}e^{-|x|}$. Use characteristic functions and the result of Exercise 7.5 to prove that $Z = X_1 + X_2 + X_3$ has the probability density

$$g(Z) = \frac{1}{16}(3 + 3|Z| + Z^2)e^{-|Z|}$$

7.8. Consider the total number S of dots on n perfect dice. Find the characteristic function corresponding to the distribution of S; then compute $E(S)$, $\sigma^2(S)$.

7.9. Determine the characteristic function corresponding to the random variable with the probability density

$$f(x) = \begin{cases} C_1 & \text{for } a \leq x \leq a + l_1 \\ C_2 & \text{for } b \leq x \leq b + l_2 \\ 0 & \text{elsewhere} \end{cases}$$

where a, b, l_1, l_2, C_1, C_2 are constants such that $l_1 > 0, l_2 > 0, C_1 > 0, C_2 > 0,$ $a + l_1 \leq b,$ and $l_1 C_1 + l_2 C_2 = 1.$

7.10. From the characteristic function, compute $E(X)$ and $(\sigma^2 X)$ for the random variable of Exercise 7.9.

7.11. Consider the continuous random variable with the probability density

$$f(x) = \begin{cases} (1/m)e^{-x/m} & \text{for } 0 \leq x \\ 0 & \text{for } x < 0 \end{cases}$$

Determine the characteristic function and the general expression for $\mu'_n(X)$. Compute $E(X)$ and $\sigma^2(X)$.

7.12. Derive a recursion formula for μ_n for a Poisson variable. Then compute $\mu_3, \mu_4.$

CHAPTER 8

Normal
Random Variables

8.1 The One-Dimensional Case

8.1.1. Most of the important properties of one-dimensional normal random variables have been stated already in some of the preceding chapters, in particular in Example 2.5.5, Theorem 5.2.2, Theorem 6.3.4, Examples 7.1.5, 7.1.6.2, 7.2.3.8, 7.2.3.9, and 7.3.5, and Theorem 7.5.5. In this section we shall add a few facts on the use of available tables of values of the one-dimensional normal probability distribution and give some examples illustrating the application of these tables.

For the normalized normal random variable the values of the probability density

$$(8.1.1.1) \qquad \varphi(x) = \frac{1}{\sqrt{2\pi}} e^{-x^2/2}$$

as well as of the cumulative probability function

$$(8.1.1.2) \qquad \Phi(x) = \frac{1}{\sqrt{2\pi}} \int_{-\infty}^{x} e^{-s^2/2} ds$$

have been computed and tabulated.* Since we clearly have

$$(8.1.1.3) \qquad \varphi(-x) = \varphi(x)$$

we obtain

$$\Phi(0) = \int_{-\infty}^{0} \varphi(x)dx = \int_{0}^{+\infty} \varphi(x)dx = \tfrac{1}{2}$$

and

$$(8.1.1.4) \quad \Phi(-x) = 1 - \int_{-x}^{+\infty} \varphi(s)ds = 1 - \int_{-\infty}^{x} \varphi(s)ds = 1 - \Phi(x)$$

---

* The integral (8.1.1.2) cannot be evaluated by quadrature. To construct tables of its values, methods of numerical integration had to be used.

In view of (8.1.1.3) and (8.1.1.4) it was sufficient to tabulate values of φ and Φ for non-negative arguments only. Short tables of these functions are given at the end of this book. For a normal variable X with known expectation x_0 and standard deviation σ, the values of the probability density

$$(8.1.1.5) \qquad f(x) = \frac{1}{\sigma\sqrt{2\pi}}\, e^{-(x-x_0)^2/2\sigma^2}$$

and of the cumulative distribution function

$$(8.1.1.6) \qquad F(x) = \frac{1}{\sigma\sqrt{2\pi}} \int_{-\infty}^{x} e^{-(s-x_0)^2/2\sigma^2} ds$$

may be easily found from tables of values for $\varphi(x)$ and $\Phi(x)$, by making use of the identities

$$(8.1.1.7) \qquad f(x) = \frac{1}{\sigma}\, \varphi\!\left(\frac{x-x_0}{\sigma}\right)$$

$$(8.1.1.8) \qquad F(x) = \Phi\!\left(\frac{x-x_0}{\sigma}\right)$$

To say that a random variable X has a normal probability distribution with expectation x_0 and variance σ^2, one often uses the abbreviation: X has the distribution $N(x_0,\sigma^2)$.

8.1.2. Example. Let X have the distribution $N(3.2,2.25)$. Compute $f(3.8)$ and $P(1.8 \leq X \leq 3.7)$. From (8.1.1.7) we obtain

$$f(3.8) = \frac{1}{1.5}\, \varphi\!\left(\frac{3.8 - 3.2}{1.5}\right)$$

$$= \frac{1}{1.5}\, \varphi(0.4) = \frac{1}{1.5}\, (0.36827) = 0.24551$$

By using (8.1.1.8) and (8.1.1.4) we compute

$$P(1.8 \leq X \leq 3.7) = F(3.7) - F(1.8) = \Phi\!\left(\frac{3.7 - 3.2}{1.5}\right) - \Phi\!\left(\frac{1.8 - 3.2}{1.5}\right)$$

$$= \Phi(0.33) - \Phi(-0.93) = \Phi(0.33) - 1 + \Phi(0.93)$$

$$= 0.629 - 1 + 0.824 = 0.453$$

8.1.3. Equation (8.1.1.8) shows that for a normal variable the d.f. depends only on the ratio $(x - x_0)/\sigma$ which is sometimes referred to as the *deviation from the expectation in σ units*. Clearly all the probabilities

$$P(x_1 \leq X \leq x_2) = \Phi\!\left(\frac{x_2 - x_0}{\sigma}\right) - \Phi\!\left(\frac{x_1 - x_0}{\sigma}\right)$$

too, depend only on the values of the deviations in σ units

$$\frac{x_2 - x_0}{\sigma}, \qquad \frac{x_1 - x_0}{\sigma}$$

The following approximate numerical values for the normal probability distribution are worth remembering:

$$P(|X - x_0| \geq 1.96\sigma) = 0.05$$
$$P(|X - x_0| \geq 2.33\sigma) = 0.02$$
$$P(|X - x_0| \geq 2.58\sigma) = 0.01$$
$$P(|X - x_0| \geq 3.30\sigma) = 0.001$$
$$P(|X - x_0| \leq 0.6745\sigma) = P(|X - x_0| \geq 0.6745\sigma) = \tfrac{1}{2}$$
$$P(|X - x_0| \leq \sigma) = 0.682$$

In words, the first of these equalities means that the probability of an outcome which differs absolutely from the mathematical expectation by 1.96σ or more, is 5/100. Similarly, the fourth equality states that the probability of an outcome deviating from the expectation by 3.3σ or more, is only 1/1000. The fifth equality tells us that the interval $(x_0 - 0.6745\sigma, x_0 + 0.6745\sigma)$ has the property that an outcome X is equally probable to fall inside as it is to fall outside of that interval. The number 0.6745σ is sometimes called the *probable error* of a normal probability distribution with standard deviation σ. The last equality amounts to saying that the probability of X falling between $x_0 - \sigma$ and $x_0 + \sigma$ is slightly more than $\tfrac{2}{3}$.

By using tables of $\Phi(x)$, one easily evaluates approximate expressions such as (7.5.1.6) or (7.5.1.7), as will be shown in the following examples.

8.1.4. Example. Evaluate approximately the probability that, in tossing a coin 2000 times, heads will appear between 1050 and 1150 times. Assuming $p = q = \tfrac{1}{2}$ and $n = 2000$, we have $\sqrt{npq} = \sqrt{500} = 22.4$, which is large enough to assure a good approximation.

From (7.5.1.7) we have

$$P(1050 \leq S \leq 1150) = \Phi\left(\frac{1150 - 1000}{22.4}\right) - \Phi\left(\frac{1050 - 1000}{22.4}\right)$$

$$= \Phi(6.73) - \Phi(2.24) = 0.0125$$

8.1.5. Example. How many times does one have to roll a perfectly symmetrical die, to have a probability of at least 0.95 that the relative frequency of the outcome five will differ from $\tfrac{1}{6}$ by not more than 0.01? This question was already treated in Example 6.5.3.4 and there we found that 27,778 throws certainly will be sufficient. By using (7.5.1.7) we are able to reduce this number considerably. We are asking for a number n so large that

$$P\left(-\frac{1}{100} \leq \frac{S}{n} - \frac{1}{6} \leq \frac{1}{100}\right) \geq 0.95$$

For P we have the approximate expression

$$P\left(-\frac{1}{100} \leq \frac{S}{n} - \frac{1}{6} \leq \frac{1}{100}\right) =$$

$$P\left\{-\frac{1}{100}\left[n\Big/\left(\frac{1}{6}\cdot\frac{5}{6}\right)\right]^{1/2} \leq \left[n\Big/\left(\frac{1}{6}\cdot\frac{5}{6}\right)\right]^{1/2}\left(\frac{S}{n} - \frac{1}{6}\right) \leq \frac{1}{100}\left[n\Big/\left(\frac{1}{6}\cdot\frac{5}{6}\right)\right]^{1/2}\right\}$$

$$= \frac{1}{\sqrt{2\pi}} \int_{-\frac{1}{100}[n/(\frac{1}{6}\cdot\frac{5}{6})]^{1/2}}^{+\frac{1}{100}[n/(\frac{1}{6}\cdot\frac{5}{6})]^{1/2}} e^{-z^2/2} dz$$

$$= 2\Phi(0.06\sqrt{n/5}) - 1$$

Hence our condition for n takes the form

$$2\Phi(0.06\sqrt{n/5}) - 1 \geq 0.95$$

or

$$\Phi(0.06\sqrt{n/5}) \geq 0.975$$

and we find from the table of Φ that this is fulfilled for $0.06\sqrt{n/5} \geq 1.96$, which is equivalent to $n \geq 5335$. Hence $n = 5335$ is approximately the required number of throws.

*8.2 Some Properties of Definite Quadratic Forms

8.2.1. Let

$$A = (a_{j,k}), \quad j, k = 1, 2, \cdots, n$$

be a $n \times n$ square matrix of real numbers, and

$$\mathbf{x} = \begin{pmatrix} x_1 \\ x_2 \\ \cdot \\ \cdot \\ \cdot \\ x_n \end{pmatrix}$$

a real vector with the n coordinates x_i, $i = 1, 2, \cdots, n$. The real polynomial of the second degree in $x_1, \cdots, x_n$

(8.2.1.1) $$Q(\mathbf{x}) = \mathbf{x}'A\mathbf{x} = \sum_{j=1}^{n} \sum_{k=1}^{n} a_{jk}x_j x_k$$

is called a *positive definite quadratic form* in $\mathbf{x}$ if $Q(\mathbf{x}) > 0$ for all values of $\mathbf{x}$ except

$$\mathbf{x} = \begin{pmatrix} 0 \\ \cdot \\ \cdot \\ \cdot \\ 0 \end{pmatrix}$$

It may be assumed without loss of generality that A is a symmetric matrix, and we shall make this assumption from now on

$$A' = A$$

8.2.2. Theorem. If $Q(\mathbf{x}) = \mathbf{x}'A\mathbf{x}$ is a positive definite quadratic form, then there exists a real linear transformation

(8.2.2.1) $$\mathbf{z} = B\mathbf{x}$$

with a matrix

$$B = (b_{j,k}), \quad j, k = 1, 2, \cdots, n$$

such that

(i) $$b_{j,k} = 0 \quad \text{if } j > k$$

(ii) $$|B| = 1$$

(iii) $$Q(\mathbf{x}) = Q(B^{-1}\mathbf{z}) = \sum_{r=1}^{n} c_r z_r^{\,2} = \mathbf{z}' \begin{pmatrix} c_1 & & & & \\ & c_2 & & 0 & \\ & & \cdot & & \\ & 0 & & \cdot & \\ & & & & c_n \end{pmatrix} \mathbf{z}$$

(iv) $$|A| = c_1 c_2 \cdots c_n$$

Proof. We have $a_{11} > 0$, for if a_{11} were ≤ 0 we could put $x_1^{\star} = 1$, $x_2^{\star} = x_3^{\star} = \cdots = x_n^{\star} = 0$ and obtain $Q(\mathbf{x}^{\star}) = a_{11} \leq 0$, contrary to the assumption that $Q(\mathbf{x}) > 0$ everywhere but at the origin. We may now write

$$Q(\mathbf{x}) = a_{11}\left[x_1 + \sum_{k=2}^{n} \frac{a_{1k}}{a_{11}} x_k \right]^2 + \sum_{j=2}^{n} \sum_{k=2}^{n} \left(a_{jk} - \frac{a_{1j}a_{1k}}{a_{11}} \right) x_j x_k$$

and introduce the notations

(8.2.2.1.1) $$b_{11} = 1, \quad b_{1k} = \frac{a_{1k}}{a_{11}}, \quad k = 2, \cdots, n$$

(8.2.2.1.2) $$z_1 = \sum_{k=1}^{n} b_{1k} x_k = x_1 + \sum_{k=2}^{n} b_{1k} x_k$$

(8.2.2.1.3) $$c_1 = a_{11}$$

(8.2.2.1.4) $$a_{jk}^{(1)} = a_{jk} - \frac{a_{1j}a_{1k}}{a_{11}}, \quad j, k = 2, \cdots, n$$

(8.2.2.1.5) $$Q(\mathbf{x}) = c_1 z_1^{\,2} + \sum_{j=2}^{n} \sum_{k=2}^{n} a_{jk}^{(1)} x_j x_k = c_1 z_1^{\,2} + Q_1(x_2, \cdots, x_n)$$

From (8.2.2.1.4) it follows that the $(n-1) \times (n-1)$ matrix of coefficients of $Q_1(x_2,\cdots,x_n)$ is symmetrical, and Q_1 is a positive definite quadratic form in $x_2, \cdots, x_n$ for, if we had $Q_1(x_2{}^\star,x_3{}^\star,\cdots,x_n{}^\star) \leq 0$ and $x_2{}^\star, x_3{}^\star, \cdots, x_n{}^\star$ not all zero we could determine from (8.2.2.1.2) an $x_1{}^\star$ such that

$$z_1 = x_1{}^\star + \sum_{k=2}^{n} b_{1k}x_k{}^\star = 0$$

and would obtain from (8.2.2.1.5) the inequality $Q(x_1{}^\star,x_2{}^\star,\cdots,x_n{}^\star) \leq 0$ with $x_1{}^\star, x_2{}^\star, \cdots, x_n{}^\star$ not all zero.

Repeating for $Q_1(x_2,x_3,\cdots,x_n)$ the argument just applied to $Q(\mathbf{x})$, we conclude that $a_{22}^{(1)} > 0$, write

$$Q_1(x_2,x_3,\cdots,x_n) = a_{22}^{(1)}\left[x_2 + \sum_{k=3}^{n} \frac{a_{2k}^{(1)}}{a_{22}^{(1)}} x_k\right]^2 + \sum_{j=3}^{n}\sum_{k=3}^{n}\left(a_{jk}^{(1)} - \frac{a_{2j}^{(1)}a_{2k}^{(1)}}{a_{22}^{(1)}}\right)x_j x_k$$

introduce the quantities

(8.2.2.2.1) $\qquad b_{22} = 1, \qquad b_{2k} = \dfrac{a_{2k}^{(1)}}{a_{22}^{(1)}}, \qquad k = 3, \cdots, n$

(8.2.2.2.2) $\qquad z^2 = \displaystyle\sum_{k=2}^{n} b_{2k}x_k = x_2 + \sum_{k=3}^{n} b_{2k}x_k$

(8.2.2.2.3) $\qquad c_2 = a_{22}^{(1)}$

(8.2.2.2.4) $\qquad a_{jk}^{(2)} = a_{jk}^{(1)} - \dfrac{a_{2j}^{(1)}a_{2k}^{(1)}}{a_{22}^{(1)}}, \qquad j, k = 3, \cdots, n$

and obtain

$$Q_1(x_2,\cdots,x_n) = c_2 z_2{}^2 + \sum_{j=3}^{n}\sum_{k=3}^{n} a_{jk}^{(2)} x_j x_k = c_2 z_2{}^2 + Q_2(x_3,\cdots,x_n)$$

so that by (8.2.2.1.5) we obtain

(8.2.2.2.5) $\qquad Q(x_1,x_2,\cdots,x_n) = c_1 z_1{}^2 + c_2 z_2{}^2 + Q_2(x_3,\cdots,x_n)$

Again $Q_2(x_3,\cdots,x_n)$ is a positive definite quadratic form and the argument may be repeated over and over again.

In the lth repetition we introduce the quantities

(8.2.2.3.1) $\qquad b_{ll} = 1, b_{lk} = \dfrac{a_{lk}^{(l-1)}}{a_{ll}^{(l-1)}}, \qquad k = l+1, \cdots, n$

(8.2.2.3.2) $\qquad z_l = \displaystyle\sum_{k=l}^{n} b_{lk}x_k = x_l + \sum_{k=l+1}^{n} b_{lk}x_k$

(8.2.2.3.3) $\qquad c_l = a_{ll}^{(l-1)}$

(8.2.2.3.4) $\qquad a_{jk}^{(l)} = a_{jk}^{(l-1)} - \dfrac{a_{lj}^{(l-1)}a_{lk}^{(l-1)}}{a_{ll}^{(l-1)}}, \qquad j, k = l+1, \cdots, n$

and obtain

(8.2.2.3.5) $\quad Q(\mathbf{x}) = c_1 z_1{}^2 + c_2 z_2{}^2 + \cdots + c_l z_l{}^2 + Q_l(x_{l+1},\cdots,x_n)$

After $n - 1$ repetitions this argument yields

$$Q(\mathbf{x}) = c_1 z_1^2 + c_2 z_2^2 + \cdots + c_{n-1} z_{n-1}^2 + Q_{n-1}(x_n)$$

where $Q_{n-1}(x_n)$ is positive definite, hence $Q_{n-1}(x_n) = a_{nn}^{(n-1)} x_n^2$ with $a_{nn}^{(n-1)} > 0$, and by introducing the quantities

(8.2.2.4.1) $b_{nn} = 1$

(8.2.2.4.2) $z_n = x_n$

(8.2.2.4.3) $c_n = a_{nn}^{(n-1)}$

we conclude

(8.2.2.4.4) $Q(\mathbf{x}) = c_1 z_1^2 + c_2 z_2^2 + \cdots + c_n z_n^2$

Equalities (8.2.2.1.2), (8.2.2.2.2), (8.2.2.3.2), and (8.2.2.4.2) determine the transformation (8.2.2.1) with the properties claimed in (i), (ii), and (iii). To verify (iv), we substitute (8.2.2.1) in (8.2.2.4.4), writing

$$C = \begin{pmatrix} c_1 & & & \\ & c_2 & & 0 \\ & & \cdot & \\ & & & \cdot \\ 0 & & & \cdot \\ & & & & c_n \end{pmatrix}$$

and obtain

$$Q(\mathbf{x}) = \mathbf{x}'A\mathbf{x} = \mathbf{z}'C\mathbf{z} = \mathbf{x}'(B'CB)\mathbf{x}$$

hence

$$A = B'CB$$

and

$$|A| = |B'| \cdot |C| \cdot |B| = |C| = c_1 c_2 \cdots c_n$$

From (iii) and (iv) follows that the determinant $|A| = |a_{jk}|$ of the matrix of coefficients of a positive definite quadratic form is positive.

The procedure described in the proof above is known as *diagonalization* of a positive definite quadratic form.

8.2.3. Theorem.   Every principal minor of the matrix of coefficients of a positive definite quadratic form is positive.

Proof.   Consider a principal minor of order h of the matrix A of $Q(\mathbf{x})$. The terms of $Q(\mathbf{x})$ which correspond to that minor form a quadratic polynomial P in h variables with coefficients which form a symmetrical $h \times h$ matrix. This polynomial P is positive definite since, if it could be ≤ 0 for values of its arguments which are not all zero, so would $Q(\mathbf{x})$.

Conversely it can be shown that, if for a quadratic form $\mathbf{x}'A\mathbf{x}$ all principal minors of A are positive, then it is positive definite.

*8.3   Multivariate Normal Probability Distribution

8.3.1.   A function

$$(8.3.1.1) \quad f(x^{(1)},x^{(2)},\cdots,x^{(n)}) = K \exp\left[-\frac{1}{2}\sum_{i=1}^{n}\sum_{j=1}^{n} A_{ij}(x^{(i)} - a_i)(x^{(j)} - a_j)\right]$$

is a *multivariate n-dimensional normal probability density* when

$$R(x^{(1)},x^{(2)},\cdots,x^{(n)}) = \sum_{i=1}^{n}\sum_{j=1}^{n} A_{ij}(x^{(i)} - a_i)(x^{(j)} - a_j)$$

is a positive definite quadratic form and K the normalizing constant.

To determine K, we write the condition

$$(8.3.1.2) \quad \int_{-\infty}^{+\infty}\cdots\int_{-\infty}^{+\infty} f(x^{(1)},\cdots,x^{(n)})dx^{(1)}\cdots dx^{(n)} = 1$$

make the change of variables

$$x_j = x^{(j)} - a_j, \quad j = 1,\cdots, n$$

and apply the diagonalizing transformation (8.2.2.1).   From (ii) in Theorem 8.2.2 we see that the Jacobian of this transformation is identically 1, hence by (iii) and (iv) of that theorem we obtain

$$\int_{-\infty}^{+\infty}\cdots\int_{-\infty}^{+\infty} f(x^{(1)},\cdots,x^{(n)})dx^{(1)}\cdots dx^{(n)}$$

$$= \int_{-\infty}^{+\infty}\cdots\int_{-\infty}^{+\infty} \exp\left(-\frac{1}{2}\sum_{r=1}^{n} c_r z_r^2\right)dz_1\cdots dz_n$$

$$= \int_{-\infty}^{+\infty} \exp\left(-\tfrac{1}{2}c_1 z_1^2\right)dz_1 \cdots \int_{-\infty}^{+\infty} \exp\left(-\tfrac{1}{2}c_n z_n^2\right)dz_n$$

$$= \sqrt{2\pi/c_1}\cdots\sqrt{2\pi/c_n}$$

$$= (2\pi)^{n/2}/\sqrt{|A_{ij}|}$$

From this and (8.3.1.2) we find

$$(8.3.1.3) \qquad\qquad K = \sqrt{|A_{ij}|}\,(2\pi)^{-n/2}$$

and (8.3.1.1) takes the form

$$(8.3.1.4) \quad f(x^{(1)},\cdots,x^{(n)}) = \sqrt{|A_{ij}|}\,(2\pi)^{-n/2}$$

$$\times \exp\left[-\frac{1}{2}\sum_{i=1}^{n}\sum_{j=1}^{n} A_{ij}(x^{(i)} - a_i)(x^{(j)} - a_j)\right]$$

8.3.2. Theorem.   All marginal probability densities of a multivariate normal probability distribution are normal probability densities.

Proof.   Without loss of generality we may consider the marginal probability density of the $(n - l)$-dimensional random variable

$$(X^{(l+1)}, X^{(l+2)}, \cdots, X^{(n)})$$

for $1 \leq l \leq n - 1$. This probability density is

$$\int_{-\infty}^{+\infty} \cdots \int_{-\infty}^{+\infty} f(x^{(1)}, \cdots, x^{(l)}, x^{(l+1)}, \cdots, x^{(n)}) dx^{(1)} \cdots dx^{(l)}$$

$$= \sqrt{|A_{ij}|} (2\pi)^{-n/2} \int_{-\infty}^{+\infty} \cdots \int_{-\infty}^{+\infty} \exp\left[-\tfrac{1}{2}Q(x_1, \cdots, x_l, x_{l+1}, \cdots, x_n)\right] dx_1 \cdots dx_l$$

where

$$Q(x_1, \cdots, x_n) = \sum_{i=l}^{n} \sum_{j=1}^{n} A_{ij} x_i x_j$$

is a positive definite quadratic form.   From the proof of Theorem 8.2.2 we recall that after the lth step we had

(8.2.2.3.5) $$Q(x_1, \cdots, x_n) = c_1 z_1^2 + \cdots + c_l z_l^2 + Q_l(x_{l+1}, \cdots, x_n)$$

where

(8.2.2.1.2) $$z_1 = x_1 + \sum_{j=2}^{n} b_{1j} x_j$$

(8.2.2.2.2) $$z_2 = x_2 + \sum_{j=3}^{n} b_{2j} x_j$$

$$\cdot$$
$$\cdot$$
$$\cdot$$

(8.2.2.3.2) $$z_l = x_l + \sum_{j=l+1}^{n} b_{lj} x_j$$

and $Q_l(x_{l+1}, \cdots, x_n)$ is a positive definite quadratic form in its arguments. The change of variables (8.2.2.1.2), (8.2.2.2.2), $\cdots$, (8.2.2.3.2) which has a Jacobian identically equal to 1 yields

$$\int_{-\infty}^{+\infty} \cdots \int_{-\infty}^{+\infty} \exp\left[-\tfrac{1}{2}Q(x_1, \cdots, x_l, x_{l+1}, \cdots, x_n)\right] dx_1 \cdots dx_l$$

$$= \exp\left[-\tfrac{1}{2}Q_l(x_{l+1}, \cdots, x_n)\right] \int_{-\infty}^{+\infty} \exp\left(-\tfrac{1}{2}c_1 z_1^2\right) dz_1 \cdots \int_{-\infty}^{+\infty} \exp\left(-\tfrac{1}{2}c_l z_l^2\right) dz_l$$

$$= K_l \exp\left[-\tfrac{1}{2}Q_l(x_{l+1}, \cdots, x_n)\right]$$

This is an expression of the same form as (8.3.1.1), which completes the proof.

By a similar argument one proves also that all conditional probability densities of a multivariate normal probability distribution are normal.

EXERCISES

8.1. What is the probability that double six will occur exactly 15 times in 500 throws? That it will occur at least 15 times in 500 throws?

8.2. Five coins are tossed simultaneously and the number of heads obtained is denoted by H. This game is repeated 150 times. What is the probability that the outcome $H = 3$ occurs exactly 50 times? Exactly 70 times? At most 70 times?

8.3. A genetically determined character a is known to occur in plants of a certain species with a probability of $\frac{1}{4}$. Two thousand specimens of this plant are to be collected. Let S be the number of specimens in these 2000 which have the character a. Determine a number m such that $P(500 - m < S < 500 + m)$ equals (a) 0.95, (b) 0.99, (c) 0.999.

8.4. A psychological test is so normalized that the scores X are normally distributed with $x_0 = 50$, $\sigma_x = 10$. Find the probabilities $P(45 < X < 55)$, $P(X < 62)$, $P(67 < X)$, $P(56 < X < 65)$.

8.5. A test, standardized as in Exercise 8.4 was given to 500 individuals. Let U be the number of those in the sixth decile, i.e., those for whom $50 \leq X \leq 60$. Compute the probability $P(160 < U < 180)$.

8.6. In firing a rifle from a given distance at a given target suppose the vertical and horizontal components of the deviation of the shot from the center of the target can be regarded as being normally and independently distributed about the center of the target with standard deviations of 3 feet. In aiming at a rectangular opening 6 inches (horizontally) by 12 inches (vertically), symmetric about the center of the target, what is the probability of firing a shot through it? What is the smallest number of shots that must be fired so that the probability is at least 0.99 of getting at least 1 shot through it?

8.7. The random variable (X_1, X_2, X_3) has the multivariate normal probability density

$$K \exp \left[-\tfrac{1}{2}(2X_1{}^2 + X_2{}^2 + 4X_3{}^2 - X_1 X_2 - 2X_1 X_3) \right].$$

Write the matrix A of coefficients of the quadratic form in the exponent and compute K. Obtain (a) the marginal probability density of (X_1, X_3) and (b) the conditional probability density of (X_1, X_3) given X_2.

CHAPTER 9

Regression
and
Correlation

9.1 Two-Dimensional Random Variables: Fundamentals

9.1.1. In the case of two- and more dimensional random variables it is of great interest not only to determine whether the single coordinates are or are not dependent but also to study their dependence in detail. In this section we shall discuss problems of dependence—or *correlation*, as it is often called—in the case of a two-dimensional random variable. The discussion will be presented for continuous random variables but, as the reader may easily verify, all the statements hold true and can be proved by quite analogous steps for the discrete case.

Using the notations introduced in (4.1) we define the following concepts: The function of *y*

(9.1.1.1)
$$E(X \mid y) = \int_{-\infty}^{+\infty} xg(x \mid y)dx$$

is called the *conditional expectation of X for given y*, and the function of *x*

(9.1.1.2)
$$E(Y \mid x) = \int_{-\infty}^{+\infty} yh(y \mid x)dy$$

the *conditional expectation of Y for given x.*

In this section we shall always assume that the variance is positive for each marginal distribution. The assumption that one of the variances σ_X^2 or σ_Y^2 is zero leads to the degenerate case in which the corresponding coordinate assumes the value of its expectation with probability 1, a case which is equivalent to a one-dimensional random variable.

The number

$$\sigma_{XY} = E[(X - E(X))(Y - E(Y))]$$

is called the *covariance* of X and Y. The number

(9.1.1.3)
$$\rho_{XY} = \frac{\sigma_{XY}}{\sigma_X \cdot \sigma_Y}$$

is called the *coefficient of correlation of X and Y.*

9.1.2. Theorem.   If X and Y are independent, we have

$$\sigma_{XY} = \rho_{XY} = 0$$

Proof.   It follows immediately from (6.3.8.2).

The converse statement is not true: from $\sigma_{XY} = \rho_{XY} = 0$ it cannot be concluded that X and Y are independent. An example will be given in 9.1.4.

The graph of $E(X \mid y)$ as a function of y

$$x = E(X \mid y)$$

is called the *regression curve* of X on Y, and the graph of $E(Y \mid x)$

$$y = E(Y \mid x)$$

is called the *regression curve* of Y on X.

9.1.3. Theorem.   If one of the regression curves is a constant, then $\sigma_{XY} = \rho_{XY} = 0$.

Proof.   Assume, for example, that $y = E(Y \mid x) = c$. Then

$$c = \int_{-\infty}^{+\infty} yh(y \mid x)dy = \int_{-\infty}^{+\infty} y\frac{f(x,y)}{g(x)}\, dy = \frac{1}{g(x)} \int_{-\infty}^{+\infty} yf(x,y)dy$$

$$cg(x) = \int_{-\infty}^{+\infty} yf(x,y)dy$$

and, by integrating both sides with respect to x,

$$c \int_{-\infty}^{+\infty} g(x)dx = c = \int_{-\infty}^{+\infty} \int_{-\infty}^{+\infty} yf(x,y)dxdy = E(Y)$$

$$c = E(Y)$$

Using this we find

$$\sigma_{XY} = E[(X - E(X))(Y - E(Y))]$$
$$= E[XY - E(X)Y - E(Y)X + E(X)E(Y)]$$
$$= E(XY) - E(X)E(Y)$$
$$= \int_{-\infty}^{+\infty} \int_{-\infty}^{+\infty} xyf(x,y)dxdy - E(X)c$$
$$= \int_{-\infty}^{+\infty} xg(x) \int_{-\infty}^{+\infty} y\frac{f(x,y)}{g(x)}\, dydx - cE(X)$$
$$= \int_{-\infty}^{+\infty} xg(x)dxE(Y \mid x) - cE(X) = 0$$

9.1.4. Example. The random variable (X,Y) with the joint probability density

$$f(x,y) = \frac{1}{2\pi\sqrt{1+y^2}} \exp\left(-\frac{x^2}{2(1+y^2)} - \frac{y^2}{2}\right)$$

has covariance zero, and yet X and Y are not independent. To see this we compute

$$h(y) = \int_{-\infty}^{+\infty} f(x,y)dx = \frac{1}{\sqrt{2\pi}} e^{-y^2/2}$$

$$g(x \mid y) = \frac{f(x,y)}{h(y)} = \frac{1}{\sqrt{2\pi(1+y^2)}} \exp\left[-\frac{x^2}{2(1+y^2)}\right]$$

Since $x \exp\left[-\dfrac{x^2}{2(1+y^2)}\right]$ is an odd function of x, we immediately obtain

$$E(X \mid y) = \frac{1}{\sqrt{2\pi(1+y^2)}} \int_{-\infty}^{+\infty} x \exp\left[-\frac{x^2}{2(1+y^2)}\right]dx = 0$$

Hence, by Theorem 9.1.3, we have

$$\sigma_{XY} = \rho_{XY} = 0$$

but $g(x \mid y)$ clearly depends on y and thus X and Y are not independent.

9.1.5. Theorem. For any random variable (X,Y) with finite σ_X and σ_X we have the inequality

(9.1.5.1) $$|\sigma_{XY}| \leq \sigma_X \sigma_Y$$

Proof. Schwarz's inequality for two variables gives

$$\sigma_{XY}^2 = \left\{\int_{-\infty}^{+\infty}\int_{-\infty}^{+\infty} [x - E(X)] \cdot [y - E(Y)]f(x,y)dxdy\right\}^2$$

$$\leq \int_{-\infty}^{+\infty}\int_{-\infty}^{+\infty} [x - E(X)]^2f(x,y)dxdy \int_{-\infty}^{+\infty}\int_{-\infty}^{+\infty} [y - E(Y)]^2f(x,y)dxdy$$

$$= \sigma_X^2 \sigma_Y^2$$

which proves (9.1.5.1) for continuous random variables.

For discrete random variables Cauchy's inequality for double series must be used instead of Schwarz's inequality.

It can be shown that the equality sign in (9.1.5.1) holds if and only if there are constants A, B, not both zero, such that the identity

(9.1.5.2) $$A[x - E(X)] = B[y - E(Y)]$$

holds for all (X,Y) except, possibly, for a set which has probability zero.

9.1.6. Theorem. For any random variable (X,Y) with finite σ_X and σ_Y we have

(9.1.6.1) $$-1 \leq \rho_{XY} \leq 1$$

Proof.   It follows immediately from 9.1.5 in view of (9.1.1.3).

Again, it can be proved that the extreme values -1 or $+1$ for ρ_{XY} are taken if and only if relationship (9.1.5.2) is fulfilled. Further comments on this matter are contained in the remarks following identity (9.3.1.5).

The coefficient of correlation ρ_{XY} is often used to describe quantitatively the dependence between X and Y. Theorems 9.1.2 and 9.1.6 and the remarks which follow these theorems present the properties of ρ_{XY} which make it a useful "measure" of dependence: (*a*) if X and Y are independent, then $\rho_{XY} = 0$, (*b*) $\rho_{XY} = \pm 1$ is necessary and sufficient for one of the variables X and Y being completely determined by the other by a relationship of the form (9.1.5.2). A drawback of ρ_{XY} as a measure of dependence is that,

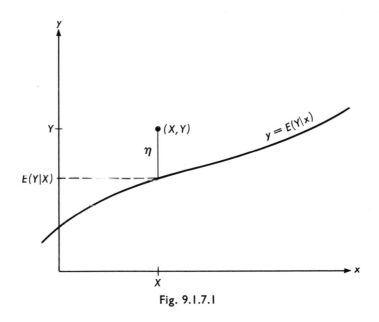

Fig. 9.1.7.1

without some additional assumptions, $\rho_{XY} = 0$ does not indicate independence, as can be seen from Example 9.1.4.

9.1.7.   Having computed $E(Y \mid x)$ for every value of x, we consider the quantity

(9.1.7.1) $\eta = Y - E(Y \mid X)$

This quantity is a random variable which may be described as the deviation, for an observed point (X,Y), of the coordinate Y from its conditional expectation computed for the observed value of X, or as the deviation of Y from the regression curve at the observed value of X (see Fig. 9.1.7.1).

9.1.7.2. Theorem. The random variable η has the expectation

(9.1.7.2.1) $$E(\eta) = 0$$

and the variance

(9.1.7.2.2) $$\sigma^2(\eta) = E(Y^2) - E[E^2(Y \mid X)]$$

Proof. The inequality

$$\eta_1 \le \eta \le \eta_2$$

is equivalent to the inequality

$$E(Y \mid X) + \eta_1 \le Y \le E(Y \mid X) + \eta_2$$

which determines a region R in the (X,Y) plane (see Fig. 9.1.7.2).

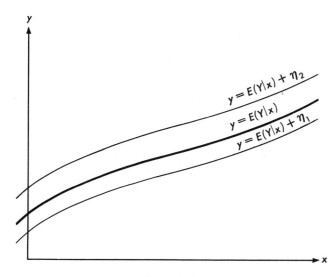

Fig. 9.1.7.2

We have

$$P(\eta_1 \le \eta \le \eta_2) = P[(X,Y) \in R]$$
$$= \iint_R f(x,y)dxdy = \int_{x=-\infty}^{+\infty} \int_{y=E(Y|x)+\eta_1}^{E(Y|x)+\eta_2} f(x,y)dydx$$
$$= \int_{x=-\infty}^{+\infty} \int_{\eta=\eta_1}^{\eta_2} f(x,E(Y \mid x) + \eta)d\eta dx$$
$$= \int_{\eta=\eta_1}^{\eta_2} \left[\int_{x=-\infty}^{+\infty} f(x,E(Y \mid x) + \eta)dx \right] d\eta = \int_{\eta_1}^{\eta_2} j(\eta)d\eta$$

hence

(9.1.7.2.3) $$j(\eta) = \int_{x=-\infty}^{+\infty} f(x,E(Y \mid x) + \eta)dx$$

is the probability density for η. From this we conclude

$$E(\eta) = \int_{-\infty}^{+\infty} \eta j(\eta) d\eta = \int_{-\infty}^{+\infty} \eta \int_{x=-\infty}^{+\infty} f(x, E(Y \mid x) + \eta) dx d\eta$$

$$= \int_{x=-\infty}^{+\infty} \int_{y=-\infty}^{+\infty} [y - E(Y \mid x)] f(x,y) dy dx$$

$$= E(Y) - \int_{x=-\infty}^{+\infty} \int_{y=-\infty}^{+\infty} E(Y \mid x) f(x,y) dy dX$$

and since

$$\int_{x=-\infty}^{+\infty} \int_{y=-\infty}^{+\infty} E(Y \mid x) f(x,y) dy dx = \int_{x=-\infty}^{+\infty} E(Y \mid x) \int_{y=-\infty}^{+\infty} f(x,y) dy dx$$

$$= \int_{x=-\infty}^{+\infty} \left[\int_{y=-\infty}^{+\infty} y \frac{f(x,y)}{g(x)} dy g(x) \right] dx = E(Y)$$

we obtain (9.1.7.2.1). To prove (9.1.7.2.2), we compute

$$\sigma^2(\eta) = E(\eta^2) = \int_{\eta=-\infty}^{+\infty} \eta^2 \int_{x=-\infty}^{+\infty} f(x, E(Y \mid x) + \eta) dx d\eta$$

$$= \int_{x=-\infty}^{+\infty} \int_{y=-\infty}^{+\infty} [y - E(Y \mid x)]^2 f(x,y) dy dx$$

$$= \int_{x=-\infty}^{+\infty} \int_{y=-\infty}^{+\infty} y^2 f(x,y) dx dy$$

$$- 2 \int_{x=-\infty}^{+\infty} E(Y \mid x) g(x) \int_{y=-\infty}^{+\infty} y \frac{f(x,y)}{g(x)} dy dx$$

$$+ \int_{x=-\infty}^{+\infty} E^2(Y \mid x) \int_{y=-\infty}^{+\infty} f(x,y) dy dx$$

$$= E(Y^2) - 2 \int_{x=-\infty}^{+\infty} E^2(Y \mid x) g(x) dx$$

$$+ \int_{-\infty}^{+\infty} E^2(Y \mid x) g(x) dx = E(Y^2) - E[E^2(Y \mid X)]$$

The number $\sigma^2(\eta)$ is called the *variance about the regression curve of Y on X*. The number

(9.1.7.2.4) $$\sigma(\eta) = \sqrt{E(Y^2) - E[E^2(Y \mid X)]}$$

is sometimes referred to as the *standard error of estimate for Y*. It is the standard deviation of η and, according to Chebyshev's inequality, can be used to estimate the probability of η scattering away from $E(\eta) = 0$, that is, of Y scattering vertically away from $E(Y \mid X)$.

Similarly, the deviation of X from its conditional expectation

(9.1.7.2.5) $$\xi = X - E(X \mid Y)$$

is a random variable with

(9.1.7.2.6) $$E(\xi) = 0$$

(9.1.7.2.7) $$\sigma^2(\xi) = E(X^2) - E[E^2(X \mid Y)]$$

The number $\sigma^2(\xi)$ is called the *variance about the regression curve of X on Y*, and

$$\sigma(\xi) = \sqrt{E(X^2) - E[E^2(X \mid Y)]}$$

is often referred to as *standard error of estimate for X*.

9.1.8. Example. Let $f(x,y)$ be the probability density of the random variable with uniform distribution in the region Q bounded by

$$y - x = 1, \quad x - y = 1, \quad y = \tfrac{1}{2}(x^2 + 2x - 2), \quad y = \tfrac{1}{2}(x^2 - 2x + 2)$$

The area of Q being 4 units, $f(x,y)$ is equal to $\tfrac{1}{4}$ for (x,y) in Q, and 0 outside of Q. The absolute probability densities are

$$g(x) = \int_{(1/2)(x^2+2x-2)}^{x+1} \tfrac{1}{4} dy = \frac{1}{2}\left(1 - \frac{x}{2}\right)\left(1 + \frac{x}{2}\right) \quad \text{for } -2 \le x \le 0$$

$$g(x) = \int_{x-1}^{(1/2)(x^2-2x+2)} \tfrac{1}{4} dy = \frac{1}{2}\left(1 - \frac{x}{2}\right)^2 \quad \text{for } 0 \le x \le 2$$

and

$$h(y) = \int_{-1-\sqrt{3+2y}}^{-1+\sqrt{3+2y}} \tfrac{1}{4} dy = \tfrac{1}{2}\sqrt{3 + 2y} \quad \text{for } -\tfrac{3}{2} \le y \le -1$$

$$h(y) = \int_{y-1}^{y+1} \tfrac{1}{4} dx = \tfrac{1}{2} \quad \text{for } -1 \le y \le \tfrac{1}{2}$$

$$h(y) = \int_{y-1}^{1-\sqrt{2y-1}} \tfrac{1}{4} dx + \int_{1+\sqrt{2y-1}}^{y+1} \tfrac{1}{4} dx = \tfrac{1}{2}(1 - \sqrt{2y - 1}) \quad \text{for } \tfrac{1}{2} \le y \le 1$$

The conditional probability densities are:

If $-\tfrac{3}{2} \le y \le -1$,

$$g(x \mid y) = \begin{cases} \dfrac{1}{2\sqrt{3 + 2y}} & \text{for } -1 - \sqrt{3 + 2y} \le x \le -1 + \sqrt{3 + 2y} \\ 0 & \text{elsewhere} \end{cases}$$

If $-1 \le y \le \tfrac{1}{2}$,

$$g(x \mid y) = \begin{cases} \tfrac{1}{2} & \text{for } y - 1 \le x \le y + 1 \\ 0 & \text{elsewhere} \end{cases}$$

If $\frac{1}{2} \leq y \leq 1$,

$$g(x \mid y) = \begin{cases} \dfrac{1}{2(1 - \sqrt{2y - 1})} & \text{for } y - 1 \leq x \leq 1 - \sqrt{2y - 1} \\[2mm] \dfrac{1}{2(1 - \sqrt{2y - 1})} & \text{for } 1 + \sqrt{2y - 1} \leq x \leq y + 1 \\[2mm] 0 & \text{elsewhere} \end{cases}$$

If $-2 \leq x \leq 0$,

$$h(y \mid x) = \begin{cases} \dfrac{1}{2 - (x^2/2)} & \text{for } \frac{1}{2}(x^2 + 2x - 2) \leq y \leq x + 1 \\[2mm] 0 & \text{elsewhere} \end{cases}$$

If $x - 1 \leq y \leq \frac{1}{2}(x^2 - 2x + 2)$,

$$h(y \mid x) = \begin{cases} \dfrac{2}{(2 - x)^2} & \text{for } x - 1 \leq y \leq \frac{1}{2}(x^2 - 2x + 2) \\[2mm] 0 & \text{elsewhere} \end{cases}$$

With these probability densities, one obtains

$$E(X) = -\tfrac{1}{3}, \qquad E(Y) - -\tfrac{1}{3}$$

$$E(X \mid y) = \begin{cases} -1 & \text{for } -\tfrac{3}{2} \leq y \leq -1 \\[1mm] y & \text{for } -1 \leq y \leq \tfrac{1}{2} \\[1mm] \dfrac{1}{2} - \dfrac{\sqrt{2y - 1}}{2} & \text{for } \tfrac{1}{2} \leq y \leq 1 \end{cases}$$

$$E(Y \mid x) = \begin{cases} x + \dfrac{x^2}{4} & \text{for } -2 \leq x \leq 0 \\[2mm] \dfrac{x^2}{4} & \text{for } 0 \leq x \leq 2 \end{cases}$$

$$E(X^2) = \tfrac{2}{3}, \qquad E(Y^2) = \tfrac{7}{15}, \qquad E(XY) = \tfrac{2}{5}$$

$$\sigma_X^2 = \tfrac{5}{9}, \qquad \sigma_Y^2 = \tfrac{16}{45}, \qquad \sigma_{XY} = \tfrac{13}{45}$$

$$\rho_{XY} = \tfrac{13}{20}$$

$$E[E^2(X \mid Y)] = \tfrac{13}{480}, \qquad E[E^2(Y \mid X)] = \tfrac{4}{15}$$

$$\sigma^2(\xi) = \tfrac{307}{408}, \qquad \sigma^2(\eta) = \tfrac{1}{5}$$

The reader is urged to prepare a careful sketch of the region Q considered in this example, and to draw the graphs of both regression curves. He will observe that these curves, besides having somewhat unexpected shapes, have entire arcs outside the region Q, i.e., in parts of the plane where the probability density of (X,Y) is zero.

9.2 Two-Dimensional Random Variables: Linear Regression, Normal Bivariate Distribution

9.2.1. The two-dimensional random variable (X,Y) is said to have *linear regression of Y on X* if

(9.2.1.1) $$E(Y \mid x) = Ax + B$$

with A and B constant, that is, if the regression curve of Y on X is a straight line which is then called the *regression line of Y on X*. Similarly, (X,Y) is said to have *linear regression of X on Y* if

(9.2.1.2) $$E(X \mid y) = Cy + D$$

with C and D constant, that is, if the regression curve of X on Y is a straight line, which is then called the *regression line of X on Y*. If (9.2.1.1) and (9.2.1.2) both hold, (X,Y) is said to have *linear regression*. The number A is called the *regression coefficient of Y on X*, and the number C the *regression coefficient of X on Y*.

The theory presented in Section 9.1 takes a particularly simple form if (X,Y) has linear regression or at least linear regression of one coordinate on the other.

9.2.2. Theorem. If (X,Y) has linear regression of Y on X then

(9.2.2.1) $$A = \rho_{XY} \cdot (\sigma_Y/\sigma_X) = \sigma_{XY}/\sigma_X{}^2$$

and

(9.2.2.2) $$B = E(Y) - AE(X) = E(Y) - (\sigma_{XY}/\sigma_X{}^2)E(X)$$

Proof. By multiplying (9.2.1.1) by $g(x)$ and integrating, one finds

$$\int_{-\infty}^{+\infty} E(Y \mid x)g(x)dx = A \int_{-\infty}^{+\infty} xg(x)dx + B \int_{-\infty}^{+\infty} g(x)dx$$

that is,

$$E(Y) = AE(X) + B$$

Similarly, by multiplying (9.2.1.1) by $xg(x)$ and integrating, one obtains

$$\int_{-\infty}^{+\infty} E(Y \mid x)xg(x)dx = A \int_{-\infty}^{+\infty} x^2g(x)dx + B \int_{-\infty}^{+\infty} xg(x)dx$$

that is,.

$$E(XY) = AE(X^2) + BE(X)$$

Solving these two equations for A and B, one obtains

$$A = \frac{E(XY) - E(X) \cdot E(Y)}{E(X^2) - E^2(X)} = \frac{\sigma_{XY}}{\sigma_X{}^2} = \frac{\sigma_{XY}}{\sigma_X \sigma_Y} \cdot \frac{\sigma_Y}{\sigma_X} = \rho_{XY} \frac{\sigma_Y}{\sigma_X}$$

$$B = E(Y) - AE(X)$$

Under the assumption of linear regression of X on Y, one finds by an analogous argument the relationships

(9.2.2.3) $$C = \rho_{XY} \frac{\sigma_X}{\sigma_Y}$$

(9.2.2.4) $$D = E(X) - CE(Y)$$

The following corollaries follow immediately from Theorem 9.2.2.

9.2.3. Corollary. If (X,Y) has linear regression, the equations of the regression lines are:

(9.2.3.1) $$y - E(Y) = \rho_{XY} \frac{\sigma_Y}{\sigma_X} [x - E(X)]$$

(9.2.3.2) $$x - E(X) = \rho_{XY} \frac{\sigma_X}{\sigma_Y} [y - E(Y)]$$

and these lines intersect at the point $(E(X),E(Y))$.

9.2.4. Corollary. If (X,Y) has linear regression, we have

(9.2.4.1) $$\operatorname{sign} A = \operatorname{sign} C$$

and

(9.2.4.2) $$\rho_{XY} = \sqrt{AC} \cdot \operatorname{sign} A = \sqrt{AC} \cdot \operatorname{sign} C$$

9.2.5. Theorem. If (X,Y) has linear regression of Y on X, then the variance about the regression line of Y on X has the value

(9.2.5.1) $$\sigma^2(\eta) = \sigma^2(Y)(1 - \rho_{XY}^2)$$

Proof

$$\sigma^2(\eta) = E(Y^2) - E[E^2(Y \mid X)]$$
$$= E(Y^2) - E\{[E(Y) + \rho_{XY}(\sigma_Y/\sigma_X)(X - E(X))]^2\}$$
$$= E(Y^2) - E^2(Y) - 2E(Y)\rho_{XY}(\sigma_Y/\sigma_X)E[X - E(X)]$$
$$\quad - \rho_{XY}^2(\sigma_Y{}^2/\sigma_X{}^2)E\{[X - E(X)]^2\}$$
$$= \sigma_Y{}^2 - \rho_{XY}^2(\sigma_Y{}^2/\sigma_X{}^2)\sigma_X{}^2$$
$$= \sigma_Y{}^2(1 - \rho_{XY}^2)$$

Relationship (9.2.5.1) may be used for computing the standard error of estimate if there is linear regression of Y on X, but its use for computing $\sigma(\eta)$ leads to incorrect results if this assumption is not fulfilled, as will be seen in more detail from equation (9.3.1.5).

Under the assumption of linear regression of X on Y, one obtains similarly

(9.2.5.2) $$\sigma^2(\xi) = \sigma^2(X)(1 - \rho_{XY}^2)$$

9.2.6. Theorem. If the random variable (X,Y) has a normal bivariate probability distribution with the probability density

$$f(x,y) = \frac{1}{2\pi} \sqrt{A_{11}A_{22} - A_{12}{}^2} \exp \left\{-\tfrac{1}{2}[A_{11}(x - x_0)^2 + 2A_{12}(x - x_0)(y - y_0) \right.$$
$$\left. + A_{22}(y - y_0)^2]\right\}$$

then it has linear regression, and the regression lines have the equations

(9.2.6.1) $$E(Y \mid x) = -(A_{12}/A_{22})(x - x_0) + y_0$$

(9.2.6.2) $$E(X \mid y) = -(A_{12}/A_{11})(y - y_0) + x_0$$

Proof. According to (4.2.1.4) we have

$$h(y \mid x) = \sqrt{\frac{A_{22}}{2\pi}} \exp \frac{-\{y - [y_0 - (A_{12}/A_{22})(x - x]\}^2 A_0)_{22}}{2}$$

This, for every value of x is a normal probability density for Y with the expectation $y_0 - (A_{12}/A_{22})(x - x_0)$, which proves (9.2.6.1). Equality (9.2.6.2) is obtained by a symmetrical argument.

From 9.2.6 it follows that all statements proven for random variables with linear regression hold true for normal bivariate random variables.

9.3 Fitting Straight Lines to Regression Curves by the Method of Least Squares

9.3.1. Let (X,Y) be a two-dimensional random variable for which the regression curve of Y on X has the equation

(9.3.1.1) $$y = E(Y \mid x)$$

We shall determine a straight line

(9.3.1.2) $$y = \alpha_0 x + \beta_0$$

best fitted to the curve (9.3.1) in that sense that the function of α, β

$$F(\alpha,\beta) = E\{[E(Y \mid X) - (\alpha X + \beta)]^2\}$$

shall have a minimum for $\alpha = \alpha_0$, $\beta = \beta_0$ The line (9.3.1.2) is called the *least-square regression line of Y on X*.

In order that α_0, β_0 minimize $F(\alpha,\beta)$, it is necessary that they fulfill the equations

$$\frac{\partial F(\alpha_0,\beta_0)}{\partial \alpha} = 2E\{[E(Y \mid X) - (\alpha_0 X + \beta_0)][(-X)\}$$

$$= -2\{E(XY) - \alpha_0 E(X^2) - \beta_0 E(X)\} = 0$$

and

$$\frac{\partial F(\alpha_0,\beta_0)}{\partial \beta} = 2E\{[E(Y \mid X) - (\alpha_0 X + \beta_0)](-1)\}$$

$$= -2\{E(Y) - \alpha_0 E(X) - \beta_0\} = 0$$

Solving these equations gives

(9.3.1.3) $$\alpha_0 = \frac{E(XY) - E(X) \cdot E(Y)}{E(X^2) - E^2(X)} = \frac{\sigma_{XY}}{\sigma_X^2}$$

(9.3.1.4) $$\beta_0 = E(Y) - \alpha_0 E(X) = E(Y) - \frac{\sigma_{XY}}{\sigma_X^2} E(X)$$

The line (9.3.1.2) with α_0 and β_0 given by (9.3.1.3) and (9.3.1.4) actually minimizes $F(\alpha,\beta)$. For if, α, β are any two real numbers, we have

$$F(\alpha,\beta) = E\{[E(Y \mid X) - (\alpha_0 X + \beta_0) + (\alpha_0 X + \beta_0) - (\alpha X + \beta)]^2\}$$

$$= E\{[E(Y \mid X) - (\alpha_0 X + \beta_0)]^2\}$$

$$+ 2E\{[E(Y \mid X) - (\alpha_0 X + \beta_0)] \cdot [(\alpha_0 X + \beta_0) - (\alpha X + \beta)]\}$$

$$+ E\{[(\alpha_0 - \alpha)X + (\beta_0 - \beta)]^2\}$$

$$= F(\alpha_0,\beta_0) + 2(\alpha_0 - \alpha)E\{[E(Y \mid X) - (\alpha_0 X + \beta_0)]X\}$$

$$+ 2(\beta_0 - \beta)E\{E(Y \mid X) - (\alpha_0 X + \beta_0)\}$$

$$+ E\{[(\alpha_0 - \alpha)X + \beta_0 - \beta)]^2\}$$

In view of (9.3.1.3) and (9.3.1.4) the two middle terms are zero and we have

$$F(\alpha,\beta) = F(\alpha_0,\beta_0) + E\{[(\alpha_0 - \alpha)X + (\beta_0 - \beta)]^2\} \geq F(\alpha_0,\beta_0)$$

It is of interest to note that the values α_0, β_0 given by (9.3.1.3) and (9.3.1.4) are the same as the values of A and B given by (9.2.2.1) and (9.2.2.2) in the case of linear regression of Y on X. Hence, if there is no linear regression of Y on X, the line with the equation (9.2.3.1) is still the least square regression line of Y on X.

By substituting in $F(\alpha,\beta)$ the values $\alpha = \alpha_0 = A$, $\beta = \beta_0 = B$, we obtain

$$
\begin{aligned}
F(A,B) &= E\{[E(Y\,|\,X) - (AX+B)]^2\} \\
&= E\{[E(Y\,|\,X) - \rho_{XY}(\sigma_X/\sigma_Y)(x-x_0) - y_0]^2\} \\
&= E\{[E(Y\,|\,X)]^2\} + \rho_{XY}{}^2(\sigma_Y{}^2/\sigma_X{}^2)\sigma_X{}^2 + y_0{}^2 \\
&\quad - 2\rho_{XY}(\sigma_Y/\sigma_X)E\{E(Y\,|\,X)(X-x_0)\} - 2y_0E\{E(Y\,|\,X)\} \\
&\quad + 2\rho_{XY}(\sigma_Y/\sigma_X)y_0E(X-x_0) \\
&= E[E^2(Y\,|\,X)] + \rho_{XY}{}^2\sigma_Y{}^2 + y_0{}^2 - 2\rho_{XY}(\sigma_Y/\sigma_X)E(XY) \\
&\quad + 2\rho_{XY}(\sigma_Y/\sigma_X)x_0y_0 - 2y_0{}^2 \\
&= E[E^2(Y\,|\,X)] - E(Y^2) - y_0{}^2 + E(Y^2) + \rho_{XY}{}^2\sigma_Y{}^2 \\
&\quad + 2\rho_{XY}(\sigma_Y/\sigma_X)[x_0y_0 - E(XY)] \\
&= -\sigma^2(\eta) + \sigma_Y{}^2 + \rho_{XY}{}^2\sigma_Y{}^2 - 2\rho_{XY}(\sigma_Y/\sigma_X)\sigma_{XY} \\
&= -\sigma^2(\eta) + \sigma_Y{}^2 - \rho_{XY}{}^2\sigma_Y{}^2
\end{aligned}
$$

and finally

(9.3.1.5) $\quad E\{[E(Y\,|\,X) - (AX+B)]^2\} + \sigma^2(\eta) = \sigma_Y{}^2(1 - \rho_{XY}{}^2)$

From (9.3.1.5) it is obvious that, if ρ_{XY} is close to either $+1$ or to -1, then $E\{[E(Y\,|\,X) - (AX+B)]^2\} = F(A,B)$ and $\sigma^2(\eta)$ are both close to zero, which means that the regression curve $E(Y\,|\,X)$ is close to the least square regression line $AX + B$ and that the scatter of Y about $E(Y\,|\,X)$ is small. In particular, for $|\rho_{XY}| = 1$, we obtain $F(A,B) = \sigma^2(\eta) = 0$ hence the regression of Y on X is linear and the scatter of Y about $E(Y\,|\,X) = AX + B$ is zero. that is Y is a linear function of X.

Another obvious consequence of (9.3.1.5) is the inequality

$$
\sigma^2(\eta) \leq \sigma_Y{}^2(1 - \rho_{XY}{}^2)
$$

in which the equality sign holds if and only if

$$
F(A,B) = 0
$$

i.e., in the case of linear regression. This means that the standard error of estimate $\sigma(\eta)$ is equal to the standard deviation σ_Y if and only if there is correlation zero *and* linear regression of Y on X.

Since the left-hand expression in (9.1.3.5) is clearly non-negative, it follows that $\rho_{XY}{}^2 \leq 1$, and this is an alternative proof of (9.1.6.1) which makes no use of Schwarz's inequality.

All the statements of this section can be repeated with the variables X and Y interchanged.

9.3.2. Example. For the probability distribution of Example 9.1.8, the least square regression lines have the constants

$$\alpha_0 = \frac{\sigma_{XY}}{\sigma_X{}^2} = \frac{13/45}{5/9} = \frac{13}{25}$$

$$\beta_0 = E(Y) - \alpha_0 E(X) = -\frac{1}{3} - \frac{13}{25}\left(-\frac{1}{3}\right) = -\frac{4}{25}$$

$$\gamma_0 = \frac{\sigma_{XY}}{\sigma_Y{}^2} = \frac{13/45}{41/90} = \frac{26}{41}$$

$$\delta_0 = E(X) - \gamma_0 E(Y) = -\frac{1}{3} - \frac{26}{41}\left(-\frac{1}{3}\right) = \frac{-5}{41}$$

Thus the equations of the least square lines are:

$$\text{Regression line of } Y \text{ on } X, \quad y = \frac{1}{25}\,(13x - 4)$$

$$\text{Regression line of } X \text{ on } Y, \quad x = \frac{1}{41}\,(26y - 5)$$

9.4 Random Variables with a Common Component. Correlation of Attributes

9.4.1. Let X, Y, Z, be mutually independent random variables with finite variances $\sigma_X{}^2, \sigma_Y{}^2, \sigma_Z{}^2$, and let U, V be the random variables defined by

$$U = X + Z$$

$$V = Y + Z$$

Then the correlation coefficient ρ_{UV} is

$$\rho_{UV} = \frac{\sigma_Z{}^2}{\sqrt{(\sigma_X{}^2 + \sigma_Z{}^2)(\sigma_Y{}^2 + \sigma_Z{}^2)}}$$

This follows immediately from the relationships

$$\begin{aligned}
\sigma_{UV} &= E(UV) - E(U) \cdot E(V) \\
&= E(XY + YZ + XZ + Z^2) - [E(X) + E(Z)] \cdot [E(Y) + E(Z)] \\
&= E(X) \cdot E(Y) + E(Y) \cdot E(Z) + E(X) \cdot E(Z) + E(Z^2) \\
&= E(X)E(Y) - E(Y)E(Z) - E(X)E(Z) - E^2(Z) \\
&= E(Z^2) - E^2(Z) = \sigma_Z{}^2 \\
\end{aligned}$$

$$\sigma_U{}^2 = \sigma_X{}^2 + \sigma_Z{}^2, \qquad \sigma_V{}^2 = \sigma_Y{}^2 + \sigma_Z{}^2$$

9.4.1.1. Example. Consider the following game. $n + l$ coins are tossed simultaneously, and the number of heads obtained is called U. Then n of these coins are picked up and tossed again, while l are left as they fell before; the number of heads on all $n + l$ coins is counted again and called V. If the number of heads on the l coins left unchanged is called Z, the number of heads on the remaining n obtained in the first tossing X, and that in the second tossing Y, then clearly $U = X + Z$, $V = Y + Z$, and the assumptions of 9.4.1 are fulfilled. Since

$$\sigma_X{}^2 = \sigma_Y{}^2 = n \cdot \tfrac{1}{2} \cdot \tfrac{1}{2}, \qquad \sigma_Z{}^2 = l \cdot \tfrac{1}{2} \cdot \tfrac{1}{2}$$

we obtain

$$\rho_{UV} = \frac{l}{n + l}$$

9.4.2. Frequently it is of interest to study the dependence between the occurrence or non-occurrence of one attribute and the occurrence or non-occurrence of another attribute, such as being inoculated or not being inoculated against a certain disease, and contracting or not contracting that disease. Let A denote the occurrence and $\bar{A}$ the non-occurrence of one attribute, and B the occurrence and $\bar{B}$ the non-occurrence of the other attribute. The only possible outcomes of any individual observation are: (A,B), $(A,\bar{B})$, $(\bar{A},B)$, $(\bar{A},\bar{B})$. Let, in n independent observations, α_n be the number of A's and β_n the number of B's observed. The quantities α_n and β_n are random variables, each with the possible values $0, 1, 2, \cdots, n$. With these notations, we have the following theorem.

9.4.2.1. Theorem. Let the probabilities of the events (A,B), $(A,\bar{B})$, $(\bar{A},B)$, $(\bar{A},\bar{B})$ be denoted by $P(A,B)$, $P(A,\bar{B})$, $P(\bar{A},B)$, $P(\bar{A},\bar{B})$ respectively, and let

$$P(A) = P(A,B) + P(A,\bar{B})$$
$$P(\bar{A}) = P(\bar{A},B) + P(\bar{A},\bar{B})$$
$$P(B) = P(A,B) + P(\bar{A},B)$$
$$P(\bar{B}) = P(A,\bar{B}) + P(\bar{A},\bar{B})$$

Then the correlation coefficient $\rho_{\alpha_n \beta_n}$ is independent of n and is equal to

$$\rho_{\alpha_n \beta_n} = \frac{P(A,B) \cdot P(\bar{A},\bar{B}) - P(A,\bar{B}) \cdot P(\bar{A},B)}{\sqrt{P(A) \cdot P(B) \cdot P(\bar{A}) \cdot P(\bar{B})}}$$

Proof. We define the auxiliary variables

$$X_i = \begin{cases} 1 & \text{if } A \text{ occurs in the } i\text{th observation} \\ 0 & \text{if } \bar{A} \text{ occurs in the } i\text{th observation} \end{cases}$$

$$Y_i = \begin{cases} 1 & \text{if } B \text{ occurs in the } i\text{th observation} \\ 0 & \text{if } \bar{B} \text{ occurs in the } i\text{th observation} \end{cases}$$

In view of the assumed independence of the observations, X_i and Y_k are independent for $i \neq k$. We have the relationships

$$P(A,B) + P(A,\bar{B}) + P(\bar{A},B) + P(\bar{A},\bar{B}) = 1$$

$$E(X_i) = P(A), \qquad \sigma_X{}^2 = P(A) \cdot P(\bar{A}) \quad \text{for } i = 1, 2, \cdots, n$$

$$E(Y_i) = P(B), \qquad \sigma_Y{}^2 = P(B) \cdot P(\bar{B}) \quad \text{for } i = 1, 2, \cdots, n$$

$$E(X_i Y_i) = 1.1.P(A,B) + 1.0.P(A,\bar{B}) + 0.1.P(\bar{A},B) + 0.0.P(\bar{A},\bar{B})$$

$$= P(A,B) \quad \text{for } i = 1, 2, \cdots, n$$

$$\alpha_n = \sum_{i=1}^{n} X_i, \qquad \beta_n = \sum_{i=1}^{n} Y_i$$

hence

$$E(\alpha_n) = nP(A), \qquad E(\beta_n) = nP(B)$$

$$E(\alpha_n \beta_n) = E\left(\sum_{i=1}^{n} X_i Y_i + \sum_{i=1}^{n} \sum_{k \neq i} X_i Y_k \right)$$

$$= \sum_{i=1}^{n} E(X_i Y_i) + \sum_{i=1}^{n} \sum_{k \neq i} E(X_i)E(Y_k)$$

$$= nP(A,B) + n(n-1)P(A) \cdot P(B)$$

$$\sigma_{\alpha_n \beta_n} = E(\alpha_n \beta_n) - E(\alpha_n) \cdot E(\beta_n) = n[P(A,B) - P(A) \cdot P(B)]$$

$$\sigma_{\alpha_n}{}^2 = \sum_{i=1}^{n} \sigma_{X_i}{}^2 = nP(A) \cdot P(\bar{A}), \qquad \sigma_{\beta_n}{}^2 = \sum_{i=1}^{n} \sigma_{Y_i}{}^2 = nP(B) \cdot P(\bar{B})$$

$$\rho_{\alpha_n \beta_n} = \frac{\sigma_{\alpha_n \beta_n}}{\sigma_{\alpha_n} \cdot \sigma_{\beta_n}} = \frac{n[P(A,B) - P(A) \cdot P(B)]}{\sqrt{nP(A) \cdot P(\bar{A})nP(B)P(\bar{B})}}$$

$$= \frac{P(A,B)P(\bar{A},\bar{B}) - P(A,\bar{B}) \cdot P(\bar{A},B)}{\sqrt{P(A) \cdot P(\bar{A}) \cdot P(B) \cdot P(\bar{B})}}$$

The correlation coefficient $\rho(\alpha_n, \beta_n)$ between the frequencies of occurrence of two attributes is sometimes referred to as *Bernoulli's coefficient of correlation*.

One verifies easily that the vanishing of Bernoulli's coefficient of correlation is necessary and sufficient for the independence of the attributes, that is, $\rho(\alpha_n, \beta_n) = 0$ is necessary and sufficient for $P(A,B) = P(A) \cdot P(B)$.

EXERCISES

9.1. The two-dimensional random variable (X,Y) has the uniform probability distribution in the rectangle with vertices at $(1,0)$, $(7,3)$, $(6,5)$, and $(0,2)$. Use geometrical considerations, write the equations of both regression curves, and plot t ese curves.

9.2. Let R be a rectangle centered at $(0,0)$ with sides of lengths $a < b$, and let the sides of length b make an angle θ, $0 \le \theta < \pi/2$, with the positive X axis. If the random variable (X,Y) has uniform probability density in R, compute σ_X, σ_Y, $\sigma_{X,Y}$, $\rho_{X,Y}$.

9.3. The random variable (X,Y) has the probability density $f(x,y) = Ce^{-(ax+by)}$ for $0 \le y \le x \le 1$, with given constants $a > 0$, $b > 0$. Compute the normalizing constant C, find the conditional probability density $h(y \mid x)$, compute the regression curve of Y on X. Sketch this regression curve for $a = 1$, $b = 2$.

9.4. Consider the random variable (X,Y) with uniform probability density in the parallelogram with the vertices $(0,0)$, $(a,0)$, $(a + b, c)$, (b,c). Can formula (9.2.5.1) or (9.2.5.2) or both be used to compute the standard errors of estimate? If yes, carry out the computations.

9.5. Find the equation of the least square regression line of Y on X for the random variable of Exercise 9.2. Taking the numerical values $\theta = \pi/4$, $a = 2$, $b = 6$, plot the regression curve as well as the least square regression line of Y on X.

9.6. Consider the independent random variables: X with distribution $N(0,1)$, Y with distribution $N(0,4)$, Z with distribution $N(0,2.25)$. For the random variables

$$V = X + Z, \qquad W = Y - Z,$$

compute v_0, w_0, σ_V^2, σ_W^2, $\sigma_{V,W}$, $\rho_{V,W}$. Show that (V,W) has linear regression, find the equations of both regression lines and plot them.

9.7. Show that the angle θ between the regression lines is such that

$$\tan \theta = \frac{1 - \rho^2}{\rho} \cdot \frac{\sigma_X \sigma_Y}{\sigma_X^2 + \sigma_Y^2}$$

What can be concluded from this about the relative location of the two regression lines for ρ close to 0 and for ρ close to 1?

CHAPTER 10

Some Important Probability Distributions

10.1 The Poisson Distribution as an Approximation to the Binomial Distribution

Let S be the number of successes in the n-fold repetition of a simple alternative with the probability p for success hence $q = 1 - p$ for failure. We know that the possible values of S are $0, 1, 2, \cdots, n$, and the corresponding probabilities

(10.1.1) $$P(n,s) = \frac{n!}{s! \, (n-s)!} p^s q^{n-s} \quad \text{for } s = 0, 1, \cdots, n$$

For large n, the De Moivre-Laplace expression (7.5.1.6) enables us to evaluate $P(n,s)$ approximately, provided that np and nq are both large numbers. If, however, one of these quantities is not large, the De Moivre-Laplace expression fails to give a good approximation. Assuming that n is large but p is small, so that np is not large, we shall derive another useful approximation to the binomial probability $P(n,s)$. Let a denote the mathematical expectation of S. We have

$$a = E(S) = pn$$

and

$$P(n,s) = \frac{n(n-1) \cdots (n-s+1)}{s! \, n^s} (np)^s (1-p)^{n-s}$$

$$= \frac{1 \cdot [1 - (1/n)] \cdots \{1 - [(s-1)/n]\}}{s!} a^s \left[\left(1 - \frac{a}{n}\right)^{n/a} \right]^a \left(1 - \frac{a}{n}\right)^{-s}$$

If p is small and n large so that $pn = a$ is not large we have the approximate equalities

$$1 \cdot \left(1 - \frac{1}{n}\right) \cdots \left(1 - \frac{s-1}{n}\right) = 1$$

$$\left[\left(1 - \frac{a}{n}\right)^{n/a}\right]^a = e^{-a}$$

$$\left(1 - \frac{a}{n}\right)^{-s} = 1$$

and thus, approximately,

(10.1.2) $$P(n,s) = \frac{a^s e^{-a}}{s!}$$

In Example 7.3.6 we have studied a random variable X which had the countable set of possible values $0, 1, 2, \cdots$, and the corresponding probabilities

(7.3.6.1) $$f(x) = \frac{a^x e^{-a}}{x!} \quad \text{for } x = 0, 1, 2, \cdots$$

and we have called this probability distribution a *Poisson distribution*. From (10.1.2) we see that, for small p and large n, the binomial probabilities $P(n,s)$ are close to the probabilities of the Poisson distribution with $a = np$.

In view of the assumed smallness of p, (10.1.2) is sometimes referred to as the formula for the *probabilities of rare events*.

10.1.3. Example. In the following table, the second line contains the binomial probabilities $P(n,s)$ for $n = 20$ and $p = \frac{1}{10}$, while the third line contains the values of (7.3.6.1) for $a = np = 2$. All probabilities are computed to three decimals.

$S =$	0	1	2	3	4	5	6	7	8
$P(20,S) =$	0.122	0.270	0.285	0.190	0.090	0.032	0.009	0.002	0.000
$\dfrac{2^S e^{-2}}{S!} =$	0.135	0.271	0.271	0.180	0.090	0.036	0.012	0.003	0.001

10.1.4. Example. A hemacytometer is a glass plate divided into $20 \times 20 = 400$ small quadratic fields. A liquid containing yeast cells was spread over the glass plate. The total number of yeast cells was, by counting under a microscope, found to be 1872. What are the probabilities that a certain field will contain 0 cells, 1 cell, 2 cells, etc.? To answer this question, let us assume that the yeast cells were uniformly distributed in the liquid so that the probability of any particular cell falling into a definite square is 1/400, and the probability of its falling outside of that square 399/400. If we fix our attention at some definite square A and consider every cell falling into that square a success, and if we assume that the single cells are independent of each other, then we have a 1872-fold repetition of the simple alternative: success = a cell falling into A, failure = a cell falling outside of A, with $p = 1/400$, $q = 399/400$. For $P(1872,S)$ we use the approximate values given by the Poisson distribution with $a = 1872 \cdot (1/400) = 4.68 \sim 4.7$ and obtain the results presented in column (2) of Table 10.1.4.

TABLE 10.1.4

(1)	(2)	(3)	(4)
s	$P(1872,s)$	$E(L_s)$	l_s
0	0.009	3.6	0
1	0.043	17.2	20
2	0.100	40.0	43
3	0.157	62.8	53
4	0.185	74.0	86
5	0.174	69.6	70
6	0.136	54.4	54
7	0.091	36.4	37
8	0.054	21.6	18
9	0.028	11.2	10
10	0.013	5.2	5
11	0.006	2.4	2
12	0.002	0.8	2
13	0.001	0.4	0
14	0.000	0.0	0
15	0.000	0.0	0
16	0.000	0.0	0
	0.999	399.6	400

For any fixed s, the mathematical expectation of the number L_s of those of the 400 squares which contain exactly s cells is $400 \cdot P(1872,s)$. These mathematical expectations $E(L_s)$ are tabulated in column (3). In column (4) are tabulated the frequencies l_s of squares of a hemacytometer which contained s yeast cells in an actual experiment in which a total of 1872 cells was counted. The agreement between expected and observed values appears quite good. In Chapter 15 it will be shown how such an agreement between expectation and observation may be judged and interpreted.

In 7.3.6 we have seen that the characteristic function corresponding to the Poisson distribution (7.3.6.1) is

(7.3.6.2) $$C_X(t) = e^{a(e^{it}-1)}$$

and that $E(X) = \sigma^2(X) = a$. By applying the method of Theorem 7.2.3 to the characteristic function (7.3.6.2), one obtains for the next few moments about the expectation the values

$$\mu_3 = a, \qquad \mu_4 = a(1 + 3a), \qquad \mu_5 = a(1 + 10a)$$

The d.f. for the Poisson distribution is

$$F(x) = \sum_{j=0}^{x} \frac{a^j e^{-a}}{j!}$$

For example, the probability that a given square of the hemacytometer in the experiment described in 10.1.4 contains not more than 4 yeast cells is

$$F(4) = 0.009 + 0.043 + 0.100 + 0.157 + 0.185 = 0.494$$

If p is constant and $n \to \infty$ (hence also $a \to \infty$), then the d.f. of the Poisson distribution approximates the d.f. corresponding to the normal probability distribution with expectation a and variance a. More accurately, if X_n denotes the random variable with a Poisson distribution in which $a = pn$, and if Y_n is the corresponding normalized random variable $Y_n = (X_n - a)/\sqrt{a}$, then the distribution functions of the variables Y_n converge to the d.f. of the normalized normal variable, that is, to

$$\frac{1}{\sqrt{2\pi}} \int_{-\infty}^{x} e^{-s^2/2} ds$$

To prove this, we observe that the characteristic function corresponding to Y_n is

$$C_{Y_n}(t) = E(e^{iY_n t})$$

$$= E(e^{iX_n(t/\sqrt{a})} e^{-it\sqrt{a}})$$

$$= e^{-it\sqrt{a}} C_{X_n}(t/\sqrt{a})$$

$$= e^{-it\sqrt{a}} \exp[a(e^{it/\sqrt{a}} - 1)]$$

In view of the expansion

$$a(e^{i(t/\sqrt{a})} - 1) = a \sum_{k=1}^{\infty} \frac{1}{k!} (it/\sqrt{a})^k$$

$$= it\sqrt{a} - \frac{t^2}{2} + \sum_{k=3}^{\infty} \frac{1}{k!} \frac{(it)^k}{a^{(k-2)/2}}$$

we have

$$C_{Y_n}(t) = \exp\left[-\frac{t^2}{2} + \sum_{k=3}^{\infty} \frac{1}{k!} \frac{(it)^k}{a^{(k-2)/2}} \right]$$

and

$$\lim_{n \to \infty} C_{Y_n}(t) = e^{-t^2/2}$$

and this limit is the characteristic function corresponding to the normalized normal variable. By Theorem 7.5.4 we conclude that the d.f. of Y_n converges to the d.f. of the normalized normal variable.

10.2 Gamma and Beta Functions

The function

$$(10.2.1) \qquad \Gamma(u) = \int_0^\infty s^{u-1}e^{-s}ds$$

defined for all $u > 0$ is known as the *gamma function*. When integrating by parts, one obtains from (10.2.1)

$$(10.2.2) \qquad \Gamma(u) = -s^{u-1}e^{-s}\big|_{s=0}^\infty + (u-1)\int_0^\infty s^{u-2}e^{-s}ds$$

$$= (u-1)\Gamma(u-1) \quad \text{for } u > 1$$

If u is a positive integer, a repeated application of this recursion formula leads to the expression

$$\Gamma(u) = (u-1)(u-2) \cdots 2.1 \cdot \Gamma(1)$$

and since

$$\Gamma(1) = \int_0^\infty e^{-s}ds = 1$$

we have

$$(10.2.3) \qquad \Gamma(u) = (u-1)(u-2) \cdots 2.1 = (u-1)!$$

for positive integers u.

The change of variables

$$s = w^2$$

transforms (10.2.1) into

$$(10.2.4) \qquad \Gamma(u) = 2\int_0^\infty w^{2u-1}e^{-w^2}dw$$

In particular, for $u = \frac{1}{2}$, we obtain by virtue of (2.5.5.2)

$$(10.2.5) \qquad \Gamma(\tfrac{1}{2}) = 2\int_0^\infty e^{-w^2}dw = \int_{-\infty}^{+\infty} e^{-w^2}dw = \sqrt{\pi}$$

The function of the two variables u and v

$$(10.2.6) \qquad B(u,v) = \int_0^1 s^{u-1}(1-s)^{v-1}ds$$

defined for all positive values of u and of v, is known as the *beta function*. The variables u, v may be interchanged

$$B(u,v) = B(v,u)$$

as can be seen immediately by replacing s in (10.2.6) by $1 - s$.

For all $u > 0$, $v > 0$ we have the relationship

$$(10.2.7) \qquad B(u,v) = \frac{\Gamma(u)\Gamma(v)}{\Gamma(u+v)}$$

To prove this, we write $\Gamma(u)$ and $\Gamma(v)$ in the form (10.2.4) and obtain

$$\Gamma(u)\Gamma(v) = 4\int_{s=0}^{\infty} s^{2u-1}e^{-s^2}ds \int_{t=0}^{\infty} t^{2v-1}e^{-v^2}dt$$

$$= 4\int_{s=0}^{\infty}\int_{t=0}^{\infty} s^{2u-1}t^{2v-1}e^{-(s^2+t^2)}dsdt$$

Changing the polar coordinates,

$$s = r\cos\theta, \qquad t = r\sin\theta, \qquad dsdt = rdrd\theta$$

we have

$$\Gamma(u)\Gamma(v) = 4\int_{\theta=0}^{\pi/2}\int_{r=0}^{\infty}(\cos\theta)^{2u-1}(\sin\theta)^{2v-1}e^{-r^2}r^{2u+2v-1}drd\theta$$

$$= \left[2\int_{\theta=0}^{\pi/2}(\cos\theta)^{2u-1}(\sin\theta)^{2v-1}d\theta\right]\left[2\int_{r=0}^{\infty}r^{2(u+v)-1}e^{-r^2}dr\right]$$

The change of variables $\sin^2\theta = z$ transforms the first factor into

$$\int_0^1 (1-z)^{u-1}z^{v-1}dz = B(u,v)$$

and the second factor is $\Gamma(u+v)$ by (10.2.4), so that

$$\Gamma(u)\Gamma(v) = B(u,v)\Gamma(u+v)$$

In view of (10.2.3), equality (10.2.7) takes for positive integer values of u and v the form

$$B(u,v) = \frac{(u-1)!\,(v-1)!}{(u+v-1)!}$$

so that the binomial coefficient $\binom{u+v-2}{u-1}$ may be expressed in the form

$$\binom{u+v-2}{u-1} = \frac{(u+v-2)!}{(u-1)!\,(v-1)!} = \frac{1}{(u+v-1)B(u,v)}$$

The function

(10.2.8) $$\Gamma_x(u) = \int_0^x s^{u-1}e^{-s}ds$$

of the variables x and u, defined for all real values $u > 0$ and $x \geq 0$, is called the *incomplete gamma function.*
Similarly, the function

(10.2.9) $$B_x(u,v) = \int_0^x s^{u-1}(1-s)^{v-1}ds$$

of the variables x, u, v, defined for all real values $u > 0$, $v > 0$, $1 \geq x \geq 0$, is known as the *incomplete beta function.*

10.3   Gamma and Beta Distributions

10.3.1.   A one-dimensional continuous random variable X whose probability density is

$$(10.3.1.1) \qquad f(x) = \begin{cases} \dfrac{1}{\Gamma(u)} x^{u-1} e^{-x} & \text{for } x > 0 \\ 0 & \text{for } x \le 0 \end{cases}$$

with $u > 0$, will be said to have a *gamma distribution with the parameter u.* Obviously $f(x) \ge 0$ and we have

$$\int_{-\infty}^{+\infty} f(x)dx = \frac{1}{\Gamma(u)} \int_0^{\infty} x^{u-1} e^{-x} dx = \frac{1}{\Gamma(u)} \Gamma(u) = 1$$

10.3.2. Theorem.   The characteristic function corresponding to a gamma distribution with parameter u is

$$(10.3.2.1) \qquad\qquad C(t) = (1 - it)^{-u}$$

The expectation and variance of a random variable with distribution (10.3.1.1) are:

$$(10.3.2.2) \qquad\qquad E(X) = u$$

$$(10.3.2.3) \qquad\qquad \sigma^2(X) = u$$

Proof.   We have

$$C(t) = E(e^{itx}) = \frac{1}{\Gamma(u)} \int_0^{\infty} x^{u-1} e^{ixt-x} dx$$

The successive derivatives of $C(t)$ are

$$C'(t) = \frac{i}{\Gamma(u)} \int_0^{\infty} x^u e^{ixt-x} dx$$

$$C''(t) = \frac{i^2}{\Gamma(u)} \int_0^{\infty} x^{u+1} e^{ixt-x} dx$$

$$\cdot \qquad\qquad \cdot$$
$$\cdot \qquad\qquad \cdot$$
$$\cdot \qquad\qquad \cdot$$

$$C^{(n)}(t) = \frac{i^n}{\Gamma(u)} \int_0^{\infty} x^{u+n-1} e^{ixt-x} dx$$

$$\cdot \qquad\qquad \cdot$$
$$\cdot \qquad\qquad \cdot$$
$$\cdot \qquad\qquad \cdot$$

For $t = 0$ we obtain

$$C^{(n)}(0) = \frac{i^n}{\Gamma(u)} \int_0^\infty x^{u+n-1} e^{-x} dx$$

$$= i^n \frac{\Gamma(u+n)}{\Gamma(u)}$$

$$= i^n \frac{(u+n-1)(u+n-2) \cdots u\Gamma(u)}{\Gamma(u)}$$

$$= i^n u(u+1) \cdots (u+n-1)$$

Hence the Maclaurin expansion for $C(t)$ is

$$C(t) = \sum_{n=0}^\infty \frac{u(u+1) \cdots (u+n-1)}{n!} (it)^n$$

and this is the expansion of $(1 - it)^{-u}$. From (10.3.2.1) we find

$$C'(t) = ui(1 - it)^{-u-1}$$

and, by Theorem 7.2.3, we conclude

$$iE(X) = C'(0) = ui$$

which proves (10.3.2.2). Similarly, from

$$C''(t) = ui^2(u+1)(1 - it)^{-u-2}$$

we obtain

$$C''(0) = i^2 \mu_2' = i^2 u(u+1)$$

and hence

$$\sigma^2(X) = \mu_2' - E^2(X) = u$$

The d.f. for a random variable with the gamma distribution (10.3.1.1) is

(10.3.2.4) $$F(x) = P(X \leq x) = \frac{1}{\Gamma(u)} \int_0^x s^{u-1} e^{-s} ds = \frac{\Gamma_x(u)}{\Gamma(u)}$$

where $\Gamma_x(u)$ is the incomplete gamma function. Extensive tables of $\Gamma_x(u)$ are available and may be used for computing $F(x)$.

A special class of random variables with gamma distributions, particularly important in statistics, is obtained if u takes a value equal to a positive integer multiple of $\frac{1}{2}$, and the random variable is transformed by setting $X = \frac{1}{2}Z$. The probability element

$$\frac{1}{\Gamma(n/2)} x^{(n/2)-1} e^{-x} dx \quad \text{for } x > 0$$

$$0 dx \quad \text{for } x \leq 0$$

is then transformed into

(10.3.2.5)
$$\frac{1}{2^{n/2}\Gamma(n/2)} z^{(n/2)-1}e^{-z/2}dz \quad \text{for } z > 0$$
$$0dz \quad \text{for } z \leq 0$$

The random variable Z which has the distribution (10.3.2.5) is, for historical reasons, called a χ^2 *variable* (*chi square variable*) with n degrees of freedom and is denoted by χ_n^2. The probability density in (10.3.2.5) is thus denoted by $f_{\chi_n^2}(u)$. The positive integer n is called the *number of degrees of freedom*.

10.3.3. Theorem. The χ^2 variable with n degrees of freedom has the characteristic function

(10.3.3.1)
$$C_{\chi_n^2}(t) = (1 - 2it)^{-n/2}$$

and its expectation and variance are

(10.3.3.2)
$$E(\chi_n^2) = n$$

(10.3.3.3)
$$\sigma^2(\chi_n^2) = 2n$$

Proof. Since $\chi_n^2 = Z = 2X$ where X has the gamma distribution with parameter $n/2$ we obtain from Theorem 10.3.2

$$C_{\chi_n^2}(t) = E(e^{iZt}) = E(e^{iX2t}) = C_X(2t) = (1 - 2it)^{-n/2}$$

and

$$E(\chi_n^2) = E(Z) = 2E(X) = n$$
$$\sigma^2(\chi_n^2) = \sigma^2(Z) = \sigma^2(2X) = 4\sigma^2(X) = 2n$$

The χ^2 variables have a reproductive property similar to that of normal and Poisson variables.

10.3.4. Theorem. (The reproductive property of χ^2 distributions). Let $U_1, U_2, \cdots, U_n$ be independent random variables, each having a χ^2 distribution, U_1 with n_1 degrees of freedom, U_2 with $n_2, \cdots, U_m$ with n_m degrees of freedom. Then the random variable

$$V = U_1 + U_2 + \cdots + U_m$$

has a χ^2 distribution with $n_1 + n_2 + \cdots + n_m$ degrees of freedom.
Proof. We have

$$C_V(t) = (1 - 2it)^{-n_1/2}(1 - 2it)^{-n_2/2} \cdots (1 - 2it)^{-n_m/2}$$
$$= (1 - 2it)^{-(n_1+n_2+\cdots+n_m)/2}$$

This is the characteristic function corresponding to a χ^2 distribution with $n_1 + n_2 + \cdots + n_m$ degrees of freedom, and according to Theorem 7.3.3 V has the χ^2 distribution with $n_1 + n_2 + \cdots + n_m$ degrees of freedom.

10.3.5.   A continuous random variable X is said to have a *beta distribution in the interval* (a,b) *with the exponents* $u > 0, v > 0$ if its probability density is

(10.3.5.1)

$$f(x) = \begin{cases} 0 & \text{for } x < b \\ \dfrac{(b-a)^{1-u-v}}{B(u,v)}(x-a)^{u-1}(b-x)^{v-1} & \text{for } a \le x \le b \\ 0 & \text{for } x > b \end{cases}$$

Obviously $f(x) \ge 0$. To verify that

$$\int_{-\infty}^{+\infty} f(x)dx = 1$$

we make the change of variables

$$x = (b-a)s + a$$

and obtain

$$\int_{-\infty}^{+\infty} f(x)dx = \frac{(b-a)^{1-u-v}}{B(u,v)} \int_a^b (x-a)^{u-1}(b-x)^{v-1}dx$$

$$= \frac{(b-a)^{1-u-v}}{B(u,v)}(b-a)^{u+v-1}\int_0^1 s^{u-1}(1-s)^{v-1}ds = 1$$

The d.f. of a random variable with the beta distribution (10.3.5.1) can be expressed in terms of the incomplete beta function by the following formulas:

(10.3.5.2)

$$F(x) = P(X \le x) = \int_{-\infty}^x f(s)ds = \frac{(b-a)^{1-u-v}}{B(u,v)} \int_a^x (s-a)^{u-1}(b-s)^{v-1}ds$$

$$= \frac{1}{B(u,v)}\int_0^{(x-a)} s^{u-1}(1-s)^{v-1}ds = \frac{B_{[(x-a)/(b-a)]}(u,v)}{B(u,v)} \quad \text{for } a \le x \le b$$

$$F(x) = 0 \quad \text{for } x < a$$
$$F(x) = 1 \quad \text{for } x > b$$

EXERCISES

10.1. The number of female insects in a given region on a given day follows a Poisson distribution with parameter m. The number of eggs laid by each insect on one day follows independently a Poisson distribution with parameter λ. Find the probability distribution of the number of eggs in that region on one day, its expectation and its variance.

10.2. The probability of hitting the center of a target is 0.02. Five hundred shots are fired. What is the probability that the number of times the center is hit is at least 5?

10.3. Find the mode of the gamma distribution with parameter u. For what values of u is the mode positive? How does it compare with the expectation?

10.4. Find the expectation, the mode, and the variance for the beta distribution (10.3.5.1). How do the expectation and the mode compare?

10.5. Plot the probability densities of the beta distribution for $a = 0$, $b = 1$ and (a) $u = v = 1$, (b) $u = 1$, $v = 2$, (c) $u = 2$, $v = 2$, and (d) $u = 2$, $v = \frac{3}{2}$.

PART II

Some Procedures
of
Statistical Inference

Problems
of Estimation

II.I   Universe and Sample.   Parameters and Statistics

In Part I we dealt mainly with problems in which the probability distributions of some random variables were assumed as known, and statements on the probability distributions of some other random variables had to be derived.   Those were problems typical for the *calculus of probabilities*.   Most of the problems dealt with in *mathematical statistics* are of a different character and have the following typical structure: the probability distribution of a certain random variable is not known, or not completely known, but a number of empirical determinations of that variable is at our disposal.   What information about the probability distribution can be derived from those available empirical data?

Let X be a random variable, and $X_1, X_2, \cdots, X_n$ independent empirical determinations of X.   Such n independent determinations $X_1, X_2, \cdots X_n$ of X are called *a random sample O_n of size n* for the variable X.   The variable X is sometimes called *the universe* from which the sample O_n was taken.   In some cases samples are considered in which the single determinations are not independent.   This will always be pointed out explicitly.

The probability distribution of a random variable determines certain constants, such as the mathematical expectation, the variance, moments of higher order, the coefficient of correlation (for a two-dimensional random variable).   Conversely, each of these constants constitutes a bit of information about the probability distribution; in fact, most of the distributions discussed in the preceding chapters were completely determined by a small number of such constants.   For example, the probability distribution of a simple alternative X is entirely determined by $E(X) = p$; a binomial distribution is determined by the two constants p and n, and can be also completely described by giving the two constants $E(X) = np$, $\sigma^2(X) = npq$ since from these two quantities we may compute p and n; a Poisson distribution is determined by one constant $E(X) = a$; a bivariate normal distribution is determined by the five constants $\sigma_X{}^2$, $\sigma_Y{}^2$, ρ_{XY}, $E(X)$, $E(Y)$.

A constant determined by the probability distribution of a random variable is called a *parameter of that distribution*. Our examples show that not only does the distribution determine the parameters, but also, conversely, often a very small number of parameters determines the distribution, if it is known that the distribution is of a certain type (simple alternative, binomial distribution, Poisson distribution, etc.).

If we know that a random variable X has a distribution which is determined by a finite number of parameters $\theta_1, \theta_2, \cdots, \theta_k$ and if a sample O_n: $X_1, X_2, \cdots, X_n$ is available, then, in order to derive from this sample some information on the distribution, we may try to derive from it approximate values for the parameters $\theta_1, \theta_2, \cdots \theta_k$. We may succeed in proving that a certain function $h_1(X_1,X_2,\cdots,X_n)$ of the values obtained in the sample O_n is very likely to be close to the parameter θ_1; another function $h_2(X_1,X_2,\cdots,X_n)$ to the parameter θ_2, etc. Any function $h(X_1,X_2,\cdots,X_n)$ of a sample of such a structure that one can compute it for any sample size n will be called a *statistic*. If a statistic is used as an approximation to a parameter, it is called *an estimate* of that parameter.

11.1.1. Example. The probability distribution of the die described in Example 6.5.3.5 would be known if we knew the probabilities p_1, p_2, p_3, p_4, p_5 of the faces marked 1, 2, 3, 4, 5 (the probability of the sixth face is $1 - p_1 - p_2 - p_3 - p_4 - p_5$), hence it is determined by these five parameters. In order to estimate, say, p_5, we consider an auxiliary simple alternative X, which we set equal to 1 if the die shows five and equal to 0 if the die shows non-five. We know that $E(X) = p_5$. We roll the die n times and obtain the n values $X_1, X_2, \cdots, X_n$. From Theorem 6.5.3 we know that

$$\frac{1}{n} \sum_{j=1}^{n} X_j$$

is, for large n, very unlikely to differ from p_5 by a sizable quantity. It is, therefore, plausible to use the statistic

$$h(X_1,X_2,\cdots,X_n) = \frac{1}{n} \sum_{j=1}^{n} X_j$$

as an estimate of the parameter p_5.

11.1.2. For given sample size n, a statistic $h(X_1,X_2,\cdots,X_n)$ is a random variable. Its set of possible values is the set of all values which the function $h(X_1,X_2,\cdots,X_n)$ assumes when each of the variables $X_1, X_2, \cdots, X_n$ goes independently through the set of possible values of X (this statement will need some modification in those cases in which the sample consists of dependent determinations of X). If the probability distribution of X is known, and the expression for $h(X_1, X_2, \cdots, X_n)$ is given, it is a problem in calculus of probabilities to derive the probability distribution of the statistic $h(X_1, X_2, \cdots, X_n)$ for each n.

Whenever a parameter θ of a distribution is to be estimated, and $h(X_1, X_2, \cdots, X_n)$ is the statistic whose value will be used as an approximation to θ, $h(X_1, X_2, \cdots, X_n)$ will be more specifically called a *point estimate* for θ. Frequently it is possible to find, for a parameter θ, two statistics $h_l(X_1, \cdots, X_n)$ and $h_u(X_1, \cdots, X_n)$ such that it can be assumed with a certain amount of confidence (in a sense to be defined later) that θ is contained in the interval (h_l, h_u), that is that $h_l < \theta < h_u$. The problem of finding such a pair of statistics, h_l and h_u, is known as the problem of *interval estimation*.

11.2 Point Estimates for E(X) and σ²(X)

11.2.1. A sequence of random variables $U_1, U_2, \cdots, U_k, \cdots$ is said to *converge stochastically* or *in probability* to the number l if, for each pair of positive numbers ε, η there exists a number $K(\varepsilon, \eta)$ such that

(11.2.1.1) $P(|U_k - l| < \varepsilon) > 1 - \eta$ for any $k > K(\varepsilon, \eta)$

In a less rigorous language this means that, for k sufficiently large, the probability becomes very close to 1 that U_k differs very little from l.

We know for example that, for a random variable X with finite variance, the arithmetic mean of n independent repetitions of X

(11.2.1.2)
$$\bar{X}_n = \frac{X_1 + X_2 + \cdots + X_n}{n}$$

converges stochastically to $E(X)$ (Theorem 6.5.5).

A statistic $h(X_1, X_2, \cdots, X_n)$ is called a *consistent point estimate* of a parameter θ if the sequence of random variables $U_k = h(X_1, X_2, \cdots, X_k)$, for $k = 1, 2, \cdots$, converges stochastically to θ.

The property of an estimate to be consistent assures us that, for a sufficiently large sample, the estimate obtained will, with high probability, be close to the parameter estimated. In view of Theorem 6.5.5, the arithmetic mean is a consistent estimate of $E(X)$ for any random variable with finite variance.

A statistic $h(X_1, X_2, \cdots, X_n)$ is called an *unbiased estimate* of a parameter θ if

(11.2.1.3) $E[h(X_1, X_2, \cdots, X_n)] = \theta$

for every positive integer value of n.

If $X_1, X_2, \cdots, X_k$ are k repetitions (independent or not) of a random variable X, we have

$$E\left(\frac{X_1 + X_2 + \cdots + X_k}{k}\right) = \frac{1}{k}\sum_{j=1}^{k} E(X_j) = \frac{1}{k} kE(X) = E(X)$$

which shows that the arithmetic mean of a sample is an unbiased estimate of the expectation of a variable.

For later reference, we summarize the properties of the arithmetic mean of a sample in the following theorem.

11.2.2. Theorem.   Let $X_1, X_2, \cdots, X_n$ be a sample of size n of a random variable X. The arithmetic mean

$$\bar{X}_n = \frac{1}{n} \sum_{j=1}^{n} X_j$$

has the expectation

$$E(\bar{X}_n) = E(X) \quad \text{for } n = 1, 2, \cdots$$

and thus is an unbiased estimate of $E(X)$. If X has a finite variance then $\bar{X}_n$ has the variance

$$\sigma^2(\bar{X}_n) = \frac{1}{n} \sigma^2(X)$$

and $\bar{X}_n$ is a consistent estimate of $E(X)$.

For an estimate of a parameter it is desirable to learn as much as possible about the probability distribution of this estimate. If one cannot derive the probability distribution, it is of great interest to compute at least the expectation of the estimate (a step which will enable us to tell if the estimate is unbiased) and its variance. The variance of the estimate, according to Chebyshev's inequality, will give us some information on the scatter of the estimate, and may enable us to determine its consistence by the use of the following theorem.

11.2.3. Theorem.   Let $h(X_1, X_2, \cdots, X_n) = H_n$ be an estimate for θ. If the conditions

(11.2.3.1) $\lim_{n \to \infty} E(H_n) = \theta$

(11.2.3.2) $\lim_{n \to \infty} \sigma^2(H_n) = 0$

are fulfilled, then H_n is a consistent estimate of θ.

Proof.   For given $\varepsilon > 0$, $\eta > 0$, we choose $N(\varepsilon, \eta)$ so that

(11.2.3.3) $|E(H_n) - \theta| < \dfrac{\varepsilon}{2}$

and

(11.2.3.4) $\sigma^2(H_n) < \dfrac{\varepsilon^2 \eta}{4}$

for any $n > N(\varepsilon, \eta)$.

For any fixed $n > N(\varepsilon, \eta)$, the set A of values of H_n such that

$$|H_n - \theta| < \varepsilon$$

contains the set B of values of H_n such that

$$|H_n - E(H_n)| < \frac{\varepsilon}{2}$$

for, in view of (11.2.3.3), we have

$$|H_n - \theta| = |H_n - E(H_n) + E(H_n) - \theta|$$

$$\leq |H_n - E(H_n)| + |E(H_n) - \theta| < |H_n - E(H_n)| + \frac{\varepsilon}{2}$$

We have, therefore, $P(A) = P(B) + P(A - B) \geq P(B)$

or

$$P(|H_n - \theta| < \varepsilon) \geq P\left(|H_n - E(H_n)| < \frac{\varepsilon}{2}\right)$$

By using Chebyshev's inequality and (11.2.3.4) we obtain

$$P\left(|H_n - E(H_n)| < \frac{\varepsilon}{2}\right)$$

$$= P\left(|H_n - E(H_n)| < \sigma(H_n)\frac{\varepsilon}{2\sigma(H_n)}\right) \geq 1 - \frac{4\sigma^2(H_n)}{\varepsilon^2} > 1 - \eta$$

and, finally, $P(|H_n - \theta| < \varepsilon) \geq 1 - \eta$ for $n > N(\varepsilon, \eta)$

11.2.4. Theorem. Let X be a random variable with finite variance σ_X^2, and $X_1, X_2, \cdots, X_n$ a sample of size n for X. If $\bar{X}_n$ denotes the arithmetic mean of the sample

$$\bar{X}_n = \frac{1}{n}\sum_{j=1}^{n} X_j$$

then the statistic

(11.2.4.1) $$\frac{s_n^2}{n-1} = \frac{1}{n-1}\sum_{j=1}^{n}(X_j - \bar{X}_n)^2$$

is an unbiased estimate for the parameter σ_X^2.

Proof. From the relationship

$$s_n^2 = \sum_{j=1}^{n}(X_j - \bar{X}_n)^2 = \sum_{j=1}^{n} X_j^2 - 2n \cdot \left(\sum_{j=1}^{n} X_j/n\right) \cdot \bar{X}_n + n\bar{X}_n^2$$

$$= \sum_{j=1}^{n} X_j^2 - n\bar{X}_n^2 = \sum_{j=1}^{n} X_j^2 - \left[\left(\sum_{j=1}^{n} X_j\right)^2 \middle/ n\right]$$

$$= \sum_{j=1}^{n} X_j^2\left(1 - \frac{1}{n}\right) - \frac{1}{n}\sum_{j=1}^{n} X_j \sum_{\substack{k=1 \\ k \neq j}}^{n} X_k$$

we obtain

$$E(s_n^2) = \left(1 - \frac{1}{n}\right)\sum_{j=1}^{n} E(X_j^2) - \frac{1}{n}\sum_{j=1}^{n} E(X_j) \sum_{\substack{k=1 \\ k \neq j}}^{n} E(X_k)$$

$$= \left(1 - \frac{1}{n}\right)nE(X^2) - \frac{1}{n} \cdot n \cdot (n-1)E^2(X)$$

$$= (n-1)[E(X^2) - E^2(X)] = (n-1)\sigma_X^2$$

or

(11.2.4.2) $$E\left(\frac{s_n^2}{n-1}\right) = \sigma_X^2$$

11.2.4.3.   According to the preceding theorem, the statistic (11.2.4.1) is an unbiased estimate for $\sigma_X{}^2$ if nothing is known about the probability distribution of X. If $E(X) = x_0$ happens to be known, and a sample of size n is available, then the statistic

$$\frac{1}{n} \sum_{j=1}^{n} (X_j - x_0)^2$$

is an unbiased estimate for $\sigma_X{}^2$, that is,

(11.2.4.3.1) $$E\!\left(\frac{1}{n} \sum_{j=1}^{n} (X_j - x_0)^2 = \sigma_X{}^2\right)$$

The proof of this statement is left to the reader.

11.2.5. Theorem.   Let X be a random variable with a finite fourth moment. Then with the notations of Theorem 11.2.4 we have

(11.2.5.1) $$\sigma^2(s_n{}^2) = \frac{n-1}{n}\, [(n-1)\mu_4 + (3-n)\mu_2{}^2]$$

Proof.   Let δ_{jk} be defined by

(11.2.5.2)
$$\delta_{jk} = 1 \quad \text{if } j = k$$
$$\delta_{jk} = 0 \quad \text{if } j \neq k$$

We have

$$X_j - \bar{X}_n = X_j - \sum_{k=1}^{n} \frac{1}{n} X_k = \sum_{k=1}^{n} \left(\delta_{jk} - \frac{1}{n}\right) X_k$$

$$s_n{}^2 = \sum_{j=1}^{n} (X_j - \bar{X}_n)^2$$

$$= \sum_{j=1}^{n} \sum_{k=1}^{n} \left(\delta_{jk} - \frac{1}{n}\right) X_k \cdot \sum_{l=1}^{n} \left(\delta_{jl} - \frac{1}{n}\right) X_l$$

$$= \sum_{k=1}^{n} \sum_{l=1}^{n} X_k X_l \sum_{j=1}^{n} \left(\delta_{jk} - \frac{1}{n}\right)\left(\delta_{jl} - \frac{1}{n}\right)$$

With the abbreviation

$$\delta_{jk} - \frac{1}{n} = A_{jk}$$

we have

$$s_n{}^2 = \sum_{k=1}^{n} \sum_{l=1}^{n} X_k X_l \sum_{j=1}^{n} A_{jk} A_{jl}$$

The numbers A_{jk} combine according to the law

(11.2.5.3) $$\sum_{j=1}^{n} A_{jk} A_{jl} = \sum_{j=1}^{n} \left(\delta_{jk} - \frac{1}{n}\right)\left(\delta_{jl} - \frac{1}{n}\right)$$

$$= \sum_{j=1}^{n} \delta_{jk}\delta_{jl} - \frac{1}{n}\sum_{j=1}^{n} \delta_{jl} - \frac{1}{n}\sum_{j=1}^{n'} \delta_{jk} + n\frac{1}{n^2}$$

$$= \delta_{kl} - \frac{1}{n} = A_{kl}$$

In view of this property of the A_{jk} we obtain

$$s_n{}^2 = \sum_{k=1}^{n} \sum_{l=1}^{n} A_{kl} X_k X_l$$

and

$$s_n{}^4 = (s_n{}^2)^2 = \sum_{k=1}^{n} \sum_{l=1}^{n} \sum_{r=1}^{n} \sum_{s=1}^{n} A_{kl} A_{rs} X_k X_l X_r X_s$$

The n^4 terms of this sum may be split up according to whether all subscripts are equal, three equal and the fourth different, etc., in the manner described in Table 11.2.5.1.

We have

$$s_n{}^4 = \Sigma_1 + \Sigma_2 + \cdots + \Sigma_{15}$$

and the mathematical expectations of the single terms are:

$$E(\Sigma_1) = \mu_4' n \cdot \left(1 - \frac{1}{n}\right)^2 = \mu_4' \frac{(n-1)^2}{n}$$

$$E(\Sigma_2) = E(\Sigma_3) = E(\Sigma_4) = E(\Sigma_5)$$

$$= \mu_3' \mu_1' n(n-1)\left(1 - \frac{1}{n}\right)\left(-\frac{1}{n}\right) = -\mu_1' \mu_3' \frac{(n-1)^2}{n}$$

$$E(\Sigma_7) = (\mu_2')^2 n(n-1)\left(1 - \frac{1}{n}\right)^2 = (\mu_2')^2 \frac{(n-1)^3}{n}$$

$$E(\Sigma_6) = E(\Sigma_8) = (\mu_2')^2 n(n-1)\left(-\frac{1}{n}\right)^2 = (\mu_2')^2 \frac{n-1}{n}$$

$$E(\Sigma_9) = \mu_2'(\mu_1')^2 n(n-1)(n-2)\left(1 - \frac{1}{n}\right)\left(-\frac{1}{n}\right)$$

$$= -(\mu_1')^2 \mu_2' \frac{(n-1)^2(n-2)}{n}$$

$$E(\Sigma_{10}) = E(\Sigma_{11}) = E(\Sigma_{12}) = E(\Sigma_{13})$$

$$= \mu_2'(\mu_1')^2 n(n-1)(n-2)\left(-\frac{1}{n}\right)^2 = (\mu_1')^2 \mu_2' \frac{(n-1)(n-2)}{n}$$

$$E(\Sigma_{14}) = -(\mu_1')^2 \mu_2' \frac{(n-1)^2(n-2)}{n}$$

$$E(\Sigma_{15}) = (\mu_1')^4 n(n-1)(n-2)(n-3)\left(-\frac{1}{n}\right)^2$$

$$= (\mu_1')^4 \frac{(n-1)(n-2)(n-3)}{n}$$

TABLE 11.2.5.1

(1) Equalities and Inequalities between Subscripts	(2) Number of Terms	(3) Partial Sum of Terms of Type Described in (1)	Abbreviation for Partial Sum in (3)
All subscripts equal			
$k = l = r = s$	n	$\sum_{k=1}^{n} A_{kk}^{2} X_{k}^{4}$	$\sum_1$
Three subscripts equal			
$k = l = r \neq s$	$n(n-1)$	$\sum_{k=1}^{n} \sum_{s \neq k} A_{kk} A_{ks} X_{k}^{3} X_{s}$	$\sum_2$
$k = l = s \neq r$	$n(n-1)$	$\sum_{k=1}^{n} \sum_{r \neq k} A_{kk} A_{rk} X_{k}^{3} X_{r}$	$\sum_3$
$k = r = s \neq l$	$n(n-1)$	$\sum_{k=1}^{n} \sum_{l \neq k} A_{kl} A_{kk} X_{k}^{3} X_{l}$	$\sum_4$
$r = s = l \neq k$	$n(n-1)$	$\sum_{l=1}^{n} \sum_{k \neq l} A_{kl} A_{ll} X_{l}^{3} X_{k}$	$\sum_5$
Two pairs equal			
$k = r \neq l = s$	$n(n-1)$	$\sum_{k=1}^{n} \sum_{l \neq k} A_{kl}^{2} X_{k}^{2} X_{l}^{2}$	$\sum_6$
$k = l \neq r = s$	$n(n-1)$	$\sum_{k=1}^{n} \sum_{r \neq k} A_{kk} A_{rr} X_{k}^{2} X_{r}^{2}$	$\sum_7$
$k = s \neq l = r$	$n(n-1)$	$\sum_{k=1}^{n} \sum_{l \neq k} A_{kl}^{2} X_{k}^{2} X_{l}^{2}$	$\sum_8$

One pair equal

$k = l,\ l \neq r,\ l \neq s,\ r \neq s$ $n(n-1)(n-2)$ $\displaystyle\sum_{k=1}^{n}\sum_{r\neq k}\sum_{\substack{s\neq k\\ s\neq r}} A_{kk}A_{rs}X_k^2 X_r X_s$ Σ_9

$k = r,\ l \neq r,\ l \neq s,\ r \neq s$ $n(n-1)(n-2)$ $\displaystyle\sum_{k=1}^{n}\sum_{l\neq k}\sum_{\substack{s\neq k\\ s\neq l}} A_{kl}A_{ks}X_k^2 X_l X_s$ Σ_{10}

$k = s,\ l \neq r,\ l \neq s,\ r \neq s$ $n(n-1)(n-2)$ $\displaystyle\sum_{k=1}^{n}\sum_{\substack{l\neq k\\ r\neq l}}\sum A_{kl}A_{rk}X_k^2 X_l X_r$ Σ_{11}

$l = r,\ k \neq r,\ k \neq s,\ r \neq s$ $n(n-1)(n-2)$ $\displaystyle\sum_{l=1}^{n}\sum_{k\neq l}\sum_{\substack{s\neq l\\ s\neq k}} A_{kl}A_{ls}X_k X_l^2 X_s$ Σ_{12}

$l = s,\ k \neq r,\ k \neq s,\ r \neq s$ $n(n-1)(n-2)$ $\displaystyle\sum_{l=1}^{n}\sum_{k\neq l}\sum_{\substack{r\neq k\\ r\neq l}} A_{kl}A_{rl}X_k X_l^2 X_r$ Σ_{13}

$r = s,\ k \neq l,\ k \neq r,\ l \neq r$ $n(n-1)(n-2)$ $\displaystyle\sum_{r=1}^{n}\sum_{k\neq r}\sum_{\substack{l\neq k\\ l\neq r}} A_{kl}A_{rr}X_k X_l X_r^2$ Σ_{14}

None equal

   $n(n-1)(n-2)(n-3)$ $\displaystyle\sum_{k=1}^{n}\sum_{l\neq k}\sum_{\substack{r\neq k\\ r\neq l}}\sum_{\substack{s\neq k\\ s\neq l\\ s\neq r}} A_{kl}A_{rs}X_k X_l X_r X_s$ Σ_{15}

Total n^4

so that we obtain

$$E(s_n{}^4) = \sum_{j=1}^{15} E(\Sigma_j)$$

$$= \frac{n-1}{n} \{(n-1)(\mu_4' - 4\mu_1'\mu_3') + (n^2 - 2n + 3)(\mu_2')^2$$

$$+ (n^2 - 5n + 6)[(\mu_1')^4 - 2(\mu_1')^2\mu_2']\}$$

Considering that, according to Theorem 7.2.2.1, we have

$$\mu_2 = \mu_2' - (\mu_1')^2, \qquad \mu_3 = \mu_3' - 3\mu_1'\mu_2' + 2(\mu_1')^3$$

$$\mu_4 = \mu_4' - 4\mu_1'\mu_3' + 3[2(\mu_1')^2\mu_2' - (\mu_1')^4]$$

we finally have

$$E(s_n{}^4) = \frac{n-1}{n} [(n-1)\mu_4 + (n^2 - 2n + 3)\mu_2{}^2]$$

This result combined with (11.2.4.2) gives

$$\sigma^2(s_n{}^2) = E(s_n{}^4) - [E(s_n{}^2)]^2$$

$$= \frac{n-1}{n} [(n-1)\mu_4 + (n^2 - 2n + 3)\mu_2{}^2] - (n-1)^2\mu_2{}^2$$

$$= \frac{n-1}{n} [(n-1)\mu_4 + (3-n)\mu_2{}^2]$$

11.2.6. Theorem.   If the random variable X has a finite fourth moment, then the statistic $s_n{}^2/(n-1)$ is a consistent estimate of the parameter $\sigma_X{}^2$.
   Proof.   According to (11.2.4.2), we have

$$E\left(\frac{s_n{}^2}{n-1}\right) = \sigma_X{}^2$$

hence obviously,

$$\lim_{n\to\infty} E\left(\frac{s_n{}^2}{n-1}\right) = \sigma_X{}^2$$

and from (11.2.5.1)

$$\sigma^2\left(\frac{s_n{}^2}{n-1}\right) = \frac{1}{(n-1)^2} \cdot \frac{n-1}{n} [(n-1)\mu_4 + (3-n)\mu_2{}^2]$$

$$= \frac{1}{n(n-1)} [(n-1)\mu_4 + (3-n)\mu_2{}^2]$$

so that

$$\lim_{n\to\infty} \sigma^2\left(\frac{s_n{}^2}{n-1}\right) = 0$$

Thus the sufficient condition of Theorem 11.2.3 is fulfilled and $s_n^2/(n-1)$ is a consistent estimate of σ_X^2.

The statistic s_n^2/n furnishes a simple example of a consistent but not unbiased estimate of a parameter. This is easily seen if one observes that

$$E\left(\frac{s_n^2}{n}\right) = \frac{1}{n} E(s_n^2) = \frac{n-1}{n}\sigma_X^2 \neq \sigma_X^2$$

so that s_n^2/n is not an unbiased estimate of σ_X^2. This statistic, however, has the properties

$$\lim_{n\to\infty} E\left(\frac{s_n^2}{n}\right) = \lim_{n\to\infty} \frac{n-1}{n}\sigma_X^2 = \sigma_X^2$$

and

$$\lim_{n\to\infty} \sigma^2\left(\frac{s_n^2}{n}\right) = \lim_{n\to\infty} \sigma^2\left(\frac{n-1}{n}\cdot\frac{s_n^2}{n-1}\right)$$

$$= \lim_{n\to\infty}\left(\frac{n-1}{n}\right)^2 \sigma^2\left(\frac{s_n^2}{n-1}\right) = \lim_{n\to\infty} \sigma^2\left(\frac{s_n^2}{n-1}\right)$$

$$= \lim_{n\to\infty} \frac{1}{n(n-1)}[(n-1)\mu_4 + (3-n)\mu_2^2]$$

so that, for μ_4 finite,

$$\lim_{n\to\infty} \sigma^2\left(\frac{s_n^2}{n}\right) = 0$$

hence s_n^2/n is a consistent estimate of σ_X^2.

Clearly for large n it hardly matters which of the two estimates, $s_n^2/(n-1)$ or s_n^2/n, is used.

It may be worth pointing out that in Theorems 11.2.2, 11.2.4, and 11.2.6 no assumptions were made on the particular type of the distribution of X. These theorems may, therefore, be applied to justify the use of $\bar{X}_n$ as an estimate for $E(X)$ and $s_n^2/(n-1)$ as an estimate for σ_X^2, for X continuous or discrete, or known to have a normal, or a Poisson, or a binomial, or some other distribution, or a distribution of which nothing is known, as long as it is known that $E(X)$ exists (see 11.6.3) or that the fourth moment is finite (if the consistency of $s_n^2/(n-1)$ is to be assured). If the type of the distribution of X is known, it may be possible to make more specific statements, as the reader will see in the case of a normal variable discussed in Chapter 12.

11.3 Point Estimates for the Arithmetic Mean of a Population. Sampling with and without Replacements

11.3.1. The term "population" is customarily used by statisticians in a very general sense, to denote not only populations of human beings but also sets of individuals of any other kind. Thus a statistician may refer to the wheat crops obtained in 150 experimental lots as a population of 150 individuals, each individual exhibiting certain numerical features such as total weight of wheat per lot, number of grains of wheat per unit of weight, and percentage of germination in each lot, or non-numerical attributes such as shape of grain, or presence or absence of certain diseases. Each recorded numerical feature or non-numerical attribute of the individuals of a population is called a *variate*. Populations in which for each individual one variate is being recorded are spoken of as *univariate* populations. If two variates are recorded for each individual, the population is called *bivariate*. Generally, if for each individual *m* variates are recorded, one speaks of an *m-variate* population.

11.3.2. Example. If, for a group of human individuals, age and sex are recorded for each individual, we have a bivariate population. Table 11.3.2.1 contains the results of such a (fictitious) census of a group of 200 college students.

TABLE 11.3.2.1

Sex \ Age	17	18	19	20	21	22	23	24	25	26	Total
Male	3	8	10	18	23	25	12	10	3	3	115
Female	4	12	20	20	16	8	4	0	1	0	85
Total	7	20	30	38	39	33	16	10	4	3	200

TABLE 11.3.2.2

Age	17	18	19	20	21	22	23	24	25	26	Total
Frequency	7	20	30	38	39	33	16	10	4	3	200

TABLE 11.3.2.3

Sex	Frequency
Male	115
Female	85
Total	200

By disregarding one variate in a bivariate population, one obtains a univariate population. For example, by disregarding the variate "sex" in Table 11.3.2.1 one obtains a univariate population with the variate "age." The values of this variate and the corresponding frequencies are contained in the top and bottom row of Table 11.3.2.1 and are tabulated separately as the frequency distribution of ages in Table 11.3.2.2.

Similarly, disregarding the variate "age," one obtains the univariate population with the variate "sex," for which the frequency distribution is given by the extreme left and right columns of Table 11.3.2.1 and is reproduced in Table 11.3.2.3.

11.3.3. When a population is studied with regard to a certain numerical variate, it is often of great interest to determine the arithmetic mean of that variate in this population. This arithmetic mean is a definite number which can be computed exactly if a complete census of the population is available. Sometimes, however, the population is so large (it may even be infinite) that a complete census appears prohibitive, and one has to resort to estimates based on a sample. Some well-known examples of such a procedure are: public opinion polls, where the variate is the individual's opinion on a certain matter,* the population consists of all individuals from a certain age upward in the country (all voters in many cases), and a complete canvassing of the population would be much too costly and time-consuming to be of practical use; studies on genetics of animals where the variates are some genetically determined features of the individual animals and the population consists of all animals of a certain genetic strain, born in the past, present, and future— clearly only a comparatively small sample of individuals bred during a short space of time can be made available for study; measurable psychological traits of human individuals; technological features of mass products in statistical quality control.

To describe the procedure by which the arithmetic mean of the variate in a population can be estimated by sampling, let us consider a population Π of N individuals and direct our attention at a variate V. Let $V_1, V_2, \cdots, V_N$ be the values of that variate for the different individuals of our population, and let

$$(11.3.3.1) \qquad \bar{V} = \frac{1}{N} \sum_{j=1}^{N} V_j$$

be the mean of V in the population, usually called the *population mean* of Π. We consider a procedure which consists in drawing an individual at random from Π and determining its value of V. Let X be the discrete random variable determined by this procedure. The possible values of X are $V_1, V_2, \cdots, V_N$ (not all necessarily different); we make the explicit *assumption that each individual is equally likely to be drawn*, and hence have for X the probabilities

$$(11.3.3.2) \qquad f(V_1) = f(V_2) = \cdots = f(V_N) = \frac{1}{N}$$

---

* To make it a numerical variate, one only has to code "yes" as 1, "no" as 0. The arithmetic mean of these numerical values is then exactly equal to the fraction of the total population whose opinion is "yes."

A sample of n individuals may be drawn from Π in two different ways: (1) one individual is drawn at a time, the value of V is recorded, then the individual is replaced, and precautions are taken that the probabilities in the next drawing are not affected by the outcome of the preceding drawings; (2) an individual is drawn, its value of V is recorded, the individual is not replaced, the next individual is drawn, its value recorded, the individual is not replaced, etc. In case (1), the successive *drawings with replacements* define independent random variables; in case (2) the successive *drawings without replacements* define a sequence of dependent random variables.

11.3.4. Theorem. Let $V_1, V_2, \cdots, V_N$ be the values of a variate for the N individuals of a population Π, and let the *population mean* be defined by (11.3.3.1) and the *population variance* by

(11.3.4.1)
$$\sigma^2(V) = \frac{1}{N} \sum_{j=1}^{N} (V_j - \bar{V})^2$$

Let $X_1, X_2, \cdots, X_n$ be a sample of size n obtained by drawings from Π with replacements. Then the *sample mean*

$$\bar{X}_n = \frac{1}{n} \sum_{k=1}^{n} X_k$$

has the properties

(11.3.4.2)
$$E(\bar{X}_n) = \bar{V}$$

(11.3.4.3)
$$\sigma^2(\bar{X}_n) = \frac{\sigma^2(V)}{n}$$

and hence is an unbiased and consistent estimate of the population mean $\bar{V}$.

Proof. According to (11.3.3.2) we have

(11.3.4.4)
$$E(X) = \sum_{j=1}^{N} V_j \frac{1}{N} = \bar{V}$$

(11.3.4.5)
$$\sigma^2(X) = \sum_{j=1}^{N} [V_j - E(X)]^2 \frac{1}{N} = \frac{1}{N} \sum_{j=1}^{N} (V_j - \bar{V})^2 = \sigma^2(V)$$

and, since $X_1, X_2, \cdots, X_n$ are independent random variables, each with the same distribution as X, we obtain according to Theorem 11.2.2

$$E(\bar{X}_n) = E(X) = \bar{V}$$

$$\sigma^2(\bar{X}_n) = \frac{\sigma^2(X)}{n} = \frac{\sigma^2(V)}{n}$$

11.3.5. Theorem. Let $X_1, X_2, \cdots, X_n$ be a sample of size n obtained from the population Π by drawings without replacements. With the notations of

Theorem 11.3.4 we have

(11.3.5.1)
$$E(\bar{X}_n) = \bar{V}$$

(11.3.5.2)
$$\sigma^2(\bar{X}_n) = \frac{\sigma^2(V)}{n} \cdot \frac{N-n}{N-1}$$

Proof. Since the addition theorem for expectations holds for dependent variables, we have

$$E(\bar{X}_n) = \frac{1}{n} \sum_{k=1}^{n} E(X_k)$$

Each of the expectations $E(X_k)$ is computed from the absolute (marginal) distribution of the random variable X_k which is defined as the value of the variate obtained in the kth drawing. The absolute distribution of X_1 has the possible values $V_1, V_2, \cdots, V_N$ each with the probability $1/N$, so that we have

$$E(X_1) = \sum_{j=1}^{N} V_j \frac{1}{N} = \bar{V}$$

The absolute distribution of X_2 has the possible values $V_1, V_2, \cdots, V_N$, and the probabilities

$$P(X_2 = V_j) = P(X_1 \neq V_j) \cdot P(X_2 = V_j \mid X_1 \neq V_j)$$

$$= \frac{N-1}{N} \cdot \frac{1}{N-1} = \frac{1}{N} \quad \text{for } j = 1, 2, \cdots, N$$

Hence, again we have

$$E(X_2) = \sum_{j=1}^{N} V_j \cdot \frac{1}{N} = \bar{V}$$

Similarly, the possible values of X_3 are $V_1, V_2, \cdots, V_N$ and the probabilities are

$$P(X_3 = V_j)$$
$$= P(X_1 \neq V_j)P(X_2 \neq V_j \mid X_1 \neq V_j) \cdot P(X_3 = V_j \mid X_1 \neq V_j, X_2 \neq V_j)$$
$$= \frac{N-1}{N} \cdot \frac{N-2}{N-1} \cdot \frac{1}{N-2} = \frac{1}{N}$$

so that

$$E(X_3) = \sum_{j=1}^{N} V_j \frac{1}{N} = \bar{V}$$

By continuing this argument one finds generally

$$E(X_k) = \bar{V} \quad \text{for } k = 1, 2, \cdots, n$$

and

$$E(\bar{X}_n) = \frac{1}{n} \cdot n\bar{V} = \bar{V}$$

To prove (11.3.5.2), we write

$$\sigma^2(\bar{X}_n) = \sigma^2\left(\frac{1}{n}\sum_{k=1}^{n} X_k\right)$$

$$= E\left[\left(\frac{1}{n}\sum_{k=1}^{n} X_k\right)^2\right] - \left[E\left(\frac{1}{n}\sum_{k=1}^{n} X_k\right)\right]^2$$

$$= \frac{1}{n^2} E\left[\left(\sum_{k=1}^{n} X_k\right)^2\right] - \bar{V}^2$$

To compute the expression

$$E\left[\left(\sum_{k=1}^{n} X_k\right)^2\right] = E\left[\sum_{k=1}^{n} X_k^2 + \sum_{k=1}^{n}\sum_{l\neq k}^{n} X_k X_l\right]$$

$$= \sum_{k=1}^{n} E(X_k^2) + \sum_{k=1}^{n}\sum_{l\neq k}^{n} E(X_k X_l)$$

we have to evaluate the quantities $E(X_k^2)$ and $E(X_k X_l)$. The quantity $E(X_k^2)$ is computed from the absolute distribution of X_k and is equal to

$$E(X_k^2) = \sum_{j=1}^{N} V_j^2 \cdot \frac{1}{N} = \frac{1}{N}\sum_{j=1}^{N} V_j^2 \quad \text{for } k = 1, 2, \cdots, n$$

To compute $E(X_k X_l)$ we need the absolute distribution of the two-dimensional random variable (X_k, X_l) for all pairs of subscripts $k \neq l$.

The probabilities $P(X_k = V_r, X_l = V_s)$ can be computed in a manner similar to that used in computing the one-dimensional probabilities $P(X_k = V_r)$, but the following alternative method is more concise. To draw n out of the N values $V_1, V_2, \cdots, V_N$ without replacements we may, equivalently, first draw the n values simultaneously and then arrange them in n places numbered $1, 2, \cdots, n$. The total number of ways of doing this is $\binom{N}{n} \cdot n!$ The total number of such drawings which yield $X_k = V_r$, $X_l = V_s$, that is, for which V_r will appear in the place numbered k and V_s in the place numbered l, is $\binom{N-2}{n-2}(n-2)!$ Hence

$$P(X_k = V_r, X_l = V_s) = \frac{\binom{N-2}{n-2}(n-2)!}{\binom{N}{n}n!} = \frac{1}{N(N-1)}$$

for any $k < l, r \neq s$. We have, therefore,

$$E(X_k X_l) = \sum_{r=1}^{N} \sum_{s \neq r} V_r V_s \frac{1}{N(N-1)}$$

$$= \frac{1}{N(N-1)} \sum_{r=1}^{N} V_r \left(\sum_{s=1}^{N} V_s - V_r \right)$$

$$= \frac{1}{N(N-1)} \left(\sum_{r=1}^{N} V_r \sum_{s=1}^{N} V_s - \sum_{r=1}^{N} V_r^2 \right)$$

$$= \frac{N}{N-1} \bar{V}^2 - \frac{1}{N(N-1)} \sum_{r=1}^{N} V_r^2$$

for any $k \neq l$. Finally, we compute

$$\sigma^2(\bar{X}_n) = \frac{1}{n^2} \left[\sum_{k=1}^{n} E(X_k^2) + \sum_{k=1}^{n} \sum_{l \neq k} E(X_k X_l) \right] - \bar{V}^2$$

$$= \frac{1}{n^2} \left[n \cdot \frac{1}{N} \sum_{j=1}^{N} V_j^2 + n(n-1) \right.$$

$$\left. \times \left(\frac{N}{N-1} \bar{V}^2 - \frac{1}{N(N-1)} \sum_{r=1}^{N} V_r^2 \right) \right] - \bar{V}^2$$

$$= \frac{N-n}{n(N-1)} \left(\frac{1}{N} \sum_{j=1}^{N} V_j^2 - \bar{V}^2 \right)$$

$$= \frac{N-n}{N-1} \cdot \frac{\sigma^2(V)}{n}$$

A comparison of Theorems 11.3.4 and 11.3.5 shows that $\bar{X}_n$ is an unbiased estimate of $\bar{V}$ in either case. It is a consistent estimate under the assumptions of 11.3.4 (sampling with replacements), whereas in 11.3.5 sampling without replacements is defined only for $n \leq N$, and for $n = N$ yields a "100% census" of the population so that $\bar{X}_N = \bar{V}$ is already the value of the parameter we wish to estimate. For $n \leq N$ the variance of $\bar{X}_n$ is smaller if the sample is obtained by drawings without replacements. If nothing else is known about the population, the magnitude of the standard deviation will, by virtue of Chebyshev's inequality, be the only available indication of the tendency of $\bar{X}_n$ to scatter away from $E(\bar{X}_n)$, and hence we will be inclined to choose that sampling procedure which has the smaller variance. If N is very large in comparison to n, the quantities $\sigma^2(V)/n$ and $[\sigma^2(V)/n] \cdot [(N-n)/(N-1)]$ differ only little, and drawings with replacements are about as efficient as those without replacements. If, however, N is not very large in relation to n, drawings without replacements are preferable.

11.3.6. Example. A model of the bivariate population of Table 11.3.2.1 was constructed by writing on each of 200 filing cards the age and the sex of one person. Then only the item "age" was considered, thus treating the cards as the univariate population of Table 11.3.2.2. A sample of $n = 40$ was taken in two different ways: with replacements and without replacements. The results are listed in Tables 11.3.6.1 and 11.3.6.2.

TABLE 11.3.6.1. Random sample of 40 ages from the population of Table 11.3.2.2, drawings with replacements				TABLE 11.3.6.2. Random sample of 40 ages from the population of Table 11.3.2.2, drawings without replacements			
21	21	19	21	20	21	18	22
21	18	20	20	20	21	22	19
22	19	22	18	20	21	21	23
18	22	21	22	25	22	24	20
24	18	21	18	22	19	20	19
20	18	24	20	19	19	20	18
21	21	24	19	18	22	18	22
18	21	20	22	18	19	22	24
21	20	24	17	18	24	22	19
20	18	17	20	21	20	17	24

The population mean of the age variate in the population of Table 11.3.2.2 is $\bar{V} = 20.7$. The estimate of this parameter obtained from the sample with replacements (Table 11.3.6.1) is $\bar{X}_{40} = 20.275$. The estimate based on the sample without replacements (Table 11.3.6.2) is $\bar{X}_{40} = 20.575$. The population variance, computed from Table 11.3.2.2, is $\sigma^2(V) = 3.79$, and, according to Theorems 11.3.4 and 11.3.5, the variance of the sample mean $\bar{X}_{40}$ is

$$\sigma^2(\bar{X}_{40}) = \frac{3.79}{40} = 0.09475$$

for drawings with replacements and

$$\sigma^2(\bar{X}_{40}) = \frac{3.79}{40} \cdot (0.8040) = (0.09475)(0.8040)$$

for drawings without replacements, the standard deviations thus being

$$\sigma(\bar{X}_{40}) = 0.3078 \quad \text{with replacements}$$

and

$$\sigma(\bar{X}_{40}) = (0.3078)(0.8967) = 0.2760 \quad \text{without replacements}$$

11.3.7. Example. From the set of cards representing the population of Table 11.3.2.1, a sample of size 40 was drawn with replacements and another sample of size 40 without replacements. The variate "sex" was noted, and the results were: in the sample with replacements 22 men and 18 women, in the sample without replacements 23 men and 17 women. If those samples are used to estimate the percentage of men in the population, one obtains $22/40 = 0.55$ from the sample with replacements and $23/40 = 0.575$ from the sample without replacements. The actual value of the estimated parameter is $115/200 = 0.575$. To examine the theory of this experiment, we code the values of our variate by writing 1 for male and 0 for female. The population mean is

$$\frac{1}{200}(115.1 + 85.0) = 0.575$$

and this is the parameter we wish to estimate. The population variance is

$$\sigma^2(V) = \frac{1}{200}[115(1 - 0.575)^2 + 85(0 - 0.575)^2] = 0.244$$

The variance of the sample mean is

$$\frac{1}{40}\sigma^2(V) = 0.00611$$

for the sample with replacements and

$$(0.00612) \cdot \frac{200 - 40}{200 - 1} = 0.00491$$

for the sample without replacements.

11.4 Stratified Sampling

11.4.1. Let us consider a population Π with the variate V, and let it be known that Π consists of m mutually exclusive subpopulations $\Pi_1, \Pi_2, \cdots, \Pi_m$

$$\Pi = \Pi_1 \cup \Pi_2 \cup \cdots \cup \Pi_m$$

Let N_j be the number of individuals in Π_j so that

$$N = \sum_{j=1}^{m} N_j$$

is the number of individuals in Π. The values of V for the N_j individuals in Π_j will be denoted by

$$V_{j,1}, V_{j,2}, \cdots, V_{j,N_j} \quad \text{for } j = 1, 2, \cdots, m$$

Let $\bar{V}$ be the population mean of Π, $\bar{V}_j$ the population mean of Π_j, $\sigma^2(V)$ the population variance of Π, and $\sigma_j^2(V)$ the population variance of Π_j, for $j = 1, 2, \cdots, m$.

The subpopulations $\Pi_1, \Pi_2, \cdots, \Pi_m$ are customarily referred to as *strata* of Π. A sample from Π obtained by taking random samples of size n_1 from Π_1, of size n_2 from $\Pi_2, \cdots$, of size n_m from Π_m, is called a *stratified sample* of total size

$$n = n_1 + n_2 + \cdots + n_m$$

The question may be asked whether for estimating $\bar{V}$ there is any advantage in taking a stratified sample instead of a random sample of the same size drawn from the whole population Π. One would expect that the advantage, if any, will depend on the amount of information available about the quantities N_j, $\bar{V}_j$, $\sigma_j^2(V)$. We shall assume that within each stratum Π_j each of the N_j individuals is equally likely to be drawn, and that the drawings are made without replacements. Let the stratified sample consist of the values of the variate

$$X_{j,1}, X_{j,2}, \cdots, X_{j,n_j} \quad \text{for } j = 1, 2, \cdots, m$$

from Π_j. We define the sample mean from Π_j

$$\bar{X}_j = \frac{1}{n_j} \sum_{k=1}^{n_j} X_{j,n_j} \quad \text{for } j = 1, 2, \cdots, m$$

and the weighted mean of the stratified sample

$$\bar{X}' = \sum_{j=1}^{m} w_j \bar{X}_j$$

where

$$\sum_{j=1}^{m} w_j = 1, \quad w_j \geq 0 \quad \text{for } j = 1, 2, \cdots, m$$

By applying Theorem 11.3.5 to each Π_j separately, we obtain

$$E(\bar{X}_j) = \bar{V}_j, \qquad \sigma^2(\bar{X}_j) = \frac{\sigma_j^2(V)}{n_j} \frac{N_j - n_j}{N_j - 1} \quad \text{for } j = 1, 2, \cdots, m$$

and hence

(11.4.1.1)
$$E(\bar{X}_n') = \sum_{j=1}^{m} w_j \bar{V}_j$$

(11.4.1.2)
$$\sigma^2(\bar{X}_n') = \sum_{j=1}^{m} w_j^2 \frac{\sigma_j^2(V)}{n_j} \frac{N_j - n_j}{N_j - 1}$$

We wish to determine the weights w_j so that $\bar{X}_n'$ is an unbiased estimate for $\bar{V}$, whatever the $\bar{V}_j$ may be. The w_j will satisfy this requirement if and only if

$$E(\bar{X}_n') = \sum_{j=1}^{m} w_j \bar{V}_j = \bar{V} = \frac{1}{N} \sum_{j=1}^{m} \sum_{k=1}^{N_j} V_{j,k} = \sum_{j=1}^{m} \frac{N_j}{N} \bar{V}_j$$

holds identically in $\bar{V}_j$, and the necessary and sufficient conditions for this identity are

$$w_j = \frac{N_j}{N}$$

We shall, therefore, consider from now on only the weighted means

(11.4.1.3)
$$\bar{X}'_n = \sum_{j=1}^{m} \frac{N_j}{N}\, \bar{X}_j$$

We have seen that $\bar{X}'_n$ is a consistent estimate of $\bar{V}$ for any choice of $n_1, n_2, \cdots, n_m$. From (11.4.1.2) we obtain

(11.4.1.4)
$$\sigma^2(\bar{X}'_n) = \sum_{j=1}^{m} \left(\frac{N_j}{N}\right)^2 \frac{\sigma_j^2(V)}{n_j}\, \frac{N_j - n_j}{N_j - 1}$$

Introducing the abbreviations

$$T_j^2 = \frac{N_j^2 \sigma_j^2(V)}{N_j - 1}$$

we obtain from (11.4.1.4) by simple algebra

(11.4.1.5)
$$\sigma^2(\bar{X}'_n) = \frac{1}{N^2}\left[\sum_{j=1}^{m} n_j \left(\frac{\sqrt{N_j}\,T_j}{n_j} - \frac{\sum_{l=1}^{m}\sqrt{N_l}\,T_l}{n}\right)^2 \right.$$
$$\left. - \sum_{j=1}^{m} T_j^2 + \frac{1}{n}\left(\sum_{j=1}^{m}\sqrt{N_j}\,T_j\right)^2 \right]$$

From this expression it can be seen that the variance of $\bar{X}'_n$ becomes smallest if the n_j are so chosen that

(11.4.1.6)
$$n_j = \frac{n}{\sum_{l=1}^{m}\sqrt{N_l}\,T_l}\,\sqrt{N_j}\,T_j \quad \text{for } j = 1, 2, \cdots, m$$

that is if the n_j are proportional to

$$\sqrt{N_j}\,T_j = \frac{N_j^{3/2}}{\sqrt{N_j - 1}}\,\sigma_j(V)$$

Two practical conclusions follow immediately from this discussion: (a) The strata Π_j should be planned, if possible, in such a way that the strata variances $\sigma_j^2(V)$ are small; then, in view of (11.4.1.4), the variance $\sigma^2(\bar{X}'_n)$ of the stratified sample will be small. (b) If N_j and $\sigma_j(V)$ are known (or can be estimated), the n_j should be chosen proportional to $N_j^{3/2}(N_j - 1)^{-1/2}\sigma_j(V)$, in order to make $\sigma^2(\bar{X}'_n)$ as small as possible. For large N_j, this is practically $N_j\sigma_j(V)$.

The information required in (b) is only rarely available. Quite often, however, one knows the ratios N_j/N, while the N_j and the $\sigma_j(V)$ are not known. In such cases it has been an accepted practice to choose the n_j proportional to N_j/N, that is,

(11.4.1.7)
$$n_j = n \cdot \frac{N_j}{N}$$

A stratified sample for which (11.4.1.7) is fulfilled is called a *representative sample*. From (11.4.1.3) and (11.4.1.7) we see that the mean of a representative sample is

$$(11.4.1.8) \qquad \bar{X}_n'' = \frac{1}{n} \sum_{j=1}^{m} \sum_{k=1}^{n_j} X_{j,k}$$

and the variance of this mean, computed from (11.4.1.4), is

$$(11.4.1.9) \qquad \sigma^2(\bar{X}_n'') = \frac{1}{n} \sum_{j=1}^{m} \frac{N_j}{N} \sigma_j^2(V) \frac{N_j - n_j}{N_j - 1}$$

To compare this variance with the variance of the mean

$$\bar{X}_n = \frac{1}{n} \sum_{l=1}^{n} X_l$$

of a random sample of size n taken from the whole population Π, we recall that

$$(11.3.5.2) \qquad \sigma^2(\bar{X}_n) = \frac{\sigma^2(V)}{n} \cdot \frac{N - n}{N - 1}$$

and compute

$$\sigma^2(V) = \frac{1}{N} \sum_{j=1}^{m} \sum_{k=1}^{N_j} (V_{j,k} - \bar{V})^2 = \frac{1}{N} \sum_{j=1}^{m} \sum_{k=1}^{N_j} (V_{j,k} - \bar{V}_j + \bar{V}_j - \bar{V})^2$$

$$= \frac{1}{N} \sum_{j=1}^{m} \sum_{k=1}^{N_j} (V_{j,k} - \bar{V}_j)^2 + \frac{1}{N} \sum_{j=1}^{m} N_j(\bar{V}_j - \bar{V})^2$$

$$= \sum_{j=1}^{m} \frac{N_j}{N} \sigma_j^2(V) + \sum_{j=1}^{m} \frac{N_j}{N} (\bar{V}_j - \bar{V})^2$$

so that (11.3.5.2) becomes

$$(11.4.1.10) \qquad \sigma^2(\bar{X}_n) = \frac{N - n}{N - 1} \cdot \frac{1}{n} \left[\sum_{j=1}^{m} \frac{N_j}{N} \sigma_j^2(V) + \frac{1}{N} \sum_{j=1}^{m} N_j(\bar{V}_j - \bar{V})^2 \right]$$

From (11.4.1.9) and (11.4.1.10) we have

$$(11.4.1.11) \qquad \sigma^2(\bar{X}_n) - \sigma^2(\bar{X}_n'') = \frac{1}{n} \sum_{j=1}^{m} \frac{N_j}{N} \sigma_j^2(V) \left[\frac{N - n}{N - 1} - \frac{N_j - n_j}{N_j - 1} \right]$$

$$+ \frac{1}{nN} \cdot \frac{N - n}{N - 1} \sum_{j=1}^{m} N_j(\bar{V}_j - \bar{V})^2$$

In view of (11.4.1.7) we have

$$\frac{N - n}{N - 1} - \frac{N_j - n_j}{N_j - 1} = \frac{N - n}{N(N - 1)} \cdot \frac{N_j - N}{N_j - 1} < 0$$

Thus the first sum on the right-hand side of (11.4.1.11) is negative, while the second sum is obviously positive unless all strata means $\bar{V}_j$ are equal. One concludes, therefore, that the variance $\sigma^2(\bar{X}_n'')$ of a representative sample need not be smaller than the variance $\sigma^2(\bar{X}_n)$ of a random sample of the same size. If $V_j = \bar{V}$ for $j = 1, 2, \cdots, m$, then only the negative term is left in the right-hand side of (11.4.1.11) and $\sigma^2(\bar{X}_n'') > \sigma^2(\bar{X}_n)$. If the $\bar{V}_j$ differ substantially while the $\sigma_j^2(V)$ are small, the right-hand side is positive and $\sigma^2(\bar{X}_n'') < \sigma^2(\bar{X}_n)$. Hence a third practical rule should be stated for planning a stratified sample: (c) In order to make the variance of the mean of a representative sample smaller than the variance of the mean of a random sample of the same size, the strata Π_j should be determined in such a way that (a) is satisfied and that the population means $\bar{V}_j$ of the strata differ as widely as possible.

If all the ratios n_j/N_j are small, then all the quantities $[(N - n)/(N - 1)] - [(N_j - n_j)/(N_j - 1)]$ are absolutely small, and the first sum in (11.4.1.11) is small. In such cases, if the $\bar{V}_j$ differ substantially, a reduction of the variance is always achieved by using a representative sample instead of a random sample.

This discussion was carried out under the assumption that all drawings were made without replacements. Similar arguments may be made *for drawings with replacements.* The results in this case are the same as those for drawings without replacements under the additional assumption that each n_j is negligibly small in relation to N_j, and hence n negligibly small in comparison with N. Since this assumption does not change (11.4.1.5), the practical rules (a) and (b) will remain unchanged. In formula (11.4.1.11), however, the brackets and hence the first sum on the right-hand side become negligible and we obtain

$$\sigma^2(\bar{X}_n) - \sigma^2(\bar{X}_n'') = \frac{1}{nN} \sum_{j=1}^{m} N_j(\bar{V}_j - \bar{V})^2$$

We conclude that, *for drawings with replacements and for a representative sample,* the variance of the mean of the representative sample always is less than the variance of the mean of the random sample, unless $V_j = \bar{V}$ for $j = 1, 2, \cdots, m$, and that the gain in variance is increased by choosing the strata so that the strata means differ widely.

11.5 Interval Estimation: Simplest Case

11.5.1. Let the random variable X have a probability distribution of a known type with a parameter θ which we wish to estimate by means of a sample $X_1, X_2, \cdots, X_n$; let $\varepsilon < 1$ be a number close to 1 (such as 0.90, or 0.95, or 0.99), and let $h_l(X_1, X_2, \cdots, X_n)$, $h_u(X_1, X_2, \cdots, X_n)$ be two statistics. The interval (h_l, h_u) will be called a *confidence interval for θ with the confidence coefficient ε* if the probability of the event $h_l(X_1, \cdots, X_n) \leq \theta \leq h_u(X_1, \cdots, X_n)$ is ε, that is, if we have

(11.5.1.1) $P(h_l \leq \theta \leq h_u) = \varepsilon$

It should be pointed out that in this definition of a confidence interval θ is a definite although not known number, not a random variable. The quantities h_l and h_u are random variables since their values depend on the random sample $X_1, X_2, \cdots, X_n$, and $P(h_l \leq \theta \leq h_u)$ in (11.5.1.1) denotes the probability that the sample will be such that h_l computed from that sample will be $\leq \theta$ and h_u computed from the same sample will be $\geq \theta$.

11.5.2. Example. Let it be known that X has a normal distribution with the standard deviation σ and an unknown expectation $E(X) = a$. In order to find a confidence interval for a with confidence coefficient $\varepsilon = 0.99$, we observe that the random variable $(\bar{X}_n - a)/(\sigma/\sqrt{n})$ has the normalized normal probability distribution so that we have

$$P\left(-T \leq \frac{\bar{X}_n - a}{\sigma/\sqrt{n}} \leq T\right) = \frac{1}{\sqrt{2\pi}} \int_{-T}^{+T} e^{-t^2/2} dt$$

Since we also have

$$P\left(-T \leq \frac{\bar{X}_n - a}{\sigma/\sqrt{n}} \leq T\right) = P\left(\bar{X}_n - T\frac{\sigma}{\sqrt{n}} \leq a \leq \bar{X}_n + T\frac{\sigma}{\sqrt{n}}\right)$$

we obtain

$$P\left(\bar{X}_n - T\frac{\sigma}{\sqrt{n}} \leq a \leq \bar{X}_n + T\frac{\sigma}{\sqrt{n}}\right) = \frac{1}{\sqrt{2\pi}} \int_{-T}^{+T} e^{-t^2/2} dt$$

From tables of the normal probability integral we find that this is equal to 0.99 for $T = 2.58$ so that we have

$$P\left(\bar{X}_n - 2.58\frac{\sigma}{\sqrt{n}} \leq a \leq \bar{X}_n + 2.58\frac{\sigma}{\sqrt{n}}\right) = 0.99$$

and thus have shown that

$$\left(\bar{X}_n - 2.58\frac{\sigma}{\sqrt{n}}, \bar{X}_n + 2.58\frac{\sigma}{\sqrt{n}}\right)$$

is a confidence interval for a with the confidence coefficient 0.99.

Here $h_l = \bar{X}_n - 2.58\,\sigma/\sqrt{n}$ and $h_u = \bar{X} + 2.58\,\sigma/\sqrt{n}$ are the statistics used as lower and upper ends of the confidence interval.

The confidence interval (h_l, h_u) is not uniquely determined by a given confidence coefficient. In our example any interval $[\bar{X}_n - T_1(\sigma/\sqrt{n}), \bar{X}_n + T_2(\sigma/\sqrt{n})]$ will be a confidence interval with $\varepsilon = 0.90$, if only T_1 and T_2 are so chosen that

$$\frac{1}{\sqrt{2\pi}} \int_{T_1}^{T_2} e^{-t^2/2} dt = 0.90$$

e.g., $T_1 = T_2 = 1.65$, or $T_1 = 1.75$ and $T_2 = 1.56$, or $T_1 = 2.8$ and $T_2 = 1.3$.

11.5.3. In 11.5.2 we obtained confidence intervals with given confidence coefficients for the expectation of a normal random variable for which the standard deviation was known. In practical applications, however, the most frequently occurring situation is this: we have a sample of a random variable X for which we wish to estimate the mathematical expectation $E(X)$ but whose variance σ^2 is not known and for which the distribution is not necessarily normal. According to 7.5.5 the variable $(\sqrt{n}/\sigma)(\bar{X} - E(X))$ has, for large n, an approximately normal probability distribution, and the method of 11.5.2 could be used if σ were known. In the next chapter we shall see how, under certain assumptions, confidence intervals can be found for $E(X)$ although σ is not known.

11.6 Sampling of a Random Variable with Cauchy's Distribution

11.6.1. From 6.1.2.4 we know that the random variable X with the probability density

$$g(x) = \frac{1}{\pi} \cdot \frac{b}{b^2 + x^2}$$

does not have a mathematical expectation, and from 7.1.4 that it has the characteristic function $C_X(t) = e^{-b|t|}$. Hence, according to Theorem 7.1.6, the random variable U with the probability density

(11.6.1.1) $$h(u) = \frac{1}{\pi} \cdot \frac{b}{b^2 + (u - a)^2}$$

has the characteristic function

(11.6.1.2) $$C_U(t) = e^{ait}C_X(t) = e^{ait - b|t|}$$

For any continuous random variable, that value for which its probability density becomes maximum is called the *mode*. Clearly $u = a$ is the mode of the random variable with the probability density (11.6.1.1). This probability density depends on two parameters a and b. We will investigate whether the arithmetic mean of a sample of U is a useful estimate for the mode a.

Let $U_1, U_2, \cdots, U_n$ be a sample of U, and

$$\bar{U}_n = \frac{1}{n} \sum_{j=1}^{n} U_j$$

Since, as can be easily concluded from 6.1.2.4, $E(U)$ does not exist, also $E(\bar{U}_n)$ does not exist and the definition of an unbiased estimate does not apply to $\bar{U}_n$. One might still hope that $\bar{U}_n$ is a consistent estimate of the mode. From (11.6.1.2) we find that

$$C_{U_1 + U_2 + \cdots + U_n}(t) = e^{nait - nb|t|}$$

and this, together with (7.1.6.1), leads to

$$C_{\bar{U}_n}(t) = e^{ait - b|t|}$$

This characteristic function is identical with $C_U(t)$ and thus, by virtue of Theorem 7.3.3, we obtain the following theorem.

11.6.2. Theorem. The arithmetic mean $\bar{U}_n$ of a sample $U_1, U_2, \cdots, U_n$ of a random variable with Cauchy's probability density (11.6.1.1) has the same probability density (11.6.1.1) as the original random variable U.

This means that the arithmetic mean of a sample of any size yields exactly as much information as a single determination of U. The sequence $\bar{U}_2, \bar{U}_3, \cdots, \bar{U}_n \cdots$ is not stochastically convergent, and $\bar{U}_n$ is not a consistent estimate of any parameter.

This example of a random variable for which the sample means do not converge stochastically with increasing sample size, does not detract from the usefulness of the sample mean as an estimate of the mathematical expectation. The reason for the singular property of Cauchy variables is the non-existence of the mathematical expectation. Such singular behavior is not possible if a random variable has at least a finite first moment, as can be seen immediately from the following theorem which will be stated here without proof.*

11.6.3. Theorem. Let X be a random variable such that $E(X)$ exists, and let $X_1, X_2, \cdots, X_n, \cdots$ be a countable sequence of independent repetitions of X. Then for any $\varepsilon > 0$ and $\eta > 0$ there exists a number $N(\varepsilon, \eta)$ such that

$$P\left(\left| \frac{X_1 + \cdots + X_n}{n} - E(X) \right| < \varepsilon \right) > 1 - \eta$$

for any $n > N(\varepsilon, \eta)$.

EXERCISES

11.1. Let X have uniform probability distribution in (a,b). If $X_1, X_2, \cdots, X_n$ is a sample of X, let

$$U = \min(X_1, X_2, \cdots, X_n), \quad V = \text{Max}(X_1, X_2, \cdots, X_n)$$

Find $E(U)$ and $E(V)$, and decide if the statistic $Z = \frac{1}{2}(U + V)$ is an unbiased estimate of $E(X)$.

---

* For a proof of this form of the law of large numbers, and an even more general statement, we refer the reader to A. N. Kolmogorov, *Foundations of the Theory of Probability*, 2nd English edition, Chelsea Publishing Company, New York, 1956, pp. 64–65.

11.2. Let X have uniform distribution in $(0,a)$, where $a > 0$ is the parameter we wish to estimate. Let $X_1, X_2, \cdots, X_n$ be a sample of X and $U = \min(X_1, \cdots, X_n)$. Find the probability distribution of the statistic $\hat{a} = (n + 1)U$, and decide: (a) if $\hat{a}$ is an unbiased estimate for a, (b) if $\hat{a}$ is a consistent estimate for a.

11.3. Weekly wages paid in a certain community to men and to women are tabulated below.

Weekly wages in $	Men	Women
40–50	4	3
50–60	32	34
60–70	102	89
70–80	126	75
80–90	118	23
90–100	104	0
100–110	62	0
110–120	31	2
120–130	12	0
130–140	4	0
140–150	2	0

Compute the population mean and the population variance of the variate: V = weekly wages for the whole population and for the two strata "men" and "women" separately.

11.4. Take a random sample, with replacements, of size 50 from the population of men's wages (use random numbers). Compute unbiased estimates of the population mean and population variance, and compare them with the values obtained in Exercise 11.3.

11.5. Assume that the actual frequency distributions tabulated in Exercise 11.3 are not known, but the number of individuals in each stratum and the strata variances computed in that exercise are known (at least approximately). A stratified sample of total size $n = 100$ is to be taken, without replacements, in order to estimate the mean weekly wages in the whole population. What part of this sample should be allotted to each stratum for greatest efficiency?

11.6. Take a pilot sample with replacements of size $n = 30$ from each of the strata "men" and "women" of Exercise 11.3 (use random numbers), and compute unbiased estimates of the population mean and population variance for each stratum. Plan a stratified sample of total size $n = 100$ without replacements, allotting parts of that sample to the two strata on the basis of the estimates of the strata variances obtained from the pilot sample and the exact number of individuals in each stratum. Do these allotments differ considerably from those obtained in Exercise 11.5?

11.7. Take a representative sample of total size $n = 100$ without replacements from the population of Exercise 11.3. Compute the sample means for each of the strata and estimate $\bar{V}$. Compare with the exact value of $\bar{V}$ computed in Exercise 11.3.

11.8. A fictitious population of employable adults (adults "in the labor force") in three different areas has the composition described in the following table.

Area	Male Employed	Male Unemployed	Female Employed	Female Unemployed
A	232	12	125	130
B	181	9	102	92
C	347	15	210	138

Assume that only the total numbers of employable men and women in each area are known, and that one wishes to estimate the fraction of unemployed persons in the total population by taking a sample without replacements of total size $n = 200$. (*a*) Stratify the population according to sex and area; then, using random numbers, obtain a representative sample and compute the required estimate. (*b*) Stratify according to sex only, take a representative sample of size $n = 200$ and compute the estimate. Compare both estimates with the true value.

11.9. Repeated independent determinations of the weight of a particle yielded the values (in grams): 0.0335, 0.0340, 0.0341, 0.0338, 0.0341, 0.0339, 0.0337, 0.0338. The technique used is known to have random errors with a normal probability distribution and a standard deviation of $\sigma = 0.001$ gram. Determine confidence intervals for the weight of the particle, with confidence coefficients $\varepsilon = 0.95, 0.99, 0.999$.

CHAPTER 12

Sampling
of Normal
Random Variables

12.1 Probability Distributions of a Linear Combination and of the Sum of Squares of Normal Random Variables

If a random variable has the probability density

(8.1.1.5)
$$f(x) = \frac{1}{\sigma\sqrt{2\pi}} e^{-(x-a)^2/2\sigma^2}$$

that is, if it has the normal probability distribution with expectation a and variance σ^2, we shall use a terminology already mentioned in 8.1.1 and say that it has the distribution $N(a,\sigma^2)$. In particular, we shall say that the normalized normal variable has the distribution $N(0,1)$.

12.1.1. Theorem. If $X_1, X_2, \cdots, X_n$ are independent random variables, distributed according to $N(a_1,\sigma_1^2)$, $N(a_2,\sigma_2^2)$, $\cdots$, $N(a_n,\sigma_n^2)$, respectively, then the random variable

$$U = k_1 X_1 + k_2 X_2 + \cdots + k_n X_n$$

is distributed according to

$$N\left(\sum_{j=1}^{n} k_j a_j, \sum_{j=1}^{n} k_j^2 \sigma_j^2\right)$$

Proof. The characteristic function corresponding to U is

$$C_U(t) = E(e^{itk_1 X_1}) \cdots E(e^{itk_n X_n})$$
$$= C_{X_1}(tk_1) \cdots C_{X_n}(tk_n)$$
$$= e^{a_1 itk_1} e^{-(\sigma_1^2 t^2 k_1^2)/2} \cdots e^{a_n itk_n} e^{-(\sigma_n^2 t^2 k_n^2)/2}$$
$$= e^{it\sum_{j=1}^{n} k_j a_j} e^{-\left(\sum_{j=1}^{n} k_j^2 \sigma_j^2 /2\right)t\right)}$$

Since this is the characteristic function corresponding to a random variable with the distribution $N\left(\sum_{j=1}^{n} k_j a_j, \sum_{j=1}^{n} k_j^2 \sigma_j^2\right)$, our conclusion follows.

12.1.2. Theorem. If X has the distribution $N(a,\sigma^2)$ and $X_1, X_2, \cdots, X_n$ is a sample of X, then

$$\bar{X} = \frac{1}{n} \sum_{j=1}^{n} X_j$$

has the distribution $N(a,\sigma_n^2/n)$.

  Proof. The statement follows immediately from 12.1.1 by putting

$$a_1 = a_2 = \cdots = a_n = a$$

$$\sigma_1^2 = \sigma_2^2 = \cdots = \sigma_n^2 = \sigma^2$$

$$k_1 = k_2 = \cdots = k_n = \frac{1}{n}$$

12.1.3. Theorem. If X and Y are independent, X has the distribution $N(x_0,\sigma_X^2)$ and Y the distribution $N(y_0,\sigma_Y^2)$, if $X_1, X_2, \cdots, X_m$ is a sample of X and $Y_1, Y_2, \cdots, Y_n$ a sample of Y, and if

$$\bar{X} = \frac{1}{m} \sum_{j=1}^{m} X_j, \quad \bar{Y} = \frac{1}{n} \sum_{k=1}^{n} Y_k$$

are the arithmetic means of these samples, then the random variable

$$U = \bar{X} - \bar{Y}$$

has the distribution

$$N\left(x_0 - y_0, \frac{\sigma_X^2}{m} + \frac{\sigma_Y^2}{n}\right)$$

  Proof. According to 12.1.2, $\bar{X}$ has the distribution $N(x_0,\sigma_X^2/m)$ and $\bar{Y}$ the distribution $N(y_0,\sigma_Y^2/n)$ hence, by 12.1.1, $U = 1 \cdot \bar{X} + (-1) \cdot \bar{Y}$ has the distribution

$$N\left(1 \cdot x_0 + (-1) \cdot y_0, \; 1^2 \cdot \frac{\sigma_X^2}{m} + (-1)^2 \frac{\sigma_Y^2}{n}\right) = N\left(x_0 - y_0, \frac{\sigma_X^2}{m} + \frac{\sigma_Y^2}{n}\right)$$

12.1.4. Theorem. Let X have the distribution $N(0,1)$, and let $X_1, X_2, \cdots, X_n$ be a sample of X. Then the random variable

$$U = X_1^2 + X_2^2 + \cdots + X_n^2$$

has a χ^2 distribution with n degrees of freedom.

Proof.   According to 5.3 the random variable $V = X^2$ has the probability element

$$\frac{1}{2\sqrt{V}}\left[\frac{1}{\sqrt{2\pi}}e^{-V/2} + \frac{1}{\sqrt{2\pi}}e^{-V/2}\right]dV = \frac{1}{\sqrt{2\pi}}V^{-1/2}e^{-V/2}dV \quad \text{for } V > 0,$$

$$0 \text{ for } V < 0$$

This is a χ^2 distribution with 1 degree of freedom (d.o.f.). Hence, by Theorem 10.3.4 U has the χ^2 distribution with n d.o.f.

12.2   Joint Distribution of Sample Mean and Sample Variance, and Related Distributions

12.2.1.   A square matrix $C = (c_{ik})$, $i, k = 1, 2, \cdots, n$, is called *orthonormal* when the sum of the squares of elements in each column is 1 and the sum of products of corresponding elements in any two different columns is 0, that is, if

(12.2.1.1) $$\sum_{i=1}^{n} c_{ij}c_{ik} = \delta_{jk}, \quad j, k = 1, 2, \cdots, n$$

or, equivalently, when

(12.2.1.2) $$C'C = I$$

where I is the identity matrix: $I = (\delta_{jk})$, $j, k = 1, \cdots, n$. For example, the 5×5 matrix

$$\begin{pmatrix} \frac{1}{\sqrt{5}}, & \frac{1}{\sqrt{5}}, & \frac{1}{\sqrt{5}}, & \frac{1}{\sqrt{5}}, & \frac{1}{\sqrt{5}} \\[2mm] \frac{1}{\sqrt{2}}, & -\frac{1}{\sqrt{2}}, & 0, & 0, & 0 \\[2mm] \frac{1}{\sqrt{6}}, & \frac{1}{\sqrt{6}}, & -\frac{2}{\sqrt{6}}, & 0, & 0 \\[2mm] \frac{1}{\sqrt{12}}, & \frac{1}{\sqrt{12}}, & \frac{1}{\sqrt{12}}, & -\frac{3}{\sqrt{12}}, & 0 \\[2mm] \frac{1}{\sqrt{20}}, & \frac{1}{\sqrt{20}}, & \frac{1}{\sqrt{20}}, & \frac{1}{\sqrt{20}}, & -\frac{4}{\sqrt{20}} \end{pmatrix}$$

is orthonormal.

12.2.2.1. Theorem. If a matrix C is orthonormal, then its determinant is $+1$ or -1.

Proof. From (12.2.1.2)

$$|C'C| = |C'| \cdot |C| = |C|^2 = |I| = 1$$

12.2.2.2. Theorem. If in a linear transformation

$$u = Cx$$

the matrix C is orthonormal, then we have the identity

$$\sum_{j=1}^{n} u_j^2 = \sum_{k=1}^{n} x_k^2$$

Proof.

$$\sum_{j=1}^{n} u_j^2 = u'u = x'C'Cx = x'Ix = x'x = \sum_{k=1}^{n} x_k^2$$

12.2.2.3. Theorem. Let $X_1, X_2, \cdots, X_n$ be independent random variables each with distribution $N(0,1)$, and let $C = (c_{jk})$ be an $n \times n$ orthonormal matrix. Then the random variables

(12.2.2.3.1) $$V_j = \sum_{k=1}^{n} c_{jk} X_k, \quad j = 1, 2, \cdots, n$$

are independent and each has distribution $N(0,1)$.

Proof. The characteristic function corresponding to the n-dimensional random variable $(V_1, V_2, \cdots, V_n)$ is

$$C_{(V_1,\cdots,V_n)}(t_1,\cdots,t_n)$$
$$= E[\exp(it_1 V_1 + \cdots + it_n V_n)]$$
$$= \left(\frac{1}{\sqrt{2\pi}}\right)^n \int_{-\infty}^{+\infty} \cdots \int_{-\infty}^{+\infty} e^{it_1 V_1 + \cdots + it_n V_n} e^{-\frac{1}{2}(X_1^2 + \cdots + X_n^2)} dX_1 \cdots dX_n$$

The change of variables (12.2.2.3.1) has a Jacobian equal to the determinant of the coefficients of the linear transformation inverse to (12.2.2.3.1), hence $+1$ or -1 by 12.2.2.1. By 12.2.2.2 we also have $X_1^2 + \cdots + X_n^2 = V_1^2 + \cdots V_n^2$; hence,

$$C_{(V_1,\cdots,V_n)}(t_1,\cdots,t_n)$$
$$= \left(\frac{1}{\sqrt{2\pi}}\right)^n \int_{-\infty}^{\infty} \cdots \int_{-\infty}^{\infty} e^{it_1 V_1 + \cdots + it_n V_n} e^{-\frac{1}{2}(V_1^2 + \cdots + V_n^2)} dV_1 \cdots dV_n$$
$$= \frac{1}{\sqrt{2\pi}} \int_{-\infty}^{\infty} e^{it_1 V_1} e^{-V_1^2/2} dV_1 \cdots \frac{1}{\sqrt{2\pi}} \int_{-\infty}^{\infty} e^{it_n V_n} e^{-V_n^2/2} dV_n$$
$$= e^{-\frac{t_1^2}{2}} \cdots e^{-\frac{t_n^2}{2}}$$

and this characteristic function corresponds to the joint distribution of n independent variables, each with distribution $N(0,1)$.

12.2.3. "Student's" Theorems

12.2.3.1.   If X is a one-dimensional random variable and $X_1, X_2, \cdots, X_n$ a sample of X, then, as we know, the statistic $\bar{X}_n$ is an unbiased estimate of $E(X)$ and the statistic

$$\frac{1}{n-1} s_n{}^2 = \frac{1}{n-1} \sum_{j=1}^{n} (X_j - \bar{X}_n)^2$$

an unbiased estimate of $\sigma_X{}^2$, and under certain general conditions these estimates are also consistent. The two statistics $\bar{X}_n$ and $s_n{}^2$, computed from the same sample, are in general not a pair of independent random variables. However if X is a normal random variable it can be shown that $\bar{X}_n$ and $s_n{}^2$ are independent. This surprising fact was first stated by a statistician who wrote under the pseudonym "Student" [W. S. Gosset]. It will be formulated in detail in the following two theorems.

12.2.3.2. Theorem.   Let $X_1, X_2, \cdots, X_n$ be independent random variables, each with probability distribution $N(0,1)$. Then the two random variables

$$U = \sqrt{n}\, \bar{X}_n = \frac{1}{\sqrt{n}} \sum_{j=1}^{n} X_j$$

$$V = s_n{}^2 = \sum_{j=1}^{n} \left(X_j - \frac{1}{n} \sum_{k=1}^{n} X_k \right)^2$$

are independent, and U has the probability distribution $N(0,1)$ while V has the χ^2 distribution with $n-1$ degrees of freedom.

Proof.   One verifies easily that the matrix

(12.2.3.2.1)

$$C = \begin{pmatrix}
\dfrac{1}{\sqrt{n}} & \dfrac{1}{\sqrt{n}} & \dfrac{1}{\sqrt{n}} & \dfrac{1}{\sqrt{n}} & \cdots & \dfrac{1}{\sqrt{n}} & \cdots & \dfrac{1}{\sqrt{n}} \\[2ex]
\dfrac{1}{\sqrt{2}} & \dfrac{-1}{\sqrt{2}} & 0 & 0 & \cdots & 0 & \cdots & 0 \\[2ex]
\dfrac{1}{\sqrt{6}} & \dfrac{1}{\sqrt{6}} & \dfrac{-2}{\sqrt{6}} & 0 & \cdots & 0 & \cdots & 0 \\[2ex]
\cdot & \cdot & \cdot & \cdot & & \cdot & & \cdot \\
\cdot & \cdot & \cdot & \cdot & & \cdot & & \cdot \\
\cdot & \cdot & \cdot & \cdot & & \cdot & & \cdot \\[1ex]
\dfrac{1}{\sqrt{j(j-1)}} & \dfrac{1}{\sqrt{j(j-1)}} & \dfrac{1}{\sqrt{j(j-1)}} & \dfrac{1}{\sqrt{j(j-1)}} & \cdots & \dfrac{1-j}{\sqrt{j(j-1)}} & \cdots & 0 \\[2ex]
\cdot & \cdot & \cdot & \cdot & & \cdot & & \cdot \\
\cdot & \cdot & \cdot & \cdot & & \cdot & & \cdot \\
\cdot & \cdot & \cdot & \cdot & & \cdot & & \cdot \\[1ex]
\dfrac{1}{\sqrt{n(n-1)}} & \dfrac{1}{\sqrt{n(n-1)}} & \dfrac{1}{\sqrt{n(n-1)}} & \dfrac{1}{\sqrt{n(n-1)}} & \cdots & \dfrac{1}{\sqrt{n(n-1)}} & \cdots & \dfrac{1-n}{\sqrt{n(n-1)}}
\end{pmatrix}$$

is orthonormal. Let $\mathbf{X}' = (X_1, X_2, \cdots, X_n)$, and let

$$\mathbf{V} = \begin{pmatrix} V_1 \\ V_2 \\ \vdots \\ V_n \end{pmatrix} = C\mathbf{X}$$

be the n-dimensional random variable obtained from our sample by linear transformation with the matrix C. By 12.2.2.3, $V_1, V_2, \cdots, V_n$ are independent, each with distribution $N(0,1)$. Therefore V_1 and $V_2^2 + \cdots + V_n^2$ are independent. We have, however,

$$\textbf{(12.2.3.2.2)} \quad V_1 = \frac{1}{\sqrt{n}} X_1 + \frac{1}{\sqrt{n}} X_2 + \cdots + \frac{1}{\sqrt{n}} X_n = \sqrt{n}\, \bar{X}_n = U$$

and by 12.2.2.2

$$V_2^2 + \cdots + V_n^2 = \sum_{k=1}^{n} V_k^2 - V_1^2$$

$$\textbf{(12.2.3.2.3)}$$

$$= \sum_{k=1}^{n} X_k^2 - \frac{1}{n}\left(\sum_{j=1}^{n} X_j\right)^2 = s_n^2 = V$$

hence U and V are independent. By (12.2.3.2.2) and Theorem 12.1.2 it follows that U has the distribution $N(0,1)$. Since $V_2, \cdots, V_n$ are independent random variables with distributions $N(0,1)$, it follows from 12.1.4 that V has χ^2 distribution with $n-1$ d.o.f.

12.2.3.3. Theorem. If X has distribution $N(a,\sigma^2)$ and $X_1, X_2, \cdots, X_n$ is a sample of X, then the random variables

$$U = \frac{\sqrt{n}}{\sigma}(\bar{X}_n - a) = \frac{\sqrt{n}}{\sigma}\left(\frac{1}{n}\sum_{j=1}^{n} X_j - a\right)$$

and

$$V = \frac{1}{\sigma^2} s_n^2 = \frac{1}{\sigma^2} \sum_{j=1}^{n} (X_j - \bar{X}_n)^2$$

are independent, and U has the distribution $N(0,1)$ while V has the χ^2 distribution with $n-1$ d.o.f.

Proof. The random variable $Y = (1/\sigma)(X - a)$ has the distribution $N(0,1)$. Let $Y_1, Y_2, \cdots, Y_n$ be the sample for Y corresponding to $X_1, X_2, \cdots, X_n$, that is

$$Y_j = (1/\sigma)(X_j - a) \quad \text{for } j = 1, 2, \cdots, n$$

We have

$$U = \frac{\sqrt{n}}{\sigma}\left(\frac{1}{n}\sum_{j=1}^{n}X_j - a\right) = \frac{1}{\sqrt{n}}\sum_{j=1}^{n}\frac{X_j - a}{\sigma} = \frac{1}{\sqrt{n}}\sum_{j=1}^{n}Y_j$$

$$V = \frac{1}{\sigma^2}\sum_{j=1}^{n}\left(X_j - \frac{1}{n}\sum_{k=1}^{n}X_k\right)^2 = \sum_{j=1}^{n}\left(\frac{X_j - a}{\sigma} - \frac{1}{n}\sum_{k=1}^{n}\frac{X_k - a}{\sigma}\right)^2$$

$$= \sum_{j=1}^{n}\left(Y_j - \frac{1}{n}\sum_{k=1}^{n}Y_k\right)^2$$

and we complete the proof by applying Theorem 12.2.3.2 to $Y_1, Y_2, \cdots, Y_n$.

Student's discovery that the statistics $\bar{X}_n$ and s_n^2 are independent admits an interesting generalization due to J. Daly. The statistic s_n^2 is a function of $X_1, X_2, \cdots, X_n$ such that a change of origin of the random variable X leaves it unchanged, that is, such that

$$g(X_1 + \xi, X_2 + \xi, \cdots, X_n + \xi) = g(X_1, X_2, \cdots, X_n)$$

for all values of ξ, $X_1, X_2, \cdots, X_n$. We shall see that any statistic having this property is independent of $\bar{X}_n$, for X distributed according to $N(0,1)$.

12.2.3.4. Theorem. Let $X_1, X_2, \cdots, X_n$ be independent random variables, each distributed according to $N(0,1)$, and $g(X_1, X_2, \cdots, X_n)$ a statistic such that the identity

(12.2.3.4.1) $g(X_1 + \xi, X_2 + \xi, \cdots, X_n + \xi) = g(X_1, + X_2, \cdots, X_n)$

is true for all values of ξ, $X_1, X_2, \cdots, X_n$. Then the random variables

$$U = \frac{1}{\sqrt{n}}\sum_{j=1}^{n}X_j = \sqrt{n}\,\bar{X}_n$$

and

$$V = g(X_1, X_2, \cdots, X_n)$$

are independent.

Proof. We transform $X_1, X_2, \cdots, X_n$ by using the same matrix (C_{jk}) as in the proof of Theorem 12.2.3.2. The transformed random variables are

$$U_1 = \sqrt{n}\,\bar{X}_n$$

$$U_j = \frac{1}{\sqrt{j(j-1)}}\left[\sum_{k=1}^{j-1}X_k + (1-j)X_j\right]$$

$$= \left(\frac{j-1}{j}\right)^{1/2}(\bar{X}_{j-1} - X_j) \quad \text{for } j = 2, \cdots, n$$

and $U_1, U_2, \cdots, U_n$ are independent. We have

$$X_2 - X_1 = -\sqrt{2}U_2$$

and

$$X_{j+1} - X_j = X_{j+1} - \frac{1}{j}\sum_{k=1}^{j} X_k - \left(\frac{j-1}{j}X_j - \frac{1}{j}\sum_{k=1}^{j-1}X_k\right)$$

$$= X_{j+1} - \bar{X}_j - \frac{j-1}{j}(X_j - \bar{X}_{j-1})$$

$$= -\left(\frac{j+1}{j}\right)^{1/2}U_{j+1} + \left(\frac{j-1}{j}\right)^{1/2}U_j \quad \text{for } j = 2, \cdots, n$$

so that

(12.2.3.4.2) $X_{j+1} - X_j = -\left(\frac{j+1}{j}\right)^{1/2}U_{j+1} + \left(\frac{j-1}{j}\right)^{1/2}U_j$

for $j = 1, 2, \cdots, n$. Let ξ have the value

(12.2.3.4.3) $\xi = -\left(X_1 + \frac{1}{\sqrt{1.2}}U_2 + \frac{1}{\sqrt{2.3}}U_3 + \cdots + \frac{1}{\sqrt{(n-1)n}}U_n\right)$

Then, as will be seen, $X_j + \xi$ is a linear function $L_j(U_2,\cdots,U_n)$ of $U_2, \cdots, U_n$, for $j = 1, 2, \cdots, n$. For we have

$$X_1 + \xi = -\left(\frac{1}{\sqrt{1.2}}U_2 + \frac{1}{\sqrt{2.3}}U_3 + \cdots\right.$$

$$\left. + \frac{1}{\sqrt{(n-1)n}}U_n\right) = L_1(U_2,\cdots,U_n)$$

and, by induction, if

$$X_j + \xi = L_j(U_2,\cdots,U_n)$$

it follows from (12.2.3.4.2) that

$$X_{j+1} + \xi = X_{j+1} - X_j + X_j + \xi$$

$$= -\left(\frac{j+1}{j}\right)^{1/2}U_{j+1} + \left(\frac{j-1}{j}\right)^{1/2}U_j$$

$$+ L_j(U_2,\cdots,U_n)$$

$$= L_{j+1}(U_2,\cdots,U_n)$$

We now use the value (12.2.3.4.3) of ξ in (12.2.3.4.1) and obtain

$$g(X_1,X_2,\cdots,X_n) = g(X_1 + \xi, X_2 + \xi,\cdots,X_n + \xi)$$

$$= g[L_1(U_2,\cdots,U_n), L_2(U_2,\cdots,U_n), \cdots, L_n(U_2,\cdots,U_n)]$$

$$= h(U_2,U_3,\cdots,U_n)$$

and since $U_2, \cdots, U_n$ are independent of U_1,

$$V = g(X_1,X_2,\cdots,X_n) = h(U_2,\cdots,U_n)$$

is independent of $U_1 = U$.

12.2.3.5. Theorem.   If the random variables U and V are independent, and if U has the distribution $N(0,1)$ and V the χ^2 distribution with m degrees of freedom, then the random variable

$$(12.2.3.5.1) \qquad\qquad T = \frac{U}{\sqrt{V/m}}$$

has the probability density

$$(12.2.3.5.2) \qquad g_m(t) = \frac{\Gamma[(m+1)/2]}{\Gamma(m/2)\sqrt{\pi m}}\left(1 + \frac{t^2}{m}\right)^{-(m+1)/2}$$

known as *Student's distribution with m degrees of freedom.*
   Proof.   The joint probability element of (U,V) is

$$f(u,v)dudv = \frac{1}{\sqrt{2\pi}}e^{-u^2/2} \cdot \frac{1}{2^{(m/2)}\Gamma(m/2)}V^{(m/2)-1}e^{-v/2}dudv$$

for any u and $v > 0$, zero for $v \leq 0$.   The change of variables

$$t = \frac{u}{\sqrt{v/m}}, \qquad s = v,$$

or

$$v = s, \qquad u = (1/\sqrt{m})ts^{1/2},$$

with the Jacobian

$$\begin{vmatrix} 1, & \dfrac{1}{2\sqrt{m}}ts^{-1/2} \\[2mm] 0, & \dfrac{1}{\sqrt{m}}s^{1/2} \end{vmatrix} = \sqrt{s/m}$$

transforms this probability element into

$$g(s,t)dsdt = \frac{1}{\sqrt{2\pi}}e^{t^2s/2m}\frac{1}{2^{m/2}\Gamma(m/2)}s^{(m/2)-1}e^{-s/2}\sqrt{s/m}\,dsdt$$

$$= \frac{1}{\sqrt{2m}\sqrt{2\pi}\,\Gamma(m/2)}e^{-(s/2)[(t^2/m)+1]}\left(\frac{s}{2}\right)^{(m-1)/2}dsdt$$

for $s > 0$, and $g(s,t)dsdt = 0$ for $s \leq 0$.   Hence the marginal probability density of t is

$$g_m(t) = \int_{-\infty}^{+\infty}g(s,t)ds$$

$$= \frac{1}{\sqrt{2m}\,\sqrt{2\pi}\,\Gamma(m/2)}\int_0^{+\infty}e^{-(s/2)[(t^2/m)+1]}\left(\frac{s}{2}\right)^{(m-1)/2}ds$$

and the change of variables

$$\frac{s}{2}\left(\frac{t^2}{m}+1\right) = \xi$$

transforms this into

$$\frac{1}{\sqrt{2m}\sqrt{2\pi}\Gamma(m/2)} \int_0^\infty e^{-\xi}\xi^{[(m+1)/2]-1}\left(\frac{t^2}{m}+1\right)^{1-[(m+1)/2]}\frac{2}{(t^2/m)+1}\,d\xi$$

$$= \left(1+\frac{t^2}{m}\right)^{-(m+1)/2}\frac{1}{\sqrt{\pi m}\,\Gamma(m/2)}\int_0^\infty e^{-\xi}\xi^{[(m+1)/2]-1}d\xi$$

$$= \frac{\Gamma[(m+1)/2]}{\Gamma(m/2)\sqrt{\pi m}}\left(1+\frac{t^2}{m}\right)^{-(m+1)/2}$$

12.2.3.6. Theorem. If X has the probability distribution $N(a,\sigma^2)$, $X_1, X_2, \cdots, X_n$ is a sample of X, and

$$\bar{X}_n = \frac{1}{n}\sum_{j=1}^n X_j \quad \text{and} \quad \frac{s_n^2}{n-1} = \frac{1}{n-1}\sum_{j=1}^n (X_j - \bar{X}_n)^2$$

are the unbiased estimates of a and σ^2, respectively, then the statistic

$$t = \frac{\sqrt{n}(\bar{X}_n - a)}{\sqrt{s_n^2/(n-1)}} = \frac{(\bar{X}_n - a)\sqrt{n(n-1)}}{\left[\sum_{j=1}^n (X_j - \bar{X}_n)^2\right]^{1/2}}$$

has Student's distribution with $n-1$ degrees of freedom.

Proof. According to Theorem 12.2.3.3 the random variables

$$U = \frac{\sqrt{n}}{\sigma}(\bar{X}_n - a)$$

and

$$V = \frac{1}{\sigma^2}\sum_{j=1}^n (X_j - \bar{X}_n)^2$$

fulfill the assumptions of Theorem 12.2.3.5 with $m = n-1$, hence

$$\frac{U}{\sqrt{V/(n-1)}} = T$$

has the Student distribution with $n-1$ d.o.f.

12.2.3.7. Theorem. Let X and X' be independent random variables, X with distribution $N(a,\sigma^2)$, and X' with distribution $N(a',\sigma^2)$, the variance σ^2 being the same for X and X'. Let $X_1, X_2, \cdots, X_n$ be a sample of X, and $X'_1, X'_2 \cdots, X'_{n'}$, a sample of X'. We use the notations

$$\bar{X} = \frac{1}{n}\sum_{j=1}^n X_j, \qquad \bar{X}' = \frac{1}{n'}\sum_{j=1}^{n'} X'_j$$

$$s^2 = \sum_{j=1}^n (X_j - \bar{X})^2, \qquad s'^2 = \sum_{j=1}^{n'} (X'_j - \bar{X}')^2$$

Then the statistic

$$(12.2.3.7.1) \qquad T = \frac{(\bar{X} - \bar{X}') - (a - a')}{\sqrt{s^2 + s'^2}} \cdot \frac{\sqrt{n + n' - 2}}{\sqrt{(1/n) + (1/n')}}$$

has the Student distribution with $n + n' - 2$ degrees of freedom.

Proof.   The random variable

$$U = \frac{(\bar{X} - \bar{X}') - (a - a')}{\sqrt{\sigma^2[(1/n) + (1/n')]}}$$

has the expectation

$$E(U) = \frac{1}{\sqrt{\sigma^2[(1/n) + (1/n')]}} [E(\bar{X}) - E(\bar{X}') - a + a'] = 0$$

and the variance

$$\sigma^2(U) = \frac{1}{\sigma^2[(1/n) + (1/n')]} [\sigma^2(\bar{X}) + \sigma^2(\bar{X}')]$$

$$= \frac{(\sigma^2/n) + (\sigma^2/n')}{\sigma^2[(1/n) + (1/n')]} = 1$$

hence U has the distribution $N(0,1)$. The random variable

$$V = \frac{s^2}{\sigma^2} + \frac{s'^2}{\sigma^2}$$

is the sum of two independent random variables, s^2/σ^2 with a χ^2 distribution with $n - 1$ d.o.f. (by Theorem 12.2.3.3), and s'^2/σ^2 with a χ^2 distribution with $n' - 1$ d.o.f. According to 10.3.4, V has the χ^2 distribution with $n + n' - 2$ d.o.f. Since $\bar{X}$ and s^2 are independent and $\bar{X}'$ and s'^2 are independent (Theorem 12.2.3.3), and since $(\bar{X}, s^2)$ and $(\bar{X}', s'^2)$ are independent two-dimensional random variables in view of the assumption that X and X' are independent, we conclude that $\bar{X} - \bar{X}'$ and $s^2 + s'^2$ are independent, and therefore U and V are independent, so that by Theorem 12.2.3.5 the random variable

$$T = \frac{U}{\sqrt{V/(n + n' - 2)}}$$

has the Student t distribution with $n + n' - 2$ d.o.f.

12.3   Interval Estimation of Expectation and of Difference of Expectations for Normal Variables

12.3.1.   From Theorem 12.2.3.5 we know that the random variable T defined by (12.2.3.5.1) has the probability

$$\int_{-t}^{t} g_m(u)du = 2\int_{0}^{t} gm(u)du$$

of falling into the interval $(-t, t)$. Thus, writing

(12.3.1.1) $p_m(t) = 2 \int_t^\infty g_m(u) du = \dfrac{2\Gamma[(m + 1)/2]}{\Gamma(m/2)\sqrt{\pi m}} \int_t^\infty [1 + (u^2/m)]^{-(m+1)/2} du$

we have

(12.3.1.2) $P(|T| \geq t) = 1 - P(-t < T < t) = p_m(t)$

The values of $p_m(t)$ have been tabulated for different m and t.

Let $X_1, X_2, \cdots, X_n$ be a sample of a normal variable X, with unknown expectation and variance. To obtain a confidence interval with a given confidence coefficient ε for the parameter $E(X) = a$, we proceed as follows. According to Theorem 12.2.3.6 and (12.3.1.2) we have

$$P(|\bar{X}_n - a| \cdot \sqrt{n(n - 1)}/s_n^2 < t) = P(|T| < t) = 1 - p_{n-1}(t)$$

and hence

$$P(\bar{X}_n - t\sqrt{s_n^2/n(n - 1)} < a < \bar{X}_n + t\sqrt{s_n^2/n(n - 1)}) = 1 - p_{n-1}(t)$$

Since $p_{n-1}(t)$ is a decreasing continuous function with

$$p_{n-1}(0) = 1, \qquad \lim_{t \to +\infty} p_{n-1}(t) = 0$$

there exists a $t_{n-1,\varepsilon}$ such that

$$1 - p_{n-1}(t_{n-1,\varepsilon}) = \varepsilon$$

Thus we obtain

(12.3.1.3)

$$P(\bar{X}_n - t_{n-1,\varepsilon}\sqrt{s_n^2/n(n - 1)} < a < \bar{X}_n + t_{n-1,\varepsilon}\sqrt{s_n^2/n(n - 1)}) = \varepsilon$$

which shows that the interval

(12.3.1.4) $(\bar{X}_n - t_{n-1,\varepsilon}\sqrt{s_n^2/n(n - 1)}, \ \bar{X}_n + t_{n-1,\varepsilon}\sqrt{s_n^2/n(n - 1)})$

is a confidence interval for a with the confidence coefficient ε. This confidence interval was obtained without the knowledge of σ_X^2, but under the assumption that X is a normal random variable. Values of $t_{n-1,\varepsilon}$ can be read off the tables of $p_{n-1}(t)$; for greater convenience, however, they have been tabulated separately for various n and the most frequently used confidence coefficients ε (see Table II at the end of the book).

12.3.2. Example.   The ratio of the weights of bromine and hydrogen which combine to form hydrobromic acid was determined experimentally. The results of ten independent determinations are given in the first column of the following table. We assume that the observed values are a sample of a normal variable X whose expectation a is the true value of the ratio, and we wish to compute from our sample a confidence interval for a with the confidence coefficient $\varepsilon = 0.999$.

X_j	$X_j - \bar{X}_{10}$		$(X_j - \bar{X}_{10})^2$
79.2863		−0.0204	0.00041616
79.3055		−0.0012	0.00000144
79.3064		−0.0003	0.00000009
79.3197	0.0130		0.00016900
79.3114	0.0047		0.00002209
79.3150	0.0083		0.00006889
79.3063		−0.0004	0.00000016
79.3141	0.0074		0.00005476
79.2915		−0.0152	0.00023104
79.3108	0.0041		0.00001681
793.0670	0.0375	−0.0375	0.00098044

The computations in the table above are self-explanatory. They yield

$$\bar{X}_{10} = 79.3067, \qquad s_{10}^2 = 0.00098044$$

$$\sqrt{s_{10}^2/10.9} = \sqrt{0.00001089} = 0.0033$$

Since $t_{9,0.999} = 4.781$ and $(4.781) \cdot (0.0033) = 0.0158$ our confidence interval is

$$(79.3067 - 0.0158,\ 79.3067 + 0.0158)$$

or

$$(79.2909,\ 79.3225)$$

It may be advisable to insert here a few remarks on the meaning of a confidence interval. From (11.5.1.1) we know that if, for a sample $X_1, X_2, \cdots, X_n$, we compute h_l and h_u, we have the probability ε that the two numbers obtained contain the parameter θ between them. Thus, if a large number of independent samples is taken, for each sample h_l and h_u are computed, and in each case the statement is made that $h_l \leq \theta \leq h_u$, then, by virtue of the law of large numbers, about 100ε per cent of all these statements will be correct and about $100(1 - \varepsilon)$ wrong. Thus, if based on the computations of Example 12.3.2, we made the statement

$$79.2909 \leq a \leq 79.3225$$

we are not certain that this statement is true; all we can say is, that if many similar sets of observations are made and the confidence interval is computed for each of these sets in the manner described in 12.3.2, and if in each case the statement is made that the parameter a lies in the computed confidence interval, only about one of such statements in a thousand may be expected to be false. For this conclusion one often uses the notation

$$a = 79.3067 \pm 0.0158 \text{ with confidence coefficient } 0.999$$

12.3.3. Theorem. For $m \to \infty$, the probability density (12.2.3.5.2) of Student's distribution converges uniformly in every finite interval to $(1/\sqrt{2\pi})e^{-t^2/2}$, that is, to the probability density of $N(0,1)$.

Proof. For m even, we write $m = 2r$ and have

(12.3.3.1) $\quad g_m(t) = \dfrac{\Gamma(r + \frac{1}{2})}{\Gamma(r)\sqrt{2r\pi}} \left(1 + \dfrac{t^2}{2r}\right)^{-1/2} \left[\left(1 + \dfrac{t^2}{2r}\right)^{2r/t^2}\right]^{-t^2/2}$

with

$$
\begin{aligned}
\frac{\Gamma(r + \frac{1}{2})}{\Gamma(r)\sqrt{2r\pi}} &= \frac{(r - \frac{1}{2})(r - \frac{3}{2}) \cdots \frac{5}{2} \cdot \frac{3}{2} \cdot \frac{1}{2} \cdot \Gamma(\frac{1}{2})}{(r - 1)(r - 2) \cdots 2 \cdot 1 \cdot \sqrt{2\pi r}} \\
&= \frac{(2r - 1)(2r - 3) \cdots 5 \cdot 3 \cdot 1 \cdot \sqrt{\pi}}{(2r - 2)(2r - 4) \cdots 4 \cdot 2 \cdot 2 \cdot \sqrt{2\pi r}} \\
&= \frac{1 \cdot 3 \cdot 5 \cdots (2r - 1)}{2 \cdot 4 \cdot 6 \cdots (2r - 2) \sqrt{2r}} \cdot \frac{1}{2}
\end{aligned}
$$

By virtue of Wallis's theorem, this has the limit $\sqrt{2/\pi} \cdot \frac{1}{2}$, and since

(12.3.3.2) $\quad \lim\limits_{r \to \infty} \left(1 + \dfrac{t^2}{2r}\right)^{2r/t^2} = e, \qquad \lim\limits_{r \to \infty} \left(1 + \dfrac{t^2}{2r}\right)^{-1/2} = 1$

we obtain from (12.3.3.1)

(12.3.3.3) $\qquad\qquad \lim\limits_{m \to \infty} g_m(t) = \dfrac{1}{\sqrt{2\pi}} e^{-t^2/2}$

The convergence in (12.3.3.2) is uniform in every finite interval, and thus is uniform in (12.3.3.3) in every finite interval. For m odd the proof is analogous.

12.3.4. From Theorem 12.3.3 it follows that

$$
\lim\limits_{m \to \infty} p_m(t) = 2 \cdot \frac{1}{\sqrt{2\pi}} \int_t^\infty e^{-x^2/2} dx
$$

so that the values of $p_m(t)$ for large m may be read off the tables of the normal probability integral. Consequently, for large n our method for obtaining confidence intervals for $E(X) = a$ requires only the use of these tables, and may be described as follows.

Let $X_1, X_2, \cdots, X_n$ be a *large* sample of a normal random variable X, with unknown expectation and variance, and let ε be a given confidence coefficient. If t_ε is a number such that

$$
\frac{1}{\sqrt{2\pi}} \int_{-t_\varepsilon}^{+t_\varepsilon} e^{-x^2/2} dx = \varepsilon
$$

then, we have approximately,

(12.3.4.1) $\quad P\left\{\overline{X}_n - t_\varepsilon \left[\dfrac{S_n^2}{n(n - 1)}\right]^{1/2} < a < \overline{X}_n + t_\varepsilon \left[\dfrac{S_n^2}{n(n - 1)}\right]^{1/2}\right\} = \varepsilon$

and thus

$$(12.3.4.2) \qquad \left\{ \bar{X} - t_\varepsilon \left[\frac{s_n^2}{n(n-1)} \right]^{1/2}, \ \bar{X}_n + t_\varepsilon \left[\sqrt{\frac{s_n^2}{n(n-1)}} \right]^{1/2} \right\}$$

is, approximately, a confidence interval with confidence coefficient ε for the parameter $a = E(X)$.

12.3.5. Example. (Confidence Interval for the Difference of Mathematical Expectations of Two Dependent Normal Variables).

In his classical paper "Student" discusses a set of experiments made to determine the difference in effect of two sleep-inducing drugs. Each of ten patients was given drug A, then, after a reasonable time, drug B. The following is a tabulation of the effects observed:

Additional Hours of Sleep Gained by Use of:

Patient	Drug A	Drug B
1	0.7	1.9
2	−1.6	0.8
3	−0.2	1.1
4	−1.2	0.1
5	−0.1	−0.1
6	3.4	4.4
7	3.7	5.5
8	0.8	1.6
9	0.0	4.6
10	2.0	3.4

Let X and Y denote the number of hours of sleep gained due to drugs A and B, respectively, and let $Z = Y - X$. We should like to find a confidence interval for $E(Z)$ with confidence coefficient 0.99. To approach this problem by our methods we assume that (X, Y) is a binormal random variable. Clearly the assumption of independence of X and Y could not be justified. However, $(-X, Y)$ is a binormal random variable, and hence Z a normal random variable. For Z we have a sample of size m, with the values tabulated below under the heading Z.

Patient	Z	Z²
1	1.2	1.44
2	2.4	5.76
3	1.3	1.69
4	1.3	1.69
5	0.0	0.00
6	1.0	1.00
7	1.8	3.24
8	0.8	0.64
9	4.6	21.16
10	1.4	1.96
	15.8	38.58

We compute

$$s_n{}^2 = \sum_{j=1}^{n}(Z_j - \bar{Z})^2 = \sum_{j=1}^{n}Z_j{}^2 - \frac{1}{n}\left(\sum_{j=1}^{n}Z_j\right)^2$$

$$= 38.58 - \tfrac{1}{10}(15.8)^2 = 13.62$$

$$\sqrt{s_n{}^2/n(n-1)} = \sqrt{13.62/10.9} = \sqrt{0.1513} = 0.389$$

$$Z_{10} = 1.58$$

find from table of Student's t

$$t_{9,0.99} = 3.250,$$

and obtain from (12.3.1.4) the confidence interval for $E(Z)$

$$(0.32, 2.84)$$

or $E(Z) = 1.58 \pm 1.26$ with confidence coefficient 0.99.

12.4   Distributions of Snedecor's F and Fisher's Z

12.4.1. Theorem.   Let U and V be independent random variables with χ^2 distributions, U with m_1, and V with m_2, degrees of freedom. Then the random variable

$$F = \frac{U/m_1}{V/m_2}$$

is a continuous random variable with the probability density

$$(12.4.1.1) \quad h(F) = \begin{cases} \dfrac{m_1{}^{m_1/2}m_2{}^{m_2/2}}{B[(m_1/2),(m_2/2)]}F^{(m_1/2)-1}(m_2 + m_1 F)^{-(m_1+m_2)/2} & \text{for } F > 0 \\ 0 & \text{for } F \le 0 \end{cases}$$

Proof.   The joint probability element of U and V is

$$(12.4.1.2) \quad \frac{1}{2^{(m_1+m_2)/2}\Gamma(m_1/2)\Gamma(m_2/2)}\, U^{(m_1/2)-1}V^{(m_2/2)-1}e^{-(U+V)/2}dUdV$$

in the quadrant $U > 0$, $V > 0$ of the (U,V) plane, zero everywhere else. The change of variables

$$F = \frac{m_2}{m_1}\frac{U}{V}, \qquad S = \frac{V}{2}$$

that is,

$$V = 2S, \qquad U = 2\frac{m_1}{m_2}FS$$

has the Jacobian

$$\begin{vmatrix} 2\dfrac{m_1}{m_2}S, & 2\dfrac{m_1}{m_2}F \\ 0, & 2 \end{vmatrix} = 4\dfrac{m_1}{m_2}S$$

and transforms (12.4.1.2) into

$$\frac{1}{\Gamma(m_1/2)\Gamma(m_2/2)}\left(\frac{m_1}{m_2}\right)^{m_1/2} F^{(m_1/2)-1}\, S^{[(m_1+m_2)/2]-1} e^{-[1+(m_1/m_2)F]S} dFdS$$

for the quadrant $F > 0$, $S > 0$, and zero everywhere else. The marginal probability element of F is obtained by integrating with respect to S:

$$h(F)dF = \frac{1}{\Gamma(m_1/2)\Gamma(m_2/2)}\left(\frac{m_1}{m_2}\right)^{m_1/2} F^{(m_1/2)-1}$$

$$\times \int_0^\infty S^{[(m_1+m_2)/2]-1} e^{-[1+(m_1/m_2)F]S} dSdF$$

The integral on the right-hand side is transformed by the substitution

$$S = \left(1 + \frac{m_1}{m_2}F\right)^{-1} R$$

into

$$\left(1 + \frac{m_1}{m_2}F\right)^{-(m_1+m_2)/2} \int_0^\infty R^{[(m_1+m_2)/2]-1} e^{-R} dR$$

$$= \left(1 + \frac{m_1}{m_2}F\right)^{-(m_1+m_2)/2} \Gamma\left(\frac{m_1+m_2}{2}\right)$$

and we finally have

$$h(F)dF = \frac{\Gamma[(m_1+m_2)/2]}{\Gamma(m_1/2)\Gamma(m_2/2)}\left(\frac{m_1}{m_2}\right)^{m_1/2} F^{(m_1/2)-1}\left(1 + \frac{m_1}{m_2}F\right)^{-(m_1+m_2)/2} dF$$

$$= \frac{m_1{}^{m_1/2}m_2{}^{m_2/2}}{B(m_1/2,\ m_2/2)} F^{(m_1/2)-1}(m_2 + m_1F)^{-(m_1+m_2)/2} dF$$

for $F > 0$, while for $F \le 0$ we obtain $h(F)dF = 0$.

The probability distribution (12.4.1.1) is known as Snedecor's F distribution with m_1 and m_2 degrees of freedom. The substitution

$$F = \frac{1 - W}{W}\cdot\frac{m_2}{m_1}\quad \text{or}\quad W = \frac{m_2}{m_2 + m_1F}$$

yields

$$h(F)dF = \frac{W^{(m_2/2)-1}(1 - W)^{(m_1/2)-1} dW}{B(m_1/2,\ m_2/2)}\quad \text{for } 0 < W < 1$$

a beta distribution.

Thus we have

$$P(F \le f) = \int_0^f h(F)dF = \frac{1}{B(m_1/2,\ m_2/2)}$$

$$\times \int_{m_2/(m_2+m_1f)}^1 W^{(m_2/2)-1}(1 - W)^{(m_1/2)-1} dW\quad \text{for } f > 0$$

which reduces the computation of the d.f. of F to tables of the incomplete beta function.

Values of f such that $P(F > f)$ is equal to a preassigned small number (0.10, 0.05, 0.01) have been tabulated.

For reasons of convenience in computation, R. A. Fisher considers instead of the random variable F the natural logarithm of the square root of F. This random variable

$$(12.4.1.3) \qquad\qquad Z = \tfrac{1}{2} \log F$$

is known as *Fisher's Z*. Its probability distribution can be easily obtained from the probability distribution of F.

12.4.2. Theorem. Let X and Y be independent random variables, with probability distributions $N(a,\sigma^2)$ and $N(a',\sigma'^2)$, respectively, and let X_1, $X_2, \cdots, X_m$ be a sample of X, and $Y_1, Y_2, \cdots, Y_n$ a sample of Y. Then the random variable

$$(12.4.2.1) \qquad F = \frac{s^2/\sigma^2(m-1)}{s'^2/\sigma'^2(n-1)} = \frac{\sum\limits_{j=1}^{m} (X_j - \bar{X}_m)^2/\sigma^2(m-1)}{\sum\limits_{k=1}^{n} (Y_k - \bar{Y}_n)^2/\sigma'^2(n-1)}$$

has Snedecor's F distribution with $m-1$ and $n-1$ degrees of freedom.

Proof. From 12.2.3.3 we know that s^2/σ^2 has the χ^2 distribution with $m-1$ degrees of freedom and s'^2/σ'^2 the χ^2 distribution with $n-1$ degrees of freedom. Since X and Y are independent, the variables s^2 and s'^2 are independent. Applying Theorem 12.4.1 with $U = s^2/\sigma^2$, $m_1 = m-1$, $V = s'^2/\sigma'^2$, $m_2 = n-1$, we obtain our theorem.

EXERCISES

12.1. To compare Student's probability density $g_m(t)$ of (12.2.3.5.2) with $\varphi(x) = (1/\sqrt{2\pi})e^{-x^2/2}$, assume as known that $g_m(0) < \varphi(0)$ for all integers $m > 0$, and prove the following statements: (a) there is exactly one value $t > 0$ such that $g_m(t) = \varphi(t)$, (b) for any $\tau > 0$, we have $P\{|T| \geq \tau\} > P\{|X| \geq \tau\}$.

12.2. Find the points of inflection of the probability density of Student's T with m degrees of freedom.

12.3. Let X have the probability density $f(x) = e^{-x}$ for $x \geq 0$, $f(x) = 0$ for $x < 0$, and let X_1, X_2 be a sample of X of size 2. Show that $U = X_1 + X_2$ and $V = X_1/X_2$ are independent random variables.

12.4. Let X have the distribution $N(a,\sigma^2)$, and let $X_1, X_2, \cdots, X_n$ be a sample of X. Obtain the joint probability element of (U,V) where

$$U = \sum_{j=1}^{k} X_j, \qquad V = \sum_{j=l}^{n} X_j, \quad 0 < l < k < n$$

12.5. Let $X_1, X_2, \cdots, X_n$ be a sample of a normal random variable X, and let $\bar{X}_n$ and s_n^2 be the sample mean and the sum of squares of deviations from the mean respectively. Let X' be one more observation of X, independent of $X_1, \cdots, X_n$. Prove that the random variable

$$\frac{X' - \bar{X}_n}{\sqrt{s_n^2}} \left(\frac{n(n-1)}{n+1} \right)^{1/2}$$

has Student's t distribution with $n - 1$ d.o.f.

12.6. Assuming that X and Y are independent random variables, each with probability distribution $N(0,1)$, consider the two-dimensional random variable (X, Y) and the random variable $R^2 = X^2 + Y^2 =$ square of distance of (X, Y) from the origin. What is the probability distribution of R^2?

12.7. If the random variable X has χ^2 distribution with m degrees of freedom, find the probability distribution of the random variable

$$Y = \frac{X}{1 + X}$$

12.8. The temperatures of twelve healthy individuals, X taken at 8 a.m. and Y taken at 4 p.m., are tabulated below:

Individual	1	2	3	4	5	6
X	98.0	97.8	97.7	98.0	98.5	98.0
Y	98.1	97.7	98.5	98.3	98.4	98.6

	7	8	9	10	11	12
X	98.2	98.6	97.9	98.0	98.1	98.2
Y	98.5	98.6	98.3	98.2	98.5	98.3

Find the confidence interval for $x_0 - y_0$ with confidence coefficient $\varepsilon = 0.98$.

CHAPTER 13

Tests
of Statistical
Hypotheses

13.1 Formulation of the Problem

13.1.1. Let X be a random variable with a probability distribution of a known type which depends on m parameters $\theta_1, \theta_2, \cdots, \theta_m$. If we knew the values of these parameters, the probability distribution of X would be completely determined. Let us consider the case in which some or all parameters are unknown, but a sample O_n: $X_1, X_2, \cdots, X_n$ is available. If nothing is known about the parameters, we may try to obtain estimates of $\theta_1, \theta_2, \cdots, \theta_m$ based on the sample O_n. In some instances, however, one has good reason to consider the *hypothesis H* that the values $\theta_1, \theta_2, \cdots, \theta_m$ are located in a certain set Ω of the m-dimensional space $(\theta_1, \theta_2, \cdots, \theta_m)$, and one wishes to determine to what extent this hypothesis is compatible with the observed sample. Methods for deciding such questions are known as *tests of statistical hypotheses*. If the set Ω consists of one point $\theta_1^0, \theta_2^0, \cdots, \theta_m^0$ the hypothesis H is called a *simple hypothesis;* if Ω consists of more than one point H is called a *composite hypothesis.*

The aim of any test of a statistical hypothesis H is to enable us to use a given sample in order to reject or to accept H.

13.1.2. Example. In a public opinion poll, taken from a very large population, 3250 persons answered a certain question with "yes" and 2812 with "no." Is it reasonable to assume that at least 60% of the total population are of the yes opinion? To answer this question let us consider the random variable X defined by questioning one person at random from the total population and writing $X = 1$ if the answer of this person is "yes", $X = 0$ if the answer is "no." Clearly X is a simple alternative with $p = P(X = 1) =$ the relative frequency of yes in the total population. In view of the assumption that this population is very large, we may consider all $3250 + 2812 = 6062$ answers as independent determinations of X. We thus have an n-fold repetition S of X, with $n = 6062$. The probability distribution of an n-fold repetition depends on the two parameters n and p. Our hypothesis H is that (n,p) is contained in the set Ω of the (n,p) space defined by $n = 6032$, $p \geq 0.6$. This is a composite hypothesis, since Ω contains more than one point. We notice that, if H is true, we have $E(S) = 6062 \cdot p \geq 3637.2$, and that the actual value $S = 3250$ is considerably less than 3637.2. The probability that S deviates from 3637.2 by as much as the observed value or by more is, by the theorem of Gauss-Laplace

$$P(S \leq 3250) = \sum_{j=0}^{3250} \binom{6062}{j} p^j (1 - p)^{6062-j}$$

$$\sim \frac{1}{\sqrt{2\pi}} \int_{-\infty}^{\frac{3250 - 6062p}{\sqrt{6062p(1-p)}}} e^{-t^2/2} dt = \psi(p)$$

For $p \geq 0.6$, the quantity $3250 - 6062p/\sqrt{6062p(1 - p)}$ is a decreasing function of p, hence

$$\max \psi(p) = \psi(0.6) = \frac{1}{\sqrt{2\pi}} \int_{-\infty}^{-10.15} e^{-t^2/2} dt < 10^{-9}$$

Therefore, if H is true, the probability of obtaining a random sample deviating from the expectation as much or more than the one actually observed would be less than 10^{-9}. We are confronted with the choice of either assuming that an event with a probability $< 10^{-9}$ has occurred or of disbelieving the hypothesis. It appears reasonable to choose this second alternative and to reject the hypothesis.

13.1.3.   The procedure illustrated in the preceding example may be generally described as follows. To test a hypothesis H, using a sample O_n, we compute the probability that, if H is true, a random sample of size n disagrees with H as much or more than O_n. If this probability is not greater than a preassigned small number, called the *significance level*, then we reject H. The significance levels most frequently chosen are 0.05, 0.03, 0.01, 0.005, or 0.001.

In this general description of testing a hypothesis, the phrase "a random sample of size n disagrees with H as much or more than O_n" requires further explanation. The "disagreement" between a hypothesis and an observed sample may often be measured in many different ways, and the question may arise which of these measures of disagreement should be used to test the hypothesis. The discussion of this question is beyond the scope of our presentation. It should be pointed out, however, that for many practical problems it is possible to determine a most advantageous way of measuring this disagreement. Some of the pertinent theory is outlined in Chapter 17.

13.2 Tests of Hypotheses, Using Confidence Intervals

13.2.1. If the probability distribution of a random variable X is of a type which depends on a parameter θ for which a confidence interval (h_l, h_u) can be obtained for any given confidence coefficient, then it is easy to indicate a test of a simple hypothesis for the parameter θ. This is true whether the distribution belongs to a type which is determined by that one parameter θ, or by θ and some more parameters. To construct a test with the given significance level α for a simple hypothesis $H: \theta = \theta_0$, one proceeds in the following manner.

A confidence interval $[h_l(X_1, X_2, \cdots, X_n), h_u(X_1, X_2, \cdots, X_n)]$ is constructed, with the confidence coefficient $1 - \alpha$. If θ is the true value of the parameter, one has

$$P[h_l(X_1, X_2, \cdots, X_n) \leq \theta \leq h_u(X_1, X_2, \cdots, X_n)] = 1 - \alpha$$

To test the hypothesis H, we assume $\theta = \theta_0$ and have

$$P[h_l(X_1, X_2, \cdots, X_n) \leq \theta_0 \leq h_u(X_1, X_2, \cdots, X_n)] = 1 - \alpha$$

or

(13.2.1.1) $P(h_u < \theta_0 \text{ or } h_l > \theta_0) = 1 - P(h_l \leq \theta \leq h_u) = \alpha$

If our sample O_n: $X_1, X_2, \cdots, X_n$ is such that $h_u(X_1, X_2, \cdots, X_n) < \theta_0$ or that $h_l(X_1, X_2, \cdots, X_n) > \theta_0$, then we interpret (13.2.1.1) as saying that a disagreement between H and a sample as great as that between H and O_n or greater has the probability α and we reject H.

13.2.2. Let us first consider the case when X has the known standard deviation σ, and nothing else is known about its probability distribution. We know that for

$$\bar{X}_n = \frac{1}{n} \sum_{j=1}^{n} X_j$$

we have

$$E(\bar{X}_n) = E(X) = x_0$$

and

$$\sigma(\bar{X}_n) = \frac{1}{\sqrt{n}} \sigma_X$$

From Chebyshev's inequality we conclude

$$P\left(|\bar{X}_n - x_0| < t \frac{\sigma_X}{\sqrt{n}}\right) \geq 1 - \frac{1}{t^2}$$

and by writing

$$1 - \frac{1}{t^2} = \varepsilon, \qquad t = \frac{1}{\sqrt{1 - \varepsilon}}$$

we obtain

$$P\left(\bar{X}_n - \frac{\sigma_X}{\sqrt{n(1 - \varepsilon)}} < x_0 < \bar{X}_n + \frac{\sigma_X}{\sqrt{n(1 - \varepsilon)}}\right) \geq \varepsilon$$

for any preassigned $0 \leq \varepsilon < 1$. This shows that

(13.2.2.1)
$$\left(\bar{X}_n - \frac{\sigma_X}{\sqrt{n(1 - \varepsilon)}}, \ \bar{X}_n + \frac{\sigma_X}{\sqrt{n(1 - \varepsilon)}}\right)$$

is a confidence interval for the parameter x_0 with a confidence coefficient $\geq \varepsilon$. Hence to test the hypothesis H: $x_0 = a$, on a significance level $\leq \alpha$, we set $\varepsilon = 1 - \alpha$ and compute for the observed sample the numbers

$$h_l = \bar{X}_n - \frac{\sigma_X}{\sqrt{n\alpha}}, \quad h_u = \bar{X}_n + \frac{\sigma_X}{\sqrt{n\alpha}}$$

If $a < h_l$ or $a > h_u$, we reject H.

13.2.3 Example. A spectroscopic method is used to determine the percentage of chromium in a certain material. In view of errors of observation, this percentage may be considered a random variable X and, assuming

TABLE 13.2.3. Determination of percentage of chromium by spectroscopic method

(1) $X = \%$ of Chromium	(2) $(X - \bar{X}_{10})^2$
28.35	0.12110
28.80	0.01040
28.80	0.01040
28.75	0.00270
29.05	0.12390
28.59	0.01166
28.75	0.00270
28.99	0.08526
28.52	0.03168
28.38	0.10112
286.98	0.50092

$$n = 10$$

$$\sum_{j=1}^{n} X_j = 286.98 \qquad s_{10}^2 = 0.50092$$

$$\bar{X}_{10} = 28.698 \qquad \frac{s_{10}^2}{9} = 0.05566$$

that there are no systematic errors, $E(X) = x_0$ may be interpreted as the true value of the percentage. From a point estimate of $\sigma_X{}^2$ computed from a large number of measurements it is known that σ_X is very nearly 0.23. A sample of the material is claimed to contain 29% chromium. Ten measurements are made and yield the results listed in column (1) of Table 13.2.3. We wish to test the claim $H: x_0 = 29$. To do this, we select a level of significance, say $\alpha = 0.02$, and compute

$$\frac{\sigma_X}{\sqrt{n\alpha}} = \frac{0.23}{\sqrt{10.(0.02)}} = 0.514$$

$$h_l = 28.698 - 0.514 = 28.184$$
$$h_u = 28.698 + 0.514 = 29.212$$

Since 29 is contained between h_l and h_u, we have no reason to reject the hypothesis.

13.2.4.   Let us now consider the case in which σ_X is known and we also know that X has a normal probability distribution. In this case a confidence interval for $E(X)$ can be obtained by the method of Example 11.5.2. The application of this method is illustrated in the following.

Since errors of observation are the result of many superimposed random components, it is usually assumed that, according to the central limit theorem, their distributions are very nearly normal. If we modify Example 13.2.3 by assuming that X has a normal distribution with $\sigma_X = 0.23$, we obtain according to 11.5.2

$$P\left(\bar{X}_{10} - T\frac{0.23}{\sqrt{10}} \le x_0 \le \bar{X}_{10} + T\frac{0.23}{\sqrt{10}}\right) = \frac{1}{\sqrt{2\pi}} \int_{-T}^{T} e^{-t^2/2}dt$$

By selecting again the level of significance $\alpha = 0.02$ and setting

$$1 - \alpha = 0.98 = \varepsilon = \frac{1}{\sqrt{2\pi}} \int_{-T}^{+T} e^{-t^2/2}dt$$

we find from the tables of the normal distribution $T = 2.33$, and compute

$$2.33 \cdot \frac{0.23}{\sqrt{10}} = 0.169$$

$$h_l = 28.698 - 0.169 = 28.529, \qquad h_u = 28.698 + 0.169 = 28.867$$

Since now $h_u < 29$, we reject H on the significance level 0.02.

13.2.5.   In most practical applications the assumption that σ_X is known is not fulfilled, and hence the methods of 13.2.3. and 13.2.4 cannot be applied.

If a small sample O_n is the only information available, a point estimate for σ_X may differ considerably from σ_X and can, therefore, not be used instead of σ_X in the procedures described in these examples.

If the only information available is the sample O_n and if it may be assumed that X has a normal probability distribution, the confidence interval (12.3.1.3) may be used to obtain a test of the hypothesis H: $x_0 = a$. For a given level of significance α one finds $t_{n-1,1-\alpha}$ from the table of Student's t and computes

(13.2.5.1)
$$h_l = \bar{X}_n - t_{n-1,1-\alpha}\sqrt{s_n^2/n(n-1)},$$
$$h_u = \bar{X}_n + t_{n-1,1-\alpha}\sqrt{s_n^2/n(n-1)}$$

If the confidence interval (h_l, h_u) contains a, H is accepted, otherwise rejected.

13.2.5.2. Example. Let us again consider the sample of size $n = 10$ consisting of the values in column (1) of Table 13.2.3 and test the hypothesis H: $x_0 = 29$. We assume that X has a normal probability distribution and that nothing is known about σ_X. For the level of significance $\alpha = 0.02$ and $n - 1 = 9$, we find $t_{9,0.98} = 2.821$. As indicated in column (2) of Table 13.2.3, we compute $s_{10}^2 = 0.50092$, and obtain for the quantities of (13.2.5) the values

$$t_{10,0.98} \cdot \sqrt{s_{10}^2/90} = 2.821\sqrt{0.50092/90} = 0.210$$

$$h_l = 28.698 - 0.210 = 28.488, \qquad h_u = 28.698 + 0.210 = 28.908$$

Since $h_u < 29$, we reject H.

13.3   Tests of Hypotheses, Using Confidence Intervals (Continued)

13.3.1. In the preceding section a number of tests were described in which confidence intervals were used and in which the hypotheses tested were of the form $E(X) = a$. Similar methods may be used to test hypotheses of the form $E(X) = E(Y)$ where X and Y are two one-dimensional random variables.

13.3.2. Let us first assume that X *and* Y are *independent* random variables and that σ_X *and* σ_Y are known but *nothing more is known* about their probability distributions.

Let $X_1, X_2, \cdots, X_m$ be a sample of X, and $Y_1, Y_2, \cdots, Y_n$ a sample of Y, and let

$$\bar{X}_m = \frac{1}{m}\sum_{j=1}^{m} X_j \quad \text{and} \quad \bar{Y}_n = \frac{1}{n}\sum_{k=1}^{n} Y_k$$

For the random variable

$$Z = \bar{X}_m - \bar{Y}_n$$

we have

$$E(Z) = E(\bar{X}_m) - E(\bar{Y}_n) = x_0 - y_0$$

$$\sigma^2(Z) = \sigma^2(\bar{X}_m) + \sigma^2(\bar{Y}_n) = \frac{\sigma_X{}^2}{m} + \frac{\sigma_Y{}^2}{n}$$

We wish to test the hypothesis H: $x_0 = y_0$ which is equivalent with $E(Z) = 0$. In view of Chebyshev's inequality we have

$$P\left(|Z - E(Z)| < t\sqrt{(\sigma_X{}^2/m) + (\sigma_Y{}^2/n)}\right) \geq 1 - \frac{1}{t^2}$$

Consequently, the interval

$$\left(\bar{X}_m - \bar{Y}_n - t\sqrt{(\sigma_X{}^2/m) + (\sigma_Y{}^2/n)}, \quad \bar{X}_m - \bar{Y}_n + t\sqrt{(\sigma_X{}^2/m) + (\sigma_Y{}^2/n)}\right)$$

is a confidence interval with a confidence coefficient $\varepsilon \geq 1 - (1/t^2)$ for $E(Z) = x_0 - y_0$. By setting $1/t^2 = \alpha$, and agreeing to reject H if either

$$h_l = \bar{X}_m - \bar{Y}_n - \frac{1}{\sqrt{\alpha}}\sqrt{(\sigma_X{}^2/m) + (\sigma_Y{}^2/n)} > 0$$

or

$$h_u = \bar{X}_m - \bar{Y}_n - \frac{1}{\sqrt{\alpha}}\sqrt{(\sigma_X{}^2/m) + (\sigma_Y{}^2/n)} < 0$$

we establish a test for H with a significance level $\leq \alpha$.

13.3.3. Example.

The molecular weight of compound A was determined 9 times, that of compound B 12 times. The results are listed in columns (1) and (3) of Table 13.3.3. The procedure used in each case is known to have a standard deviation $\sigma = 0.05$. It is claimed that A and B have the same molecular weight. If X and Y are the random variables obtained by single measurements of the molecular weights of A and of B, respectively, then we have $\sigma_X = \sigma_Y = 0.05$ and we wish to test the hypothesis H: $E(X) = E(Y)$. The computations of Table 13.3.3 yield, $\bar{X}_9 = 174.233$, $\bar{Y}_{12} = 174.272$. For the level of significance $\alpha = 0.02$ we thus have

$$\frac{1}{\sqrt{\alpha}}\sqrt{(\sigma_X{}^2/m) + (\sigma_Y{}^2/n)} = \frac{1}{\sqrt{0.02}}\sqrt{[(0.05)^2/9] + [(0.05)^2/12]} = 0.156$$

$$h_l = -0.039 - 0.156 = -0.195, \qquad h_u = -0.039 + 0.156 = +0.117$$

Since $h_l < 0 < h_u$, we have no reason to reject H.

13.3.4.

If σ_X and σ_Y are known and the probability distributions of X and Y are assumed to be *normal, we know that $Z = \bar{X}_m - \bar{Y}_n$ has a normal probability distribution with $E(Z) = x_0 - y_0$ and*

$$\sigma_Z = \sqrt{(\sigma_X{}^2/m) + (\sigma_Y{}^2/n)}$$

so that we have

$$P(|\bar{X}_m - \bar{Y}_n - (x_0 - y_0)| \le T) = \frac{1}{\sqrt{2\pi}} \int_{-T/\sqrt{(\sigma_X^2/m)+(\sigma_Y^2/n)}}^{+T/\sqrt{(\sigma_X^2/m)+(\sigma_Y^2/n)}} e^{-t^2/2}dt$$

For given σ_X, σ_Y, m, n and confidence coefficient ε, one finds T_1, such that the right-hand side equals ε and hence

$$h_l = \bar{X}_m - \bar{Y}_n - T_1, \qquad h_u = \bar{X}_m - \bar{Y}_n + T_1$$

is a confidence interval for $x_0 - y_0$ with confidence coefficient ε. To test H: $x_0 - y_0 = 0$, one will determine T_1 for $\varepsilon = 1 - \alpha$ where α is the required level of significance, compute h_l and h_u, and reject H if either $0 < h_l$ or $h_u < 0$.

TABLE 13.3.3. $X =$ measurements of molecular weight of compound A; $Y =$ measurements of molecular weight of compound B

(1) X	(2) $(X - \bar{X}_9)^2$	(3) Y	(4) $(Y - \bar{Y}_{12})^2$
174.18	0.002704	174.19	0.006724
174.29	0.003364	174.40	0.016384
174.23	0.000004	174.20	0.005184
174.30	0.004624	174.35	0.006084
174.36	0.016384	174.32	0.002304
174.18	0.002704	174.14	0.017424
174.11	0.014884	174.27	0.000004
174.20	0.001024	174.30	0.000784
174.25	0.000324	174.18	0.008464
		174.34	0.004624
		174.28	0.000064
		174.30	0.000784
1568.10	0.046016	2091.27	0.068828

$$m = 9 \qquad\qquad n = 12$$
$$\sum X = 1568.10 \qquad\qquad \sum Y = 2091.27$$
$$\bar{X}_9 = 174.233 \qquad\qquad \bar{Y}_{12} = 174.272$$
$$\sum (X - \bar{X}_9)^2 = 0.046016 \qquad \sum (Y - \bar{Y}_{12})^2 = 0.068828$$

13.3.4.1. Example. Let us assume that X and Y in the data of Table 13.3.3 are normal random variables with $\sigma_X = \sigma_Y = 0.05$. For $\alpha = 0.02$. $\varepsilon = 1 - \alpha = 0.98$, we find

$$\frac{1}{\sqrt{2\pi}} \int_{-2.33}^{2.33} e^{-t^2/2}dt = 0.98$$

$$\sqrt{(\sigma_X^2/m) + (\sigma_Y^2/n)} = \sqrt{[(0.05)^2/9] + [(0.05)^2/12]} = 0.022$$

hence $T_1 = (2.33)(0.022) = 0.051$. We then obtain

$$h_l = -0.039 - 0.051 = -0.090, \qquad h_u = -0.039 + 0.051 = 0.012$$

and since $-0.090 < 0 < 0.012$, we accept H. If the significance level is chosen at $\alpha = 0.10$, we find from the table of the normal distribution

$$\frac{1}{\sqrt{2\pi}} \int_{-1.64}^{1.64} e^{-t^2/2}dt = 0.90$$

hence

$$T_1 = (1.64)(0.022) = 0.036, \qquad h_l = 0.039 - 0.036 = -0.075,$$

$$h_u = -0.003$$

Since now $h_u < 0$, we reject H on the 10% significance level.

13.3.5. Again, as in the one-sample problem considered in 13.2.5, most frequently the standard deviations σ_X and σ_Y are not known, and all the information needed must be obtained from the available samples of X and Y. In this case, if it may be assumed that X and Y are independent random variables with normal probability distributions and that both have *the same* (although not known) *variance* σ^2, a test of the hypothesis H: $x_0 = y_0$ may be obtained in the following manner.

According to Theorem 12.2.3.7 the statistic

$$T = \frac{(\bar{X}_m - \bar{Y}_n) - (x_0 - y_0)}{\sqrt{s_m^2 + s_n^2}} \cdot \frac{\sqrt{m + n - 2}}{\sqrt{(1/m) + (1/n)}}$$

has the probability density $g_{m+n-2}(T)$. We have, therefore,

$$P(|T| < t) = 1 - p_{m+n-2}(t)$$

and

$$P\left[\bar{X}_m - \bar{Y}_n - t\sqrt{(1/m) + (1/n)} \cdot \sqrt{\frac{s_m^2 + s_n'^2}{m + n - 2}} < x_0 - y_0 \right.$$

$$\left. < \bar{X}_m - \bar{Y}_n + t\sqrt{(1/m) + (1/n)} \cdot \sqrt{\frac{s_m^2 + s_n'^2}{(m + n - 2)}} \right]$$

$$= 1 - p_{m+n-2}(t)$$

Thus

$$h_l = \bar{X}_m - \bar{Y}_n - t\sqrt{(1/m) + (1/n)} \cdot \sqrt{(s_m^2 + s_n'^2)/(m + n - 2)}$$

$$h_u = \bar{X}_m - \bar{Y}_n + t\sqrt{(1/m) + (1/n)} \cdot \sqrt{(s_m^2 + s_n'^2)/(m + n - 2)}$$

defines a confidence interval for $x_0 - y_0$ with confidence coefficient $1 - p_{m+n-2}(t)$. To have a test for H: $x_0 - y_0 = 0$ with the level of significance α, one finds t_1 such that $p_{m+n-2}(t_1) = \alpha$; H is rejected if $h_l > 0$ or $h_u < 0$, accepted if $h_l \leq 0 \leq h_u$.

13.3.5.1. Example.   The number of red blood cells per cubic millimeter was determined for 20 men and 12 women selected at random. The results are given in columns (1) and (3) of Table 13.3.5.1. If it is assumed that the number of red cells per cubic millimeter is, for each sex, a normal random

TABLE 13.3.5.1. Number of red blood cells in millions per cubic millimeter for 20 men (X) and 12 women (Y)

(1) X	(2) $(X - \bar{X}_{20})^2$	(3) Y	(4) $(\bar{Y} - \bar{Y}_{12})^2$
4.27	0.4310	3.89	0.1444
4.40	0.2772	3.95	0.1024
4.52	0.1652	3.97	0.0900
4.56	0.1343	4.15	0.0144
4.58	0.1201	4.20	0.0049
4.64	0.0821	4.26	0.0001
4.72	0.0426	4.31	0.0016
4.80	0.0160	4.38	0.0121
4.84	0.0075	4.40	0.0169
4.89	0.0013	4.45	0.0324
4.93	0.0000	4.56	0.0841
4.97	0.0019	4.72	0.2025
5.00	0.0054		
5.02	0.0087		
5.15	0.0500		
5.20	0.0748		
5.36	0.1879		
5.49	0.3175		
5.57	0.4141		
5.62	0.4809		
98.53	2.8185	51.24	0.7058

$$m = 20 \qquad n = 12$$
$$\bar{X}_{20} = 4.9265 \qquad \bar{Y}_{12} = 4.270$$
$$s_{20}^2 = 2.8185 \qquad s_{12}^2 = 0.7058$$

variable with the same standard deviation, would the samples of Table 13.3.5.1 indicate a sex difference in the mathematical expectations? Let X be the number of red blood cells per cubic millimeter for men, and Y for women. We assume that X and Y are independent normal random variables and that $\sigma_X = \sigma_Y$ and wish to test the hypothesis $H: x_0 = y_0$ on the 5% level of significance. The computations of Table 13.3.5.1 yield

$$m = 20, \qquad \bar{X}_{20} = 4.927, \qquad s_{20}^2 = 2.8185$$
$$n = 12, \qquad \bar{Y}_{12} = 4.270, \qquad s_{12}'^2 = 0.7058$$

For $m + n - 2 = 30$ d.o.f., and the confidence coefficient $1 - 0.05 = 0.95$ we find from the table of Student's t the value $t_1 = 2.042$, and hence

$$t\sqrt{(1/m) + (1/n)}\sqrt{(s_m^2 + s_n'^2)/(m + n - 2)}$$

$$= 2.042\sqrt{\tfrac{1}{20} + \tfrac{1}{12}}\sqrt{(2.8185 + 0.7058)/30} = 0.256$$

$$h_l = 4.927 - 4.270 - 0.256 = 0.401$$

$$h_u = 4.927 - 4.270 + 0.256 = 0.913$$

Since $0 < h_l$, we reject H on the 5% significance level.

13.3.6.   The assumption $\sigma_X = \sigma_Y$ made in the preceding example was somewhat arbitrary. The estimates based on the available samples would be

Estimate for $\sigma_X{}^2$: $\dfrac{s_{20}^2}{19} = 0.1483$

Estimate for $\sigma_Y{}^2$: $\dfrac{s_{12}'^2}{11} = 0.0642$

and by taking square roots, we would obtain 0.3851 as an estimate for σ_X and 0.2534 for σ_Y. Is that discrepancy between estimates based on small samples compatible with the assumption that the parameters σ_X and σ_Y are equal? This leads to the following problem.

Let X and Y be independent normal random variables with unknown expectations and variances. Available are a sample O_m for X and a sample O_n' for Y. We wish to test the hypothesis $H\colon \sigma_X{}^2 = \sigma_Y{}^2$. From Theorem 12.4.2 we see that, if H is true, the statistic

$$F = \frac{\sum\limits_{j=1}^{m}(X_j - \bar{X}_m)^2/(m - 1)}{\sum\limits_{k=1}^{n}(Y_k - \bar{Y}_n)^2/(n - 1)} = \frac{s_m^2}{s_n^2}\cdot\frac{n - 1}{m - 1}$$

has the Snedecor F distribution with $m - 1$ and $n - 1$ d.o.f. Since $\dfrac{s_m^2}{m - 1}$ and $\dfrac{s_n'^2}{n - 1}$ are unbiased and consistent estimates of $\sigma_X{}^2$ and $\sigma_Y{}^2$, respectively, one would expect that if H is true the observed value of F should not differ very much from 1. To test H one computes, therefore, the probability that, if H is true, the ratio of the larger one of the two estimates to the smaller one will exceed 1 by as much or more than the observed value of F. If this probability is less than the given level of significance α, one rejects H, otherwise one accepts it. To compute this probability, one uses the tables of the F distribution in the following manner.

Let the unbiased estimates of the common variance $\sigma_X{}^2 = \sigma_Y{}^2 = \sigma^2$, obtained from the two samples be denoted by

$$v_1 = \sum_{j=1}^{m} \frac{(X_j - \bar{X}_m)^2}{(m-1)}$$

$$v_2 = \sum_{k=1}^{n} \frac{(Y_k - \bar{Y}_n)^2}{(n-1)}$$

Then v_1/v_2 has the F distribution with $m-1, n-1$ d.o.f. and v_2/v_1 has the F distribution with $n-1, m-1$ d.o.f. Let α be the significance level on which H is to be tested, and $f_1 = f_{m-1,n-1,\alpha/2}$, $f_2 = f_{n-1,m-1,\alpha/2}$, two numbers such that

$$P\left(\frac{v_1}{v_2} > f_1\right) = P\left(\frac{v_2}{v_1} > f_2\right) = \frac{\alpha}{2}$$

Since $f_1 > 1$ and $f_2 > 1$, we have

$P(v_1 > v_2$ and $v_1/v_2 > f_1$, or $v_2 > v_1$ and $v_2/v_1 > f_2)$
$= P(v_1 > v_2$ and $v_1/v_2 > f_1) + P(v_2 > v_1$ and $v_2/v_1 > f_2)$
$= P(v_1/v_2 > f_1) + P(v_2/v_1 > f_2) = \alpha$

Only one of the two events, $v_1/v_2 > f_1$ or $v_2/v_1 > f_2$ can occur, so that in practical applications it is sufficient to look up in tables only one of the critical values f_1 or f_2. This value must, however, correspond to $\alpha/2$, that is, to *half of the desired significance level*, a requirement often omitted in statistical tables and instructions for using them.

13.3.6.1. Example. We assume that the variables X and Y of Example 13.3.5.1 are independent and normal, and wish to test the hypothesis H: $\sigma_X{}^2 = \sigma_Y{}^2$ on the 5% level of significance. From the computations in 13.3.5.1, we have the larger estimate $s_{20}{}^2/19 = 0.1483$ and the smaller estimate $s_{12}'^2 /11 = 0.0642$. From tables of the F distribution one finds that, for 19 and 11 d.o.f. $f_{19,11,0.025} = 3.24$, and since the observed value of $(s_{20}{}^2/19)/(s_{12}{}^2/11) = 0.1483/0.0642 = 2.31$ is less than 3.24 we accept H on the 0.05 significance level.

If a problem of the kind illustrated in Example 13.3.5.1 is treated, practical considerations sometimes justify the assumption that $\sigma_X{}^2 = \sigma_Y{}^2$. Such is for example the case if X and Y are scientific measurements carried out by the same observer with the same apparatus, and all random deviations are due to errors of observation.

Very often, however, the equality $\sigma_X{}^2 = \sigma_Y{}^2$ cannot be taken for granted. In such cases it has been a frequent practice to precede the test for equality of expectations by the test for equality of variances. Although the exact theory of this procedure will not be given here, a few words on its meaning may be in order.

Let X and Y be independent random variables, known to have normal probability distributions. Samples O_m of X and O_n of Y are available. We wish to test the hypothesis $H: \sigma_X^2 = \sigma_Y^2$ and $E(X) = E(Y)$. For this purpose we choose $\alpha > 0$ and apply the F test for equality of variances as described in 13.3.6. If it is significant on the level α, we reject H. If it is not significant, we apply the t test for equality of expectations. If the value of t is significant on the level α we reject H. If neither F nor t is significant, we accept H.

In this test H is rejected if either F is significant on the level α, or if F is not significant but t is significant on the level α. Hence it appears plausible that the probability of rejecting H, if it is true, is greater than α. For practical use it may be assumed that this probability is about 2α, so that the test has the significance level of approximately 2α.

EXERCISES

13.1. In 3000 throws of a die, the face marked 3 appeared 442 times. Use the Gauss-Laplace approximation and test the hypothesis $H: P(3) = \frac{1}{6}$ on the 5% level of significance.

13.2. It is claimed that the average life length of a floodlight bulb is 24 hours. Twelve bulbs were tested and had the life lengths $X:$ 16.0, 18.5, 18.0, 22.0, 25.2, 24.3, 24.5, 20.3, 17.2, 19.3, 20.1, 24.0. Assume a normal distribution and test the hypothesis $E(X) = 24$ on the 2% level of significance.

13.3. The hypothesis is made that the expected body temperature of healthy individuals taken at 4:00 p.m. is not greater than that taken at 8:00 a.m.; in the notations of Exercise 12.8 this would be $H: E(Y) \leq E(X)$. Propose a test for this (one-sided) hypothesis, and apply it to the data of Exercise 12.8 on the 2% level of significance, assuming normal distribution.

CHAPTER 14

Sampling of a Normal Bivariate Random Variable. Multivariate Correlation and Regression

14.1 Joint Probability Distribution of Estimates for x_0, y_0, σ_x^2, σ_y^2, and ρ

Let (X,Y) be a bivariate normal random variable with the probability density written according to (4.2.1.1) and (4.2.2.6).

$$
\begin{aligned}
f(x,y) &= \frac{1}{2\pi} \sqrt{A_{11}A_{22} - A_{12}^2}\, \exp\left\{-\tfrac{1}{2}[A_{11}(x-x_0)^2 \right. \\
&\qquad\qquad \left. + 2A_{12}(x-x_0)(y-y_0) + A_{22}(y-y_0)^2]\right\} \\
&= \frac{1}{2\pi\sigma_x\sigma_y\sqrt{1-\rho^2}}\, \exp\left\{-\frac{1}{2(1-\rho)^2}\right. \\
&\qquad \left. \times \left[\frac{(x-x_0)^2}{\sigma_X^2} - \frac{2\rho(x-x_0)(Y-y_0)}{\sigma_x\sigma_y} + \frac{(Y-y_0)^2}{\sigma_y^2}\right]\right\}
\end{aligned}
$$

We consider a sample $(X_1,Y_1), (X_2,Y_2), \cdots, (X_n,Y_n)$ of (X,Y), and form the following five statistics

(14.1.1) $\qquad \bar{X} = \frac{1}{n}\sum_{j=1}^{n} X_j$

(14.1.2) $\qquad \bar{Y} = \frac{1}{n}\sum_{j=1}^{n} Y_j$

(14.1.3) $W = \dfrac{s_x{}^2}{n} = \dfrac{1}{n}\sum\limits_{j=1}^{n}(X_j - \bar{X})^2 = \dfrac{1}{n}\sum\limits_{j=1}^{n} X_j{}^2 - \bar{X}^2$

(14.1.4) $Z = \dfrac{s_y{}^2}{n} = \dfrac{1}{n}\sum\limits_{j=1}^{n}(Y_j - \bar{Y})^2 = \dfrac{1}{n}\sum\limits_{j=1}^{n} Y_j{}^2 - \bar{Y}^2$

(14.1.5) $R = \dfrac{1}{n}\sum\limits_{j=1}^{n}(X_j - \bar{Y})(Y_j - \bar{Y}) = \dfrac{1}{n}\sum\limits_{j=1}^{n} X_j Y_j - \bar{X}\bar{Y}$

We know that $\bar{X}$ and $\bar{Y}$ are unbiased and consistent estimates for x_0 and y_0, and that W and Z are consistent estimates for $\sigma_x{}^2$ and $\sigma_y{}^2$. By arguments analogous to that in 11.2.4 it can also be shown that $[n/(n-1)]W$ is an unbiased estimate for $\sigma_x{}^2$, $[n/(n-1)]Z$ an unbiased estimate for $\sigma_y{}^2$, and $[n/(n-1)]R$ an unbiased estimate for the covariance $\sigma_{x,y}$. Furthermore, it can be proved by a reasoning similar to that in 11.2.6 that R is a consistent estimate for $\sigma_{x,y}$.

The following theorem is due to R. A. Fisher. Its proof is too lengthy to be given here.

14.1.6. Theorem.   The joint probability density of the five-dimensional random variable $(\bar{X}, \bar{Y}, W, Z, R)$ is

(14.1.6.1) $f(\bar{X}, \bar{Y}, W, Z, R) = f_1(\bar{X}, \bar{Y}) \cdot f_2(W, Z, R)$

where

(14.1.6.2)

$$f_1(\bar{X}, \bar{Y}) = \frac{n}{2\pi}\sqrt{A_{11}A_{22} - A_{12}{}^2}\, \exp\{-(n/2)[A_{11}(\bar{X} - x_0)^2$$
$$+ 2A_{12}(\bar{X} - x_0)(\bar{Y} - y_0) + A_{22}(\bar{Y} - y_0)^2]\}$$

$$= \frac{n}{2\pi\sigma_x\sigma_y\sqrt{1 - \rho^2}}\, \exp\left\{-\frac{n}{2(1-\rho^2)}\left[\frac{(\bar{X} - x_0)^2}{\sigma_x{}^2}\right.\right.$$
$$\left.\left. - \frac{2\rho(\bar{X} - x_0)(\bar{Y} - y_0)}{\sigma_x\sigma_y} + \frac{(\bar{Y} - y_0)^2}{\sigma_y{}^2}\right]\right\}$$

(14.1.6.3)

$$f_2(W, Z, R) = \frac{n^{n-1}}{4\pi(n-3)!}(\sqrt{A_{11}A_{22} - A_{12}{}^2})^{n-1}(WZ - R^2)^{(n-4)/2}$$
$$\times \exp[-(n/2)(A_{11}W + 2A_{12}R + A_{22}Z)]$$

for $R_2 < WZ$, $W > 0$, zero elsewhere.

In particular it follows that $(\bar{X}, \bar{Y})$ and (W, Z, R) are independent random variables with the probability densities $f_1(\bar{X}, \bar{Y})$ and $f_2(W, Z, R)$ respectively.

14.2 Probability Distribution of the Sample Correlation
Coefficient $r = R/\sqrt{WZ}$

Since W,Z and R are consistent estimates of σ_x^2, σ_y^2 and σ_{xy}, respectively, the statistic

$$(14.2.1) \qquad\qquad r = \frac{R}{\sqrt{WZ}}$$

called the *sample correlation-coefficient*, is a consistent estimate of the parameter $\rho = \sigma_{xy}/\sigma_x\sigma_y$, that is, of the coefficient of correlation of X and Y. To derive the probability distribution of r, we make in (14.1.6.3) the change of variables (14.2.1) and obtain the joint probability element

$$g(W,Z,r)dWdZdr = f_2(W,Z,\sqrt{WZ}r)\sqrt{WZ}dWdZdr$$

$$= \frac{n^{n-1}}{4\pi(n-3)!}(\sigma_x\sigma_y\sqrt{1-\rho^2})^{-(n-1)}(WZ)^{(n-3)/2}(1-r^2)^{(n-4)/2}$$

$$\times \exp\left[-\frac{n}{2(1-\rho^2)}\left(\frac{W}{\sigma_x^2} - \frac{2\rho\sqrt{WZ}}{\sigma_x\sigma_y}r + \frac{Z}{\sigma_y^2}\right)\right]dWdZdr$$

for $W > 0$, $Z > 0$, $-1 \leq r \leq +1$, zero elsewhere.

Using the expansion

$$\exp\left[\frac{n\rho\sqrt{WZ}r}{(1-\rho^2)\sigma_x\sigma_y}\right] = \sum_{k=0}^{\infty} \frac{1}{k!}\left(\frac{n\rho\sqrt{WZ}r}{(1-\rho^2)\sigma_x\sigma_y}\right)^k$$

and integrating with respect to W and Z yields for the absolute probability density of r

$$h(r) = \int_0^{+\infty}\int_0^{+\infty} g(W,Z,r)dWdZ$$

$$= \frac{n^{n-1}}{4\pi(n-3)!}(\sigma_x\sigma_y\sqrt{1-\rho^2})^{-(n-1)}(1-r^2)^{(n-4)/2}$$

$$\sum_{k=0}^{\infty}\frac{1}{k!}\left(\frac{n\rho r}{(1-\rho^2)\sigma_x\sigma_y}\right)^k\int_0^{+\infty}W^{(n+k-3)/2}\exp\left[-\frac{n}{2(1-\rho^2)\sigma_x^2}W\right]dW$$

$$\times \int_0^{+\infty}Z^{(n+k-3)/2}\exp\left[-\frac{n}{2(1-\rho^2)\sigma_y^2}Z\right]dZ.$$

Since we have

$$\int_0^{+\infty}t^{(n+k-3)/2}\exp\left[-\frac{n}{2(1-\rho^2)\sigma^2}t\right]dt$$

$$= \left[\frac{2(1-\rho^2)\sigma^2}{n}\right]^{(n+k-1)/2}\Gamma\left(\frac{n+k-1}{2}\right)$$

the expression for $h(r)$ becomes

(14.2.2)

$$h(r) = \frac{2^{n-3}(1 - \rho^2)^{(n-1)/2}}{\pi(n - 3)!} (1 - r^2)^{(n-4)/2} \sum_{k=0}^{\infty} \frac{1}{k!} (2\rho r)^k \Gamma^2\left(\frac{n + k - 1}{2}\right)$$

for $-1 \leq r \leq +1$, and zero elsewhere. It is rather remarkable that $h(r)$, although derived from (14.1.6.3), does not depend on σ_x and σ_y, but only on ρ and n.

In the special case $\rho = 0$, $h(r)$ reduces to

(14.2.3)
$$h_0(r) = \frac{2^{n-3}\Gamma^2[(n - 1)/2]}{\pi(n - 3)!} (1 - r^2)^{(n-4)/2}$$

Extensive tables have been published for the probability distribution (14.2.2). This probability distribution varies considerably with ρ so that the tabulation had to be made for a number of different values of ρ. In practical use, however, these tables may be conveniently replaced by one concise auxiliary table and the table of the normal distribution; this great simplification was made possible by R. A. Fisher who made the observation that the random variable

(14.2.4.1)
$$z = \tfrac{1}{2} \log \frac{1 + r}{1 - r}$$

has a distribution which approximates very closely the normal distribution

$$N\left(\zeta + \frac{\rho}{2(n - 1)}, \frac{1}{n - 3}\right)$$

where

(14.2.4.2)
$$\zeta = \tfrac{1}{2} \log \frac{1 + \rho}{1 - \rho}$$

This approximation is quite good even for values of n as small as 10. Some of the practical advantages achieved by the use of Fisher's approximation will be discussed in 14.3.

In the case of $\rho = 0$ a tabulation of (14.2.3) becomes unnecessary in view of the following theorem.

14.2.5. Theorem. If (X, Y) has a normal bivariate probability density with the correlation coefficient $\rho = 0$, then the random variable

(14.2.5.1)
$$t = \sqrt{n - 2} \frac{r}{\sqrt{1 - r^2}} \quad \text{for } n \geq 3$$

has exactly the Student distribution with $n - 2$ degrees of freedom.

Proof. The transformation

$$r = t(t^2 + n - 2)^{-1/2}$$

inverse to (14.2.5.1), yields the probability element

$$l(t)dt = h_0(r)dr = C_n\left(1 - \frac{t^2}{t^2 + n - 2}\right)^{(n-4)/2}$$

$$\cdot (t^2 + n - 2)^{-1/2}[1 - t^2(t^2 + n - 2)^{-1}]dt$$

$$= C_n(n - 2)^{(n-2)/2}(t^2 + n - 2)^{-(n-1)/2}dt$$

$$= C_n'\left(1 + \frac{t^2}{n - 2}\right)^{-(n-1)/2}dt$$

which is the probability element of the Student distribution with $n - 2$ d.o.f.

14.3 Testing Hypotheses on the Values of Correlation Coefficients

14.3.1. Let us consider a random variable (X,Y) which may be assumed to have a bivariate normal probability distribution, with unknown parameters x_0, y_0, σ_x, σ_y, ρ. A sample $(X_1,Y_2), \cdots, (X_n,Y_n)$ of (X,Y) is available. We wish to test the hypothesis H: X and Y are independent. According to 4.2.3, our problem is equivalent to testing the hypothesis $\rho = 0$. Under this hypothesis Theorem 14.2.5 applies and we have $E(t) = 0$ for t defined by (14.2.5.1). We compute $r = r_1$ from our sample, and if the corresponding value $t = t_1$ is such that $P(|t| > t_1)$ is less than a chosen significance level for $n - 2$ d.o.f., we reject H. In that case it is customary to say that the value $r = r_1$ of the correlation coefficient is significantly different from zero or, in short, that $r = r_1$ is significant.

14.3.1.1. Example. We choose $\alpha = 0.01$. A sample of size $n = 12$ yielded $r = 0.382$. We compute

$$t = \sqrt{10}\,\frac{0.382}{\sqrt{1 - (0.382)^2}} = 1.307$$

For 10 d.o.f. we have from the table of Student's t $P(|t| > 1.37) > 0.2$. Thus $r = 0.382$ is not significant and we do not reject the hypothesis that X and Y are independent.

14.3.1.2. Example. A sample of size $n = 25$ yielded $r = 0.643$. Choosing the significance level 0.01, we compute

$$t = \sqrt{23}\,\frac{0.643}{\sqrt{1 - (0.643)^2}} = 4.11$$

and find from the t table the value $P(|t| > 4.11) < 0.001$. Hence $r = 0.643$ is significant, and we reject the hypothesis that X and Y are independent.

14.3.2. Sometimes one has reason to assume that ρ has a definite numerical value ρ_1 and wishes to test the hypothesis $H:\ \rho = \rho_1$ on hand of a sample. In problems of this kind one may use either the tables of the exact distribution (14.2.2), or the approximation given by (14.2.4.1) and (14.2.4.2). We shall illustrate the second method only.

14.3.2.1. Example. It is known that in normal adult individuals certain two psychological traits have a correlation coefficient of about 0.800. A sample of 15 individuals affected with a diagnosed pathological condition is available, and for those individuals the correlation coefficient of the same two traits is $r = 0.530$. Is this discrepancy significant on the 0.05 level of significance? According to Fisher's approximation, $Z = \frac{1}{2}[\log (1 + r) - \log (1 - r)]$ is approximately normal with $E(Z) = \zeta + (0.800/28)$ and $\sigma_Z = 1/\sqrt{12}$. Since

$$\zeta = \tfrac{1}{2}[\log (1 + 0.800) - \log (1 - 0.800)] = 1.10$$

we have

$$E(Z) = 1.10 + 0.03 = 1.13 \quad \text{and} \quad \sigma^2(Z) = \tfrac{1}{12}$$

The observed value $r = 0.530$ yields

$$Z = \tfrac{1}{2}[\log (1 + 0.530) - \log (1 - 0.530)] = 0.59$$

Using the table of the normal distribution we obtain

$$P\left(\frac{|Z - E(Z)|}{\sigma_Z} > \frac{|0.59 - 1.13|}{1/\sqrt{12}}\right) = P(|X| > 1.87) = 0.061 > 0.05$$

Thus the sample correlation coefficient 0.530 does not differ significantly from 0.800 on the 5% level.

14.3.3. Another problem which can be treated by using Fisher's approximation is this: There is reason to assume that the two bivariate normal random variables (X,Y) and (U,V) have the same correlation coefficient $\rho_{xy} = \rho_{uv} = \rho$. We wish to test this hypothesis, using the available independent samples $(X_1 Y_1),\ \cdots,\ (X_m, Y_m)$ and $(U_1, V_1),\ \cdots,\ (U_n, V_n)$. To do this we compute the sample correlation coefficients r_{xy} and r_{uv}. Under our hypothesis, the random variable

$$Z_{xy} = \tfrac{1}{2}[\log (1 + r_{xy}) - \log (1 - r_{xy})]$$

has approximately the distribution

$$N\left(\zeta + \frac{\rho}{2(m - 1)},\ \frac{1}{m - 3}\right)$$

and the random variable

$$Z_{uv} = \tfrac{1}{2}[\log (1 + r_{uv}) - \log (1 - r_{uv})]$$

has the distribution

$$N\left(\zeta + \frac{\rho}{2(n-1)}, \frac{1}{n-3}\right)$$

where ζ is the same in both distributions namely,

$$\zeta = \tfrac{1}{2}[\log(1+\rho) - \log(1-\rho)]$$

Since the samples are independent, Z_{xy} and Z_{uv} are independent, and $Z_{xy} - Z_{uv}$ has approximately the normal distribution

$$N\left[\frac{\rho}{2}\left(\frac{1}{m-1} - \frac{1}{n-1}\right), \frac{1}{m-3} + \frac{1}{n-3}\right].$$

One can then test, in the manner usual for normal variables, whether the observed value $Z_{xy} - Z_{uv}$ differs significantly from

$$\frac{\rho}{2}\left(\frac{1}{m-1} - \frac{1}{n-1}\right).$$

If $m = n$ or m is close to n, or if m and n are fairly large, this quantity is practically zero, and the test can be carried out by using the table of the normal distribution, without knowledge of the value of the parameter ρ.

14.3.3.1. Example. Two traits observed in men are denoted by (X,Y), observed in women by (U,V). We assume that (X,Y) and (U,V) are normal bivariate random variables, and wish to test the hypothesis that there is no sex difference in the correlation coefficient, that is, that $\rho_{xy} = \rho_{uv}$. From a sample of (X,Y) of size $m = 25$ we compute $r_{xy} = 0.43$, and from a sample of (U,V) of size $n = 22$ we obtain $r_{uv} = 0.15$. We first observe that

$$\frac{|\rho|}{2}\left|\frac{1}{24} - \frac{1}{21}\right| < \frac{1}{336}$$

which is very close to 0. We may thus assume that $Z_{xy} - Z_{uv}$ has a normal distribution with expectation 0 and variance

$$\frac{1}{22} + \frac{1}{19} = \frac{41}{418}$$

From the observed values of r_{xy} and r_{uv} we obtain

$$Z_{xy} = 0.46, \qquad Z_{uv} = 0.15, \quad \text{and} \quad P(|Z_{xy} - Z_{uv}| \geq |0.46 - 0.15|)$$
$$= P(|Z_{xy} - Z_{uv}| \geq 0.31)$$
$$= P\left(\frac{|Z_{xy} - Z_{uv}|}{\sqrt{41/418}} \geq \frac{0.31}{\sqrt{41/418}}\right)$$
$$= P(|T| \geq 0.99)$$

where T has the distribution $N(0,1)$. This is not significant at any of the usual significance levels, and we have no reason to reject the hypothesis $\rho_{xy} = \rho_{uv}$.

14.4   Distribution of Sample Regression Coefficients and Testing Hypotheses on Regression Coefficients

14.4.1.   In 9.2. we discussed the parameters

$$A = \rho_{XY}\frac{\sigma_Y}{\sigma_X} = \frac{\sigma_{XY}}{\sigma_X{}^2}, \qquad C = \rho_{XY}\frac{\sigma_X}{\sigma_Y} = \frac{\sigma_{XY}}{\sigma_Y{}^2}$$

and called them the regression coefficient of Y on X and the regression coefficient of X on Y, respectively.   The statistics

(14.4.1.1) $$a = \frac{R}{W}, \qquad c = \frac{R}{Z}$$

are used as estimates of A and C.   Since W and Z are consistent estimates of $\sigma_X{}^2$ and $\sigma_Y{}^2$ and for a very wide class of random variables (X,Y), in particular in the case of a normal bivariate distribution, R is a consistent estimate of σ_{XY}, it follows that a and c are consistent estimates of A and C.

From the joint probability density $f_2(W,Z,R)$ in (14.1.6.3) the probability densities of a and c can be explicitly derived.   These probability densities, however, depend on σ_X, σ_Y and ρ_{XY}, and thus are of little practical use; for, if σ_X, σ_Y and ρ_{XY} are known, the parameters A and C can be exactly computed, and there is no need for estimates.   The following theorem due to M. S. Bartlett is therefore of particular interest.

14.4.2. Theorem.   If (X,Y) has the normal bivariate probability distribution given in 14.1, then each of the statistics

$$t_1 = \sqrt{\frac{W(n-2)}{Z(1-r^2)}}\,(a-A)$$

$$t_2 = \sqrt{\frac{Z(n-2)}{W(1-r^2)}}\,(c-C)$$

has the Student distribution with $n - 2$ degrees of freedom.

Proof.   We make the change of variables

(14.4.2.1) $$\overline{W} = W, \qquad \overline{R} = \frac{WZ - R^2}{W}, \qquad \overline{Z} = \sqrt{W}\left(\frac{R}{W} - A\right)$$

for $W > 0, Z > 0, WZ - R^2 > 0$.   The inverse transformation

(14.4.2.2) $W = \overline{W}, \quad Z = \overline{R} + (A\sqrt{\overline{W}} + \overline{Z})^2, \quad R = \overline{Z}\sqrt{\overline{W}} + A\overline{W}$

for $\overline{W} > 0$, $\overline{R} > 0$, has the Jacobian $\sqrt{\overline{W}}$. We also have

$$WZ - R^2 = \overline{W}\overline{R}$$

and

$$\frac{1}{1 - \rho^2}\left(\frac{W}{\sigma_X{}^2} - \frac{2\rho}{\sigma_X\sigma_Y}R + \frac{Z}{\sigma_Y{}^2}\right) = \frac{\overline{W}}{\sigma_X{}^2} + \frac{\overline{R}}{\sigma_Y{}^2(1 - \rho^2)} + \frac{\overline{Z}^2}{\sigma_Y{}^2(1 - \rho^2)}$$

We thus obtain

$$f_2(W,Z,R)dWdZdR = K(WZ - R^2)^{(n-4)/2}$$

$$\times \exp\left[\frac{-n}{2(1 - \rho^2)}\left(\frac{W}{\sigma_X{}^2} - \frac{2\rho}{\sigma_X\sigma_Y}R + \frac{Z}{\sigma_Y{}^2}\right)\right]dWdZdR$$

$$= K(\overline{W}\overline{R})^{(n-4)/2}\exp\left\{-\frac{n}{2}\left[\frac{\overline{W}}{\sigma_X{}^2} + \frac{\overline{R}}{\sigma_Y{}^2(1 - \rho^2)}\right.\right.$$

$$\left.\left.+ \frac{\overline{Z}^2}{\sigma_Y{}^2(1 - \rho^2)}\right]\right\}\sqrt{\overline{W}}d\overline{W}d\overline{Z}d\overline{R}$$

$$= K\overline{W}^{(n-3)/2}e^{-n\overline{W}/2\sigma_X{}^2}\overline{R}^{(n-4)/2}$$

$$\times e^{-n\overline{R}/2\sigma_Y{}^2(1 - \rho^2)}e^{-n\overline{Z}^2/2\sigma_Y{}^2(1 - \rho^2)}d\overline{W}d\overline{Z}d\overline{R}$$

$$= \hat{f}(\overline{W},\overline{Z},\overline{R})d\overline{W}d\overline{Z}d\overline{R}\quad \text{for } \overline{W} > 0,\ \overline{R} > 0$$

This shows that the joint probability density of $\overline{W},\overline{Z},\overline{R}$ can be split into factors which depend only on $\overline{W}$, on $\overline{Z}$, on $\overline{R}$, respectively; hence the random variables $\overline{W},\overline{Z},\overline{R}$ are independent. In particular, the probability densities of $\overline{Z}$ and $\overline{R}$ are

$$g(\overline{Z}) = K_1 \cdot e^{-n\overline{Z}^2/2\sigma_Y{}^2(1 - \rho^2)}\qquad \text{for all values of } \overline{Z}$$

$$h(\overline{R}) = \begin{cases} K_2 \cdot \overline{R}^{(n-4)/2}e^{-n\overline{R}/2\sigma_Y{}^2(1 - \rho^2)} & \text{for } \overline{R} > 0 \\ 0 & \text{elsewhere} \end{cases}$$

that is $\sqrt{n}\overline{Z}\sigma_Y\sqrt{1 - \rho^2}$ has the distribution $N(0,1)$, and $n\overline{R}/\sigma_Y{}^2(1 - \rho^2)$ has the χ^2 distribution with $n - 2$ d.o.f. According to Theorem 12.2.3.5, the random variable

$$t_1 = \frac{\sqrt{n}\overline{Z}/\sigma_Y\sqrt{1 - \rho^2}}{\sqrt{[n\overline{R}/\sigma_Y{}^2(1 - \rho^2)]/(n - 2)}} = \sqrt{\frac{W(n - 2)}{Z(1 - r^2)}}(a - A)\ ,$$

has therefore the Student distribution with $n - 2$ d.o.f.

Frequently it is of interest to decide whether a regression coefficient is zero, that is, to test the hypothesis that, say, $A = 0$. Under this hypothesis, the random variable t_1 defined in Theorem 14.4.2 becomes

$$t_1 = \sqrt{W(n - 2)/Z(1 - r^2)}\ a = \sqrt{n - 2}\ (r/\sqrt{1 - r^2})$$

which is the variable discussed in 14.2.5 where we assumed $\rho = 0$. This is not surprising if one considers that the hypotheses $A = 0$ and $\rho = 0$ are equivalent.

TABLE 14.4.3

(1) X	(2) Y	(3) $X' = X - \tilde{X}$	(4) $Y' = Y - \tilde{Y}$	(5) X'^2	(6) Y'^2	(7) $X'Y'$
23.1	31.5	−0.9	−1.5	0.81	2.25	1.35
23.4	32.1	−0.6	−0.9	0.36	0.81	0.54
23.8	32.1	−0.2	−0.9	0.04	0.81	0.18
24.0	32.8	0	−0.2	0.00	0.04	
24.1	32.7	0.1	−0.3	0.01	0.09	−0.03
24.2	32.7	0.2	−0.3	0.04	0.09	−0.06
24.2	32.8	0.2	−0.2	0.04	0.04	−0.04
24.3	32.5	0.3	−0.5	0.09	0.25	−0.15
24.3	32.7	0.3	−0.3	0.09	0.09	−0.09
24.3	33.1	0.3	0.1	0.09	0.01	0.03
24.4	32.8	0.4	−0.2	0.16	0.04	−0.08
24.5	33.0	0.5		0.25		
24.5	33.2	0.5	0.2	0.25	0.04	0.10
24.7	33.1	0.7	0.1	0.49	0.01	0.07
25.1	33.7	1.1	0.7	1.21	0.49	0.77
25.6	33.9	1.6	0.9	2.56	0.81	1.44
		−1.7 6.2	−5.3 2.0			−0.45 4.48
		4.5	3.3	6.49	5.87	4.03

$$n = 16$$

$$\tilde{X} = 24 \qquad\qquad \tilde{Y} = 33$$

$$\sum X' = 4.5 \qquad\qquad \sum Y' = -3.3$$

$$\sum X'^2 = 6.49 \qquad\qquad \sum Y'^2 = 5.87$$

$$\sum X'Y' = 4.03$$

$$W = \frac{1}{n}\sum X'^2 - \left(\frac{1}{n}\sum X'\right)^2 = 0.3265, \qquad Z = \frac{1}{n}\sum Y'^2 - \left(\frac{1}{n}\sum Y'\right)^2 = 0.3243$$

$$R = \frac{1}{n}\sum X'Y' - \left(\frac{1}{n}\sum X'\right)\left(\frac{1}{n}\sum Y'\right) = 0.3099$$

$$r = \frac{R}{\sqrt{WZ}} = 0.9522$$

$$a = \frac{R}{W} = 0.9490$$

14.4.3. Example. In a living zoological species S the measurements X of one bone and Y of another bone are known to have a regression coefficient of Y on X equal to 0.75. For a fossil collection of fragments of 16 skeletons the measurements given in Table 14.4.3 were obtained. It is conjectured that those skeletons belonged to animals of the species S. We wish to test this conjecture on the 5% significance level by testing the hypothesis $A = 0.75$ on hand of the sample of Table 14.4.3. From the computations indicated in that table we obtain

$$t_1 = \sqrt{(0.3265)14/(0.3244)(1 - 0.9524^2)}(0.949 - 0.75) = 2.447$$

Since for 14 d.o.f. we have $P(|t| > 2.447) < 0.05$, we reject the hypothesis and conclude that the fossil bones did not belong to animals of the species S.

*14.5   Outline of Multivariate Correlation and Regression Theory

14.5.1. The problems and methods dealing with the study of dependence between coordinates of a two-dimensional random variable, as outlined in Chapter 9 and the preceding sections of Chapter 14, can be extended to the case of multidimensional random variables. We shall now give an extension to the n-dimensional case of the theory of Chapter 9, that is, the theory of the most important parameters used in describing and evaluating the various kinds of dependence which occur in general n-variate random variables. The sampling theory of various statistics for multivariate normal distributions, which would be a generalization to n dimensions of the contents of Sections 14.1–14.4, is much too voluminous a part of statistical theory to be included here.

14.5.2. Some Matrix Notations.   Let

$$\mathbf{X} = (X_{ij}), \quad i = 1, \cdots, r; \, j = 1, \cdots, s$$

be an $r \times s$ matrix whose elements are random variables. The probability distribution of $\mathbf{X}$ will be considered known when the joint probability distribution of all the X_{ij} (i.e., of an $r \times s$ dimensional random variable) is known.

We define the expectation of $\mathbf{X}$ as the $r \times s$ matrix whose elements are the marginal expectations of the X_{ij}, so that

$$E(\mathbf{X}) = \mathbf{X}_0 = (E(X_{ij})) \quad i = 1, \cdots, r; \, j = 1, \cdots, s$$

In particular if $\mathbf{X}$ is a vector, i.e., an $r \times 1$ matrix,

$$\mathbf{X} = \begin{pmatrix} X_1 \\ \cdot \\ \cdot \\ \cdot \\ X_r \end{pmatrix}$$

we have

$$E(\mathbf{X}) = \mathbf{X}_0 = \begin{pmatrix} E(X_1) \\ \cdot \\ \cdot \\ \cdot \\ E(X_r) \end{pmatrix}$$

which is again a vector, and

$$E(\mathbf{X}'\mathbf{X}) = E\left(\sum_{j=1}^{r} X_j^2\right) = \sum_{j=1}^{r} E(X_j^2)$$

which is a scalar, and

$$E(\mathbf{X}\mathbf{X}') = E(X_i X_j) = (EX_i X_j), \quad i = 1, \cdots, r; \; j = 1, \cdots, r$$

which is an $r \times r$ matrix.

Furthermore, for a random vector $\mathbf{X}$ we have

$$E[(\mathbf{X} - \mathbf{X}_0)'(\mathbf{X} - \mathbf{X}_0)] = E\sum_{j=1}^{r} (X_j - EX_j)^2 = \sum_{j=1}^{r} \sigma^2(X_j)$$

where $\sigma^2(X_j)$ is the marginal variance of X_j, and

$$E[(\mathbf{X} - \mathbf{X}_0)(\mathbf{X} - \mathbf{X}_0)'] = (E[(X_i - EX_i)(X_j - EX_i)])$$
$$= (\sigma_{X_i X_j}), \quad i = 1, \cdots, r; \; j = 1, \cdots, r$$

This last matrix has as its diagonal elements the variances $\sigma^2(X_1), \cdots, \sigma^2(X_r)$, and as non-diagonal elements the covariances $\sigma_{X_i X_j}$ of all pairs of different coordinates of the r-dimensional random variable represented by the random vector $\mathbf{X}$; it is called the *covariance matrix* of the r-dimensional random variable $\mathbf{X}$ and will be denoted by

$$\overset{+}{\sum}_{\mathbf{X}} = (\sigma_{X_i X_j}), \quad i = 1, \cdots, r; \; j = 1, \cdots, r$$

Obviously $\overset{+}{\sum}_{\mathbf{X}}$ is a symmetric matrix. We shall use the abbreviations

$$\sigma_{X_i X_j} = \sigma_{ij}$$
$$\sigma^2(X_i) = \sigma_i^2 = \sigma_{ii}$$

For the two-dimensional marginal distribution of every pair of coordinates (X_i, X_j) we have the *total correlation coefficient*

$$\rho_{X_i, X_j} = \frac{\sigma_{ij}}{\sigma_i \sigma_j} = \rho_{ij}$$

The matrix

$$\mathbf{P} = (\rho_{ij})$$

is called the *correlation matrix* of $\mathbf{X}$. Its diagonal elements are $\rho_{ii} = 1$, $i = 1, \cdots, r$, the matrix P is symmetrical, and we have

$$\mathbf{P} = (\rho_{ij}) = \left(\frac{\sigma_{ij}}{\sigma_i \sigma_j}\right)$$

Hence the determinant of P is

$$|P| = \frac{1}{\sigma_1^2 \cdots \sigma_r^2} |\Sigma|$$

and the cofactors are

$$P_{ik} = \frac{\sigma_i \sigma_k}{\sigma_1^2 \cdots \sigma_r^2} \Sigma_{ik}$$

where Σ_{ik} is the corresponding cofactor of Σ. We shall write $|\Sigma|$ for the determinant of the matrix Σ, whereas Σ_{ik} will be used to denote a cofactor, i.e., already a determinant with the proper sign.

We note that every covariance matrix is positive semi-definite. For let

$$Y = X - X_0$$

then

$$\Sigma_X = E(YY')$$

and the quadratic form with the coefficient matrix Σ_X is

$$Q(s) = s' \Sigma_X s = s'E(YY')s = E(s'YY's)$$
$$= E[(s'Y)(s'Y)']$$

But $s'Y$ is a scalar, i.e., a one-dimensional random variable, hence $(s'Y)(s'Y)' = (s'Y)^2$, and this is a non-negative one-dimensional random variable so that $Q(s) = E[(s'Y)^2] \geq 0$ for all values of s.

14.5.3. Regression Surface and Least Square Regression Plane.
We consider a p-dimensional random variable

$$X = \begin{pmatrix} X_1 \\ \cdot \\ \cdot \\ \cdot \\ X_p \end{pmatrix}$$

with a *positive definite* covariance matrix

$$\Sigma = (\sigma_{ij}), \quad i = 1, \cdots, p; \ j = 1, \cdots, p$$

The hyper-surface described by

(14.5.3.1) $x_1 = E(X_1 \mid x_2, \cdots, x_p) = \lambda(x_2, \cdots, x_p)$

is called the *regression surface of X_1 on $X_2, \cdots, X_p$.*

For simplicity of notations we will assume from now on

$$E(X_1) = E(X_2) = \cdots = E(X_p) = 0$$

This can be done wthout loss of generality, since we have only to replace X_i by $X_i - E(X_i)$ in the following arguments to obtain the general case.

We now consider hyperplanes in the X space of the form

(14.5.3.2) $x_1 = \beta_2 x_2 + \beta_3 x_3 + \cdots + \beta_p x_p = L(x_2, \cdots, x_p; \beta_2, \cdots, \beta_p)$

Among these hyperplanes we determine that one which minimizes the expression

(14.5.3.3) $D(\beta_2,\cdots,\beta_p) = E[X_1 - L(X_2,\cdots,X_p; \beta_2,\cdots,\beta_p)]^2$

Since D can be shown to be a differentiable function of the β's which assumes its minimum at a finite point of the $(\beta_2,\cdots,\beta_p)$ space, this minimum is found by solving the system of equations

(14.5.3.4) $$\frac{\partial D}{\partial \beta_j} = 0, \quad j = 2,\cdots,p$$

The solutions of equations (14.5.3.4) are traditionally denoted by

$$\beta_{12.34\cdots p}, \beta_{13.24\cdots p}, \cdots, \beta_{1p.23\cdots p-1}$$

and the corresponding hyperplane

(14.5.3.5) $x_1 = \beta_{12.34\cdots p}x_2 + \beta_{13.24\cdots p}x_3 + \cdots + \beta_{1p.23\cdots p-1}x_p$

is called the *least square regression plane of X_1 on $X_2, \cdots, X_p$*

Clearly X_1 has been singled out here only for the purposes of exposition, and all arguments can be repeated by singling out any coordinate X_i and studying its regression on $X_1,\cdots, X_{i-1}, X_{i+1},\cdots, X_p$. The least square regression plane corresponding to (14.5.3.5) will then have an equation

$$x_i = \beta_{i1.23\cdots(i-1),(i+1)\cdots p}x_1 + \cdots + \beta_{ip.12\cdots(i-1),(i+1),\cdots(p-1)}x_p$$

with the coefficient of x_j, for $j = 1, 2, \cdots, i-1, i+1, \cdots, p$ denoted by $\beta_{ij.1,2,\cdots p}$, where in the subscripts after the dot the values i and j are omitted. This coefficient is called the *least square regression coefficient of X_i on X_j*, and whenever there is no danger of misunderstanding we shall abbreviate the notation by writing

$$\beta_{ij.12\cdots p} = \beta_{ij}$$

The equations (14.5.3.4) can be written explicitly in the form

(14.5.3.6) $-\dfrac{1}{2}\dfrac{\partial D}{\partial \beta_{1j}} = E(X_1 X_j) - \beta_{12}E(X_2 X_j) - \cdots - \beta_{1j}E(X_j^2) - \cdots$

$$- \beta_{1p}E(X_p X_j) = 0 \quad \text{for } j = 2, \cdots, p$$

or

(14.5.3.6.1)
$$\sigma_{22}\beta_{12} + \sigma_{23}\beta_{13} + \cdots + \sigma_{2p}\beta_{1p} = \sigma_{21}$$
$$\sigma_{32}\beta_{12} + \sigma_{33}\beta_{13} + \cdots + \sigma_{3p}\beta_{1p} = \sigma_{31}$$
$$\vdots$$
$$\sigma_{p2}\beta_{12} + \sigma_{p3}\beta_{13} + \cdots + \sigma_{pp}\beta_{1p} = \sigma_{p1}$$

Since the determinant of (14.5.3.6.1) is positive (Σ being positive definite and our determinant the principal minor Σ_{11}), (14.5.3.6.1) has the unique solution

$$(14.5.3.6.2) \qquad \beta_{1k} = \frac{-\Sigma_{1k}}{\Sigma_{11}} = -\frac{\sigma_1}{\sigma_k} \cdot \frac{P_{1k}}{P_{11}}$$

By an analogous argument one obtains for the least square regression coefficient of X_i on X_k

$$(14.5.3.6.3) \qquad \beta_{ik.12\cdots p} = \beta_{ik} = -\frac{\Sigma_{ik}}{\Sigma_{ii}} = -\frac{\sigma_i}{\sigma_k} \cdot \frac{P_{ik}}{P_{ii}}$$

It may be pointed out once again that among the subscripts of $\beta_{ik.12\cdots p}$ there are two preceding the dot, also called *primary subscripts*, which do not appear among those following the dot, the so-called *secondary subscripts*. The order of the primary subscripts is of material importance, while the secondary subscripts can be permuted without affecting the meaning of the regression coefficient.

14.5.4. Residuals. Residual Variance

14.5.4.1. When a value of the p-dimensionl random variable $\mathbf{X}$ is observed, the difference between its first coordinate X_1 and the value obtained by substituting in the right side of (14.5.3.5) the observed values of $X_2, \cdots, X_p$ is denoted by

$$(14.5.4.1.1) \qquad X_{1.23\cdots p} = X_1 - \beta_{12}X_2 - \cdots - \beta_{1p}X_p$$

and is called the *residual of X_1 with respect to $X_2, \cdots, X_p$*. Clearly the residual $X_{1.23\cdots p}$ is a one-dimensional random variable, and it is of some interest to study its expectation, variance, and dependence on other random variables.

14.5.4.2. Theorem. The residual is uncorrelated with any one of the subtracted variables (i.e., coordinates of $\mathbf{X}$ whose subscript appears among the secondary subscripts of the residual).

Proof. According to (14.5.3.6) we have for any $j \neq 1$

$$E(X_j X_{1.23\cdots p}) = E(X_1 X_j) - \beta_{12}E(X_2 X_j) - \cdots - \beta_{1j}E(X_j^2) - \cdots$$
$$- \beta_{1p}E(X_p X_j) = 0$$

hence, $\sigma(X_j, X_{1.23\cdots p}) = 0$.

14.5.4.3. Introducing the values (14.5.3.6.2) for the regression coefficients, one obtains for the residual

$$(14.5.4.3.1) \qquad X_{1.23\cdots p} = \frac{1}{\Sigma_{11}} \sum_{j=1}^{p} \Sigma_{1j} X_j$$

and concludes immediately

(14.5.4.3.2)
$$E(X_{1.23\cdots p}) = 0$$

(14.5.4.3.3)
$$E(X_1 X_{1.23\cdots p}) = \frac{|\overset{+}{\Sigma}|}{\overset{+}{\Sigma}_{11}}$$

The variance of the residual, also called the *residual variance*, is therefore given by (14.5.4.3.3); the traditional notation for the residual variance and its value are

(14.5.4.3.4)
$$\sigma^2_{1.23\cdots p} = \frac{|\overset{+}{\Sigma}|}{\overset{+}{\Sigma}_{11}} = \sigma_1{}^2 \frac{|P|}{P_{11}}$$

In this section again X_1 was singled out among the p coordinates of **X**, and everything could be repeated by choosing X_j instead of X_1.

14.5.5. Least Square Regression on a Subset of Coordinates

14.5.5.1.   In a p-dimensional random variable

$$\mathbf{X} = \begin{pmatrix} X_1 \\ X_2 \\ \cdot \\ \cdot \\ \cdot \\ X_p \end{pmatrix}$$

one may select a number $k < p$ of coordinates, $X_1, X_2, \cdots, X_k$, say, and consider the marginal probability distribution of $(X_1, \cdots, X_k)$. One then can obtain a least square regression plane of X_1 on $X_2, \cdots, X_k$, which may be written

(14.5.5.1.1) $$x_1 = \beta_{12.3\cdots k} x_2 + \cdots + \beta_{1k.2\cdots k-1} x_k$$

The corresponding residual is the one-dimensional random variable

(14.5.5.1.2) $$X_{1.23\cdots k} = X_1 - \beta_{12.3\cdots k} X_2 - \cdots - \beta_{1k.2\cdots k-1} X_k$$

All arguments and statements made about the original p-dimensional random variable may be repeated for each selection of the primary subscript, which is 1 in (14.5.5.1.2), and the $k - 1$ secondary subscripts which in (14.5.5.1.2) are $2, \cdots, k$.

14.5.5.2. Theorem.   Any two residuals are uncorrelated (i.e., their covariance is zero) if the primary and secondary subscripts of the one are all among the secondary subscripts of the other.

Proof. Let $X_{i.(i+1)(i+2)\cdots k}$ and $X_{h.\cdots i(i+1)\cdots l}$ be two residuals with $h < i$, $l \geq k$, so that all (primary and secondary) subscripts of $X_{i.\cdots}$ are among the secondary subscripts of $X_{h.\cdots}$. Then

$$X_{i.\cdots} = X_i - \sum_{j=i+1}^{k} \alpha_j X_j$$

$$X_{h.\cdots} = X_h - (\gamma_{h+1}X_{h+1} + \cdots + \gamma_j X_j + \cdots + \gamma_k X_k + \cdots + \gamma_l X_l)$$

so that each coordinate in the right-hand expression for $X_{i.\cdots}$ is one of the subtracted coordinates in the expression for $X_{h.\cdots}$; hence the residuals have covariance zero by 14.5.4.2.

14.5.5.3. Theorem. The following covariances are equal:

(14.5.5.3.1) $\sigma(X_{1.34\cdots p}, X_{2.34\cdots p}) = \sigma(X_1, X_{2.34\cdots p}) = \sigma(X_{1.34\cdots p}, X_2)$

Proof.

$$\sigma(X_{1.34\cdots p}, X_{2.34\cdots p}) = E\left\{\left(X_1 - \sum_{j=3}^{p} \alpha_j X_j\right) X_{2.34\cdots p}\right\}$$

$$= E(X_1 X_{2.34\cdots p}) - \sum_{j=3}^{p} \alpha_j E(X_j X_{2.34\cdots p})$$

$$= \sigma(X_1, X_{2.34\cdots p}) - \sum_{j=3}^{p} \alpha_j \sigma(X_j, X_{2.34\cdots p})$$

$$= \sigma(X_1, X_{2.3\cdots p})$$

14.5.5.4. The regression coefficients (14.5.3.6.2), (14.5.3.6.3) can also be written in the form

(14.5.5.4.1) $$\beta_{12.34\cdots p} = \frac{\sigma(X_{1.34\cdots p}, X_{2.34\cdots p})}{\sigma^2(X_{2.34\cdots p})}$$

To see this we observe that by 14.5.4.2 and 14.5.5.3 we have

$$0 = \sigma(X_{2.34\cdots p}, X_{1.23\cdots p})$$
$$= E\{X_{2.34\cdots p}[X_1 - \beta_{12.34\cdots p}X_2 - \beta_{13.24\cdots p}X_3 - \cdots]$$
$$= \sigma(X_{1.34\cdots p}, X_{2.34\cdots p}) - \beta_{12.34\cdots p}\sigma^2(X_{2.34\cdots p})$$

14.5.5.5. Theorem. For any integer r, $1 \leq r \leq p$, we have the identity

(14.5.5.5.1) $X_r = X_{r.12\cdots(r-1)} + \beta_{r,r-1.12\cdots r-2}X_{r-1.12\cdots r-2}$
$$+ \cdots + \beta_{r,r-s.12\cdots r-s-1}X_{r-s.12\cdots r-s-1} + \cdots + \beta_{r1}X_1$$

Proof. To determine constants α_r, $\alpha_{r-1}, \cdots, \alpha_{r-s}, \cdots, \alpha_1$ so that the identity holds

$$X_r = \sum_{s=0}^{r-1} \alpha_{r-s} X_{r-s.12\cdots r-s-1}$$

we multiply this equality by $X_{r-t.12\cdots r-t-1}$, for fixed integer t and take expectations of both sides. By 14.5.5.3 and 14.5.5.1 we obtain

$$\sigma(X_{r.12\cdots r-t-1}, X_{r-t.12\cdots r-t-1}) = \sum_{s=0}^{r-1} \alpha_{r-s}\sigma(X_{r-s.12\cdots r-s-1}, X_{r-t.12\cdots r-t-1})$$

$$= \alpha_{r-t}\sigma^2(X_{r-t.12\cdots r-t-1}),$$

hence by (14.5.5.4)

$$\alpha_{r-t} = \frac{\sigma(X_{r.12\cdots r-t-1}, X_{r-t.12\cdots r-t-1})}{\sigma^2(X_{r-t.12\cdots r-t-1})}$$

$$= \beta_{r.r-t.12\cdots r-t-1}$$

14.5.6. Partial Correlation. In studying the correlation between two coordinates X_1 and X_2, say, of a p-dimensional random variable one considers, besides the total correlation coefficient ρ_{12}, the correlation coefficient between the residuals $X_{1.34\cdots p}$ and $X_{2.34\cdots p}$, called the *partial correlation coefficient* and denoted by

$$\rho_{12.34\cdots p} = \frac{\sigma(X_{1.34\cdots p}, X_{2.34\cdots p})}{\sqrt{\sigma^2(X_{1.34\cdots p})\sigma^2(X_{2.34\cdots p})}}$$

It can be shown that all partial correlation coefficients can be expressed in terms of the total correlation coefficients. For explicit formulas the reader is referred, for example, to Cramér, Section 23.4.*

14.5.7. Multiple Correlation. It can be shown that of all linear combinations of $X_2, \cdots, X_p$ the least square regression plane of X_1 on $X_2, \cdots, X_p$ yields the largest correlation coefficient with X_1. This correlation coefficient is called the *multiple correlation coefficient* of X_1 and $X_2, \cdots, X_p$, and is denoted by $\rho_{1(2,3,\cdots,p)}$, so that

$$\rho_{1(2,3,\cdots,p)} = \frac{\sigma\left(X_1, \sum_{r=2}^{p} \beta_{1r}X_r\right)}{\sqrt{\sigma^2(X_1)\sigma^2\left(\sum_{r=2}^{p} \beta_{1r}X_r\right)}}$$

A more detailed discussion may be found in Cramér, Section 23.5.*

EXERCISES

14.1. Consider the probability density $h_0(r)$ of the sample correlation coefficient r, for $\rho = 0$ and $n = 3$. What is the formula for $h_0(r)$ in this case (evaluate the

---

* H. Cramér, *Mathematical Methods of Statistics*, Princeton University Press, Princeton, N.J., 1946.

constant factor)? Does $h_0(r)$ have a maximum or a minimum? Sketch the curve $y = h_0(r)$.

14.2. For two physiological indices X, Y, the correlation coefficient in a sample of 33 normal individuals was 0.808. In another sample of 56 individuals suffering from a disease, this correlation coefficient is 0.360. It is claimed that this disease has no effect on the correlation coefficient. Is this contention tenable at the 5% significance level?

14.3. R. A. Fisher reports that, for the twenty years 1885–1904, the mean wheat yield of eastern England was found to have a correlation coefficient of -0.629 with the autumn rainfall. Is this correlation significant on the 1% level?

14.4. The following table contains the ages of husband (X) and wife (Y) of twenty couples selected at random. Test the hypothesis that X and Y are independent. State all assumptions.

X	22 24 26 26 27 27 28 28 29 30 30 30 31 32 33 34 35 35 36 37
Y	18 20 20 24 22 24 27 24 21 25 29 32 27 27 30 27 30 31 30 32

14.5. Let

$$\mathbf{x} = \begin{pmatrix} X_1 \\ \cdot \\ \cdot \\ \cdot \\ X_p \end{pmatrix}$$

be a p-dimensional random variable with expectations

$$\mu = \begin{pmatrix} \mu_1 \\ \cdot \\ \cdot \\ \cdot \\ \mu_p \end{pmatrix}$$

and covariance matrix

$$\sum = (\sigma_{ik})$$

Consider a linear function

$$Y = \sum_{i=1}^{p} a_i X_i$$

What are the expectation and the variance of Y?

14.6. With the notations of Exercise 14.5, find the correlation coefficient between two linear functions

$$Y = \sum_{i=1}^{p} a_i X_i \quad \text{and} \quad Z = \sum_{i=1}^{p} b_i X_i$$

14.7. Consider the random variables $X_1, X_2, \cdots, X_m, Y_1, Y_2, \cdots, Y_n$, all with expectation zero. The correlation coefficient between any two of the random variables $X_1, X_2, \cdots, X_m$ is $\rho_{X_j X_k} = \rho_1$, for $j \neq k$; the correlation coefficient between any two of the random variables $Y_1, Y_2, \cdots, Y_n$ is $\rho_{Y_j Y_k} = \rho_2$, for $j \neq k$; the correlation coefficient between any of the X's and any of the Y's is $\rho_{X_j Y_k} = \rho^*$, for $j = 1, \cdots, m$ and $k = 1, \cdots, n$. All the variances of the X's are equal: $\sigma^2(X_j) = \sigma_1^2$, $j = 1, \cdots, m$, and all the variances of the Y's are equal: $\sigma^2(Y_k) = \sigma_2^2$, $k = 1, \cdots, n$. Let

$$\bar{X} = \frac{1}{m} \sum_{j=1}^{m} X_j, \qquad \bar{Y} = \frac{1}{n} \sum_{k=1}^{n} Y_k$$

Find the correlation coefficient between $\bar{X}$ and $\bar{Y}$.

The x^2 Test
of Goodness
# of Fit

15.1 χ^2 as an Approximation to the Multinomial Probability Distribution

Let X be a random variable of any number of dimensions, and $E_1, E_2, \cdots,$ E_k be mutually exclusive and exhaustive events for X, so that

$$P(E_1) + P(E_2) + \cdots + P(E_k) = 1$$

We abbreviate

$$P(E_j) = p_j \quad \text{for } j = 1, 2, \cdots, k$$

15.1.1. Theorem. The probability that in n independent determinations of X the event E_1 will occur exactly m_1 times, E_2 exactly m_2 times, $\cdots$, E_k exactly m_k times, with

$$m_1 + m_2 + \cdots + m_k = n$$

is equal to

(15.1.1.1) $\quad p_n(m_1, m_2, \cdots, m_k) = \dfrac{n!}{m_1!\, m_2! \cdots m_k!}\, p_1{}^{m_1} p_2{}^{m_2} \cdots p_k{}^{m_k}$

Proof. (by induction). For $k = 2$ and any integer $n > 0$ our theorem reduces to Theorem 3.7.1 (Bernoulli's theorem). We assume that it is true for $k < K$ and any integer $n > 0$. To evaluate $P_n(m_1, m_2, \cdots, m_K)$ we make the (clearly immaterial) assumption that the n determinations of X are obtained in succession so that there is a 1st, 2nd, $\cdots$, nth outcome; we then have $P_n(m_1, m_2, \cdots, m_{K-1}, m_K) = $ (probability that E_K occurs in some m_K determinations) $\cdot$ (probability that in the remaining $n - m_K$ determinations E_1

occurs m_1 times, E_2 occurs m_2 times, $\cdots$, E_{K-1} occurs m_{K-1} times)

$$= \frac{n!}{m_K!\,(n-m_K)!}\,p_K{}^{m_K}P_{n-m_K}(m_1,\cdots,m_{K-1})$$

$$= \frac{n!}{m_K!\,(n-m_K)!}\,p_K{}^{m_K}\frac{(n-m_K)!}{m_1!\,m_2!\cdots m_{K-1}!}\,p_1{}^{m_1}p_2{}^{m_2}\cdots p_{K-1}^{m_{K-1}}$$

$$= \frac{n!}{m_1!\,m_1!\cdots m_{K-1}!\,m_K!}\,p_1{}^{m_1}p_2{}^{m_2}\cdots p_{K-1}^{m_{K-1}}p_K{}^{m_K}$$

The probability distribution (15.1.1.1) is known as the *multinomial distribution*.

We shall now derive an approximate expression for $p_n(m_1,m_2,\cdots,m_k)$ analogous to the deMoivre-Laplace approximation (7.5.1.6) for the binomial probability. Let us first assume n and all $m_j (j = 1,2,\cdots,k)$ so large that all factorials in (15.1.1) may be replaced by the corresponding values of Stirling's formula (7.5.1.1). We then obtain the approximation

(15.1.1.2)

$$P_n(m_1,\cdots,m_k) \sim \frac{(2\pi)^{1/2}n^{n+1/2}e^{-n}}{(2\pi)^{k/2}m_1^{m_1+1/2}\cdots m_k^{m_k+1/2}e^{-(m_1+\cdots+m_k)}}\,p_1{}^{m_1}\cdots p_k{}^{m_k}$$

$$= \frac{(np_1/m_1)^{m_1+1/2}\cdots(np_k/m_k)^{m_k+1/2}}{(2\pi n)^{(k-1)/2}(p_1\cdots p_k)^{1/2}}$$

If we consider the simple alternative, E_j with probability p_j, non-E_j with probability $1 - p_j$, and interpret our n trials as an n-fold repetition of this alternative, we obtain

$$E(m_j) = np_j, \qquad \sigma^2(m_j) = np_j(1-p_j) \quad \text{for } j = 1, 2, \cdots, k$$

The quantities in the right-hand term of (15.1.1.2) have accordingly a simple intuitive meaning: m_j is the observed number of outcomes E_j, np_j is the expected number of such outcomes. The normalized random variable corresponding to m_j is

(15.1.1.3)
$$t_j = \frac{m_j - np_j}{\sqrt{np_j(1 - p_j)}} = \frac{m_j - np_j}{\sigma_j}$$

where σ_j is an abbreviation for $\sigma(m_j)$. Expressing m_j in terms of t_j in (15.1.1.2) we find

(15.1.1.4) $P_n(m_1,\cdots,m_k) \sim \dfrac{\left(1+\dfrac{t_1\sigma_1}{np_1}\right)^{-t_1\sigma_1-np_1-1/2}\cdots\left(1+\dfrac{t_k\sigma_k}{np_k}\right)^{-t_k\sigma_k-np_k-1/2}}{2\pi n^{(k-1)/2}(p_1\cdots p_k)^{1/2}}$

$$= \frac{U}{L}$$

The natural logarithm of the numerator may be written in the form

$$\ln U = -\sum_{j=1}^{k}(t_j\sigma_j + np_j + \tfrac{1}{2})\,\ln\left(1 + \frac{t_j\sigma_j}{np_j}\right)$$

$$= -\sum_{j=1}^{k}(t_j\sigma_j + np_j + \tfrac{1}{2})\sum_{l=1}^{\infty}\frac{(-1)^{l+1}}{l}\left(\frac{t_j\sigma_j}{np_j}\right)^l$$

Here $\ln[1 + (t_j\sigma_j/np_j)]$ was expanded into a power series whose convergence is assured for all m_j for which $|t_j\sigma_j/np_j| < 1$. Replacing σ_j by its value $\sqrt{np_j(1 - p_j)}$ and ordering by decreasing powers of n gives

(15.1.1.4.1) $\ln U = -\sum_{j=1}^{k} t_j \sqrt{p_j(1 - p_j)}\,n^{1/2} + \sum_{j=1}^{k}(\tfrac{1}{2}t_j{}^2 q_j - q_j t_j{}^2) + R(n)$

where $R(n)$ contains only terms with $n^{-1/2}, n^{-1}, n^{-3/2}, \cdots$. Since

$$\sum_{j-1}^{k} t_j \sqrt{p_j(1 - p_j)}\,n^{1/2} = \sum_{j=1}^{k}(m_j - np_j) = \sum_{j=1}^{k}m_j - n\sum_{j=1}^{k}p_j = 0$$

and

$$\sum_{j=1}^{k}(\tfrac{1}{2}t_j{}^2 q_j - q_j t_j{}^2) = -\tfrac{1}{2}\sum_{j=1}^{\lambda}\frac{(m_j - np_j)^0}{np_j}$$

we rewrite (15.1.1.4) in the form

(15.1.1.5) $P_n(m_1,\cdots,m_k) \sim C_n \exp\left[-\tfrac{1}{2}\sum_{j=1}^{k}\frac{(m_j - np_j)^2}{np_j}\right]$

$$= C_n e^{-\chi^2/2}$$

where

(15.1.1.6) $\chi^2 = \sum_{j=1}^{k}\frac{(m_j - np_j)^2}{np_j}$

and C_n is a constant depending only on n:

$$C_n = (2\pi n)^{(1-k)/2}(p_1 p_2 \cdots p_k)^{-1/2}$$

It follows from the preceding derivation that (15.1.1.5) is a good approximation if all the expected values np_j are sufficiently large.

It can be seen that, if the approximation (15.1.1.5) is applicable, a set of values $m_1, m_2, \cdots, m_k$ has smaller probability if the corresponding quantity χ^2 in (15.1.1.6) is large, and has greater probability if the χ^2 is small. Now χ^2 is small if and only if all m_j are close to their mathematical expectations np_j. Hence the magnitude of χ^2 appears to be a reasonably good indicator of whether or not all m_j are close to their expected values and, at the same time, whether they are more or less likely to occur.

15.2 Probability Distribution of χ^2

15.2.1.   The quantity χ^2 in (15.1.1.6) is, for given n, a discrete one-dimensional random variable. The set of all its possible values is obtained by letting

$m_1, m_2, \cdots, m_k$ go through all non-negative integer values such that

$$\sum_{j=1}^{k} m_j = n$$

For given n the probability distribution of χ^2 is too complicated to be of practical use except for small values of k and n when it can be determined explicitly. We shall see, however, that for $n \to +\infty$ this probability distribution has a simple limit. For a finite integer n, we consider the random variables

(15.2.1.1) $X_j = \dfrac{m_j - np_j}{\sqrt{n}} = \sqrt{p_j(1-p_j)}\, t_j, \quad \text{for } j = 1, 2, \cdots, k$

where the random variables t_j are defined in (15.1.1.3). One clearly has

(15.2.1.2) $\sum_{j=1}^{k} X_j = 0$

and hence

$$
\begin{aligned}
\chi^2 &= \sum_{j=1}^{k} \frac{X_j^2}{p_j} = \sum_{j=1}^{k-1} \frac{X_j^2}{p_j} + \frac{1}{p_k}\left(\sum_{j=1}^{k-1} X_j\right)^2 \\
&= \sum_{j=1}^{k-1} \frac{X_j^2}{p_j} + \sum_{j=1}^{k-1} \frac{X_j^2}{p_k} + \frac{1}{p_k}\sum_{\substack{r=1 \\ r \neq s}}^{k-1}\sum_{s=1}^{k-1} X_r X_s \\
&= \sum_{r=1}^{k-1}\sum_{s=1}^{k-1} A_{rs} X_r X_s
\end{aligned}
$$

where

$$
A_{rs} = \begin{cases} \dfrac{1}{p_r} + \dfrac{1}{p_k} & \text{if } r = s \\[2mm] \dfrac{1}{p_k} & \text{if } r \neq s \end{cases}
$$

The characteristic function corresponding to χ^2 is

$$C_{\chi^2}(t) = \sum_{m_1 + \cdots + m_k = n} e^{it\chi^2} P_n(m_1, \cdots, m_k)$$

By introducing in (15.1.1.5) the correction terms $S(n)$ from Stirling's formula and $R(n)$ from (15.1.1.4.1), we have

$$P_k(m_1, \cdots, m_k) = (2\pi n)^{(1-k)/2}(p_1 p_2 \cdots p_k)^{-1/2} e^{-\chi^2/2 + R(n) + S(n)}$$

where $T(n) = R(n) + S(n)$ tends to zero with $n \to \infty$, uniformly with regard to $m_1, \cdots, m_k$. We obtain, therefore,

$$
\begin{aligned}
C_{\chi^2}(t) &= (2\pi n)^{(1-k)/2}(p_1 p_2 \cdots p_k)^{-1/2} \sum_{m_1 + \cdots + m_k = n} e^{[it - (1/2)]\chi^2 + T(n)} \\
&= (2\pi)^{(1-k)/2}(p_1 p_2 \cdots p_k)^{-1/2} \sum_{m_1 + \cdots + m_k = n} \exp\left[(it - \tfrac{1}{2})\sum_{r=1}^{k-1}\sum_{s=1}^{k-1} A_{rs} X_r X_s\right] \\
&\quad \times \left(\frac{1}{\sqrt{n}}\right)^{k-1} e^{T(n)}
\end{aligned}
$$

As m_j changes from one of its possible values to the next, X_j in (15.2.1.1) changes by

$$\Delta X_j = \frac{1}{\sqrt{n}}$$

We may, therefore, write

$$C_{\chi^2}(t) = (2\pi)^{(1-k)/2}(p_1 \cdots p_k)^{-1/2} \sum_{m_1 + \cdots + m_k = n} \exp\left[(it - \tfrac{1}{2})\sum_{r=1}^{k-1}\sum_{s=1}^{k-1} A_{rs}X_r X_s\right]$$

$$\times \Delta X_1 \cdots \Delta X_{k-1} e^{T(n)}$$

As $n \to \infty$, this tends to the limit

$$(2\pi)^{(1-k)/2}(p_1 \cdots p_k)^{-1/2} \int_{-\infty}^{+\infty} \cdots \int_{-\infty}^{+\infty} \exp\left[(it - \tfrac{1}{2})\sum_{r=1}^{k-1}\sum_{s=1}^{k-1} A_{rs}X_r X_s\right]$$

$$\times dX_1 \cdots dX_{k-1}$$

The determinant $|A_{rs}|$ is equal to $1/(p_1 \cdots p_k)$, as can be shown by simple induction. The form

$$\sum_{r=1}^{k-1}\sum_{s=1}^{k-1} A_{rs}X_r X_s$$

is positive definite since it is identically equal to χ^2. Hence the real linear transformation of 8.2.2 may be applied. The Jacobian is 1 and using the identity

$$\int_{-\infty}^{+\infty} e^{-ys^2} ds = \sqrt{\frac{\pi}{y}}$$

and by Theorem 8.2.2 we obtain

$$\int_{-\infty}^{+\infty} \cdots \int_{-\infty}^{+\infty} \exp\left[(it - \tfrac{1}{2})\sum_{r=1}^{k-1}\sum_{s=1}^{k-1} A_{rs}X_r X_s\right]dX_1 \cdots dX_{k-1}$$

$$= \int_{-\infty}^{+\infty} \cdots \int_{-\infty}^{+\infty} \exp\left[(it - \tfrac{1}{2})\sum_{r=1}^{k-1} C_r Z_r^2\right]dZ_1 \cdots dZ_{k-1}$$

$$= \prod_{r=1}^{k-1} \int_{-\infty}^{+\infty} \exp\left[(it - \tfrac{1}{2})C_r Z_r^2\right]dZ_r = \prod_{r=1}^{k-1}\sqrt{\frac{\pi}{(\tfrac{1}{2} - it)C_r}}$$

$$= (2\pi)^{(k-1)/2}(1 - 2ti)^{-(k-1)/2}\frac{1}{\sqrt{|A_{rs}|}}$$

$$= (2\pi)^{(k-1)/2}(1 - 2ti)^{-(k-1)/2}\sqrt{p_1 \cdots p_k}$$

From this we conclude

$$\lim_{n\to\infty} C_{\chi^2}(t) = (1 - 2ti)^{-(k-1)/2}$$

According to Theorem 10.3.3 this is the characteristic function corresponding to a random variable with the probability distribution (10.3.2.5) for $k - 1$

d.o.f., and hence we conclude by virtue of Theorem 7.5.4 that the d.f. of χ^2 converges for $n \to \infty$ to the d.f. of a χ^2 variable with $k - 1$ d.o.f.

We summarize this result.

15.2.2. Theorem.   For χ^2 defined by (15.1.1.6) we have

(15.2.2.1)

$$\lim_{n \to \infty} P(\chi^2 < u) = \frac{1}{2^{(k-1)/2}\Gamma[(k-1)/2]} \int_0^u U^{[(k-1)/2]-1} e^{-U/2} dU \quad \text{for } u > 0$$

The importance of this theorem is due to the fact that the right-hand side depends only on the number k of the events $E_1, \cdots, E_k$ described in the beginning of 15.1, but does not depend on $P(E_1), \cdots, P(E_k)$. General estimates of the speed of the convergence in (15.2.2.1) are not available, but numerical computations indicate that the right-hand side is a good approximation to $P(\chi^2 < u)$ as soon as $np_j \geq 10$ for all j.

Values of the right-hand side of (15.2.2.1) have been tabulated for different k and u; some of these values are given in Table III at the end of the book.

15.3 χ^2 Test of a Simple Hypothesis

15.3.1.   If a random variable X and events $E_1, E_2, \cdots, E_k$ for this random variable are studied, we may wish to test the hypothesis H that the probabilities $P(E_j)$, for $j = 1, 2, \cdots, k$, have definite numerical values:

$$P(E_j) = p_j \quad \text{for } j = 1, 2, \cdots, k$$

Let a sample of size n be given and let m_j be the number of outcomes E_j in that sample. The quantity χ^2 in (15.1.1.6), as has been pointed out in 15.1, is small if the sample agrees well with H, large if there is considerable disagreement. We, shall, therefore, test H by computing χ^2 from the sample and, if

TABLE 15.3.2

(1) j, Number of Points	(2) m_j, Observed Frequency	(3) np_j, Expected Frequency	(4) $\dfrac{(m_j - np_j)^2}{np_j}$
1	16	17	0.06
2	17	17	0.00
3	19	17	0.24
4	18	17	0.06
5	9	17	3.76
6	23	17	2.12
Total	102	102	6.24

the value obtained is $\chi_{(s)}^2$, we find from Table III the probability $P(\chi^2 \geq \chi_{(s)}^2)$ for $k - 1$ degrees of freedom. If this probability is less than a preassigned level of significance α, we reject H.

15.3.2. Example. We wish to test, on the significance level $\alpha = 0.10$, the hypothesis that a die is honest. We roll it 102 times and obtain the results listed in columns (1) and (2) of Table 15.3.2. Our events are the different faces of the die, the hypothesis H is: $P(1) = P(2) = P(3) = P(4) = P(5) = P(6) = \frac{1}{6}$, and we have $k = 6$, $n = 102$. From the computations of Table 15.3.2 we obtain $\chi^2 = 6.24$, and find from Table III that $P(\chi^2 \geq 6.24) > 0.20$ for 5 d.o.f. Since this is >0.10, we conclude that there is no reason to doubt the correctness of the die.

15.3.3. Example. For a certain survey, 6000 families were taken at random from all the families in the United States. We wish to check up on the randomness of this sample. For this purpose we compare the distribution of the size of families in the sample with the distribution of the size of families in the United States known from census data.

Under the assumption that in view of the large total population the single drawings without replacements may be considered practically independent, our hypothesis is that the probability of drawing for the sample a family of a given size is equal to the fraction of families of this size in the total population. The computations of Table 15.3.3 yield $\chi^2 = 41.75$ for $k = 4$, and we find from Table III that $P(\chi^2 \geq 41.75) < 0.001$ for 3 d.o.f. Thus at the 0.001 significance level we reject the hypothesis that the sample was the result of random drawings from the total 29,904,663 families.

TABLE 15.3.3

(1)	(2)	(3)	(4)	(5)	(6)
Family Size, Persons	Number of Families in Total Population from Census Data	p_j, Fraction of Families in Total Population	m_j, Number of Families in Sample	$6000\,p_j = e_j$	$\dfrac{(m_j - e_j)^2}{e_j}$
1–2	9,340,298	0.312	2,047	1,872	16.36
3–4	11,461,215	0.383	2,308	2,298	0.04
5–6	5,847,662	0.196	1,110	1,176	3.70
7 or more	3,255,488	0.109	535	654	21.65
Total	29,904,663	1.000	6,000	6,000	41.75

15.3.4. Example. An aptitude test is so calibrated that its per cent score X follows a normal distribution with $E(X) = 60$ and $\sigma_X = 18$. An alternate test is being constructed; it was given to 500 individuals and the frequency distribution of scores Y listed in columns (1) and (2) of Table 15.3.4 was obtained. Is this alternate test equivalent with the original test? Our hypothesis is that, for the alternate test, the probability of a score Y to fall into any given interval (a,b) is the same as for the original test, namely

$$P(a \le Y \le b) = \frac{1}{\sqrt{2\pi}} \int_{(a-60)/18}^{(b-60)/18} e^{-t^2/2}\, dt$$

These probabilities, computed from table of $\Phi(x)$ for the intervals of column (1), are listed in column (3) of Table 15.3.4. Since the expected frequencies in

TABLE 15.3.4

(1) Per Cent Score Y	(2) m_j	(3) p_j	(4) $500\, p_j = e_j$	(5) $\dfrac{(m_j - e_j)^2}{e_j}$
0–10	2	0.00272	1.36	0.3012
10–20	3	0.01049	5.25	0.9643
20–30	20	0.03425	17.12	0.4845
30–40	40	0.08604	43.02	0.2120
40–50	80	0.15424	77.12	0.1076
50–60	110	0.21226	106.13	0.1411
60–70	105	0.21226	106.13	0.0120
70–80	70	0.15424	77.12	0.6573
80–90	48	0.08604	43.02	0.5765
90 or more	22	0.04746	23.73	0.1261
Total	500	1.00000	500.00	3.5826

column (4) are rather small for the first two lines, we pool these two with the third one and obtain the modified Table 15.3.4.1. From this table we compute

TABLE 15.3.4.1

(1) Score Y	(2) m_j	(3) p_j	(4) $500\, p_j = e_j$	(5) $\dfrac{(m_j - e_j)^2}{e_j}$
0–30	25	0.04746	23.73	0.0680
30–40	40	0.08604	43.02	0.2120
40–50	80	0.15424	77.12	0.1076
50–60	110	0.21226	106.13	0.1411
60–70	105	0.21226	106.13	0.0120
70–80	70	0.15424	77.12	0.6573
80–90	48	0.08604	43.02	0.5765
90–100	22	0.04746	23.73	0.1261
Total	500	1.00000	500.00	1.9006

$\chi^2(s) = 1.9006$, and since for 7 d.o.f. $P(\chi^2 \geq 1.9006) > 0.90$, there is no reason to doubt the hypothesis on any of the conventional significance levels.

15.4 χ^2 Test of Goodness of Fit When Parameters Are Estimated from Samples. Theorem on Contingency Tables

15.4.1. In 15.3 we described a method of testing the agreement ("goodness of fit") between a sample and a hypothetical probability distribution for which all parameters were numerically given (a simple hypothesis). More often, however, one wishes to test the more general (composite) hypothesis that an available set of observations is a sample of a random variable which has a probability distribution of a given type, but some or all parameters needed to determine this distribution are not known. For example, one may wish to test the hypothesis that a sample was obtained from a random variable X which has a normal probability distribution with unknown $E(X)$ and σ_X. In such cases the unknown parameters are first estimated from the sample, the point estimates obtained are entered into the probability distribution of the given type which thus becomes completely determined, and then the goodness of fit is tested. One may ask several questions in this connection: (a) What procedure of estimation should be used? (b) What modifications does this procedure introduce into the test of goodness of fit discussed in 15.3?

15.4.2. To answer question (a) one will be inclined to estimate the unknown parameters so as to render the "measure of goodness of fit" χ^2 as small as possible. This procedure of estimation may be called the "minimum χ^2 method" of estimation. To describe this method, let us assume that the l parameters $\theta_1, \theta_2, \cdots \theta_l$ must be determined in order to specify the probability distribution. Each of the probabilities $p_j = P(E_j)$, for $j = 1, 2, \cdots, k$, is then a function of these parameters

(15.4.2.1)
$$p_j = p_j(\theta_1, \theta_2, \cdots, \theta_l)$$

To minimize χ^2 by calculus, we would have to solve the equations

(15.4.2.2)
$$\frac{\partial \chi^2}{\partial \theta_r} = \frac{\partial}{\partial \theta_r} \sum_{j=1}^{k} \frac{(m_j - np_j)^2}{np_j}$$

$$= -2 \sum_{j=1}^{k} \left[\frac{m_j - np_j}{p_j} + \frac{(m_j - np_j)^2}{2np_j^2} \right] \frac{\partial p_j}{\partial \theta_r} = 0$$

for $r = 1, 2, \cdots, l$. This system of equations is quite complicated and difficult to solve, even when the p_j are fairly simple functions of the θ_r. It is, however, intuitively plausible that if the hypothesis is true the terms $(m_j - np_j)^2/2np_j^2$ will, for large n, have little effect on the values of the roots of (15.4.2.2). We shall omit those terms and thus replace (15.4.2.2) by the simpler system of equations

(15.4.2.3)
$$\sum_{j=1}^{k} \frac{m_j - np_j}{p_j} \cdot \frac{\partial p_j}{\partial \theta_r} = 0 \quad \text{for } r = 1, 2, \cdots, l$$

In view of

$$\sum_{j=1}^{k} p_j = 1$$

we have

$$\sum_{i=1}^{k} \frac{m_j - np_j}{p_j} \frac{\partial p_j}{\partial \theta_r} = \sum_{j=1}^{k} \frac{m_j}{p_j} \frac{\partial p_j}{\partial \theta_r} - n \frac{\partial}{\partial \theta_r} \sum_{j=1}^{k} p_j$$

$$= \sum_{j=1}^{k} \frac{m_j}{p_j} \frac{\partial p_j}{\partial \theta_r}$$

and (15.4.2.3) may be replaced by

(15.4.2.4)
$$\sum_{j=1}^{k} \frac{m_j}{p_j} \frac{\partial p_j}{\partial \theta_r} = 0 \quad \text{for } r = 1, 2, \cdots l$$

The procedure of estimating $\theta_1, \theta_2, \cdots, \theta_l$ by solving the system (15.4.2.3) or (15.4.2.4) will be called the "modified minimum χ^2 method." In this presentation, we shall restrict our discussion to this modified method only, without attempting to give a rigorous justification for this method.

Question (b) is answered by the general principle that if the p_j are computed according to (15.4.2.1) with the parameters θ_r estimated from the sample by means of the equations (15.4.2.3) and are entered into the expression for χ^2, the quantity χ^2 so obtained has, for large n, approximately the χ^2 distribution with $k - l - 1$ d.o.f., where l is the number of parameters estimated. This principle is a special case of the following general theorem.

15.4.3. Theorem.   Let X be a random variable and $E_1, E_2, \cdots, E_k$ mutually exclusive and exhaustive events for X such that the probabilities

$$p_j = P(E_j) \quad \text{for } j = 1, 2, \cdots, k$$

depend on l parameters $\theta_1, \theta_2, \cdots, \theta_l$. Let $O_1, O_2, \cdots, O_s$ be s independent samples, of size $m_{1.}, m_{2.}, \cdots, m_{s.}$, respectively, and let m_{ij} be the number of occurrences of E_j in sample O_i, so that

$$\sum_{j=1}^{k} m_{ij} = m_{i.} \quad \text{for } i = 1, 2, \cdots, s$$

Let the quantity χ^2 be defined by

(15.4.3.1)
$$\chi^2 = \sum_{i=1}^{s} \sum_{j=1}^{k} \frac{(m_{ij} - m_{i.}p_j)^2}{m_{i.}p_j}$$

If the parameters $\theta_1, \theta_2, \cdots, \theta_l$ are not known but are estimated by the modified minimum χ^2 method applied to (15.4.3.1) and then substituted in this expression for χ^2, the resulting random variable χ^2 has, for large

$$n = \sum_{i=1}^{s} m_{i.}$$

approximately the χ^2 distribution with $ks - (s + l)$ d.o.f.

For the exact formulation of the assumptions of this theorem and for the proof, the reader is referred to Cramér* where, to our knowledge, for the first time it was proved rigorously under sufficiently general assumptions to cover all the practical applications in which it has been used. The proof is much too difficult to be reproduced here.

15.4.4. The theorem in 15.4.3 may be interpreted on a model known as a *contingency table* (Table 15.4.4). Let the s rows of an $s \times k$ table correspond to the independent samples $O_1, O_2, \cdots, O_s$, and the k columns to the events $E_1, E_2, \cdots, E_k$; let the entries of the table be the observed frequencies m_{ij} of event E_j in sample O_i. The numbers m_{ij} are usually called the *observed cell*

TABLE 15.4.4

i \ j	1	2	$\cdots$	k	Marginal totals
1	m_{11}	m_{12}	$\cdots$	m_{1k}	$m_{1.}$
2	m_{21}	m_{22}	$\cdots$	m_{2k}	$m_{2.}$
.	.	.			.
.	.	.			.
.	.	.			.
s	m_{s1}	m_{s2}	$\cdots$	m_{sk}	$m_{s.}$
Marginal totals	$m_{.1}$	$m_{.2}$	$\cdots$	$m_{.k}$	n

frequencies. The theorem tells us that if the marginal totals $m_1, m_2, \cdots, m_s$ are given beforehand; if, then, the independent samples $O_1, O_2, \cdots, O_s$ are obtained; if the l parameters $\theta_1, \theta_2, \cdot \, \cdot, \theta_l$ are estimated from the observed cell frequencies by the modified minimum χ^2 method, substituted in p_j and these p_j entered in (15.4.3.1), then the random variable χ^2 defined by (15.4.3.1) has, for n large, approximately the χ^2 distribution with a number of degrees of freedom equal to the number of cells decreased by the number of parameters estimated and by the number of totals given.

* H. Cramér, *Mathematical Methods of Statistics*, Princeton University Press, Princeton, N.J., 1946, pp. 424–434 and 466.

If only one sample of a given size n is available, we have $s = 1$, and the resulting quantity χ^2 has for large n approximately the χ^2 distribution with the number of degrees of freedom equal to the number of cells, decreased by the number of parameters estimated and by an additional unit.

If only one sample is available and the hypothetical probability distribution is completely specified, so that no parameters need to be estimated, we have $s = 1, l = 0$, and the resulting χ^2 has approximately the χ^2 distribution with the number of degrees of freedom equal to the number of cells decreased by a unit. This is the special case treated in Theorem 15.2.2.

15.5   Contingency Tables: Tests of Homogeneity

15.5.1.   We consider an $s \times k$ table for which the totals $m_1, m_2, \cdots, m_s$. are given, and wish to test the hypothesis H that each row is a sample of the same random variable (*homogeneity hypothesis*). This is equivalent with the hypothesis that there exist numbers $\theta_j = p_j = P(E_j)$, $j = 1, 2, \cdots, k$, which are the parameters to be estimated. Since we must have

$$\sum_{j=1}^{k} \theta_j = \sum_{j=1}^{k} p_j = 1$$

only $(k - 1)$ of these parameters need be estimated, and the kth is then determined. Expression (15.4.3.1) becomes

(15.5.1.1)
$$\chi^2 = \sum_{i=1}^{s} \sum_{j=1}^{k} \frac{(m_{ij} - m_{i.}\theta_j)^2}{m_{i.}\theta_j}$$

and the equations (15.4.2.3) of the modified minimum χ^2 method are

$$\sum_{i=1}^{s} \sum_{j=1}^{k} \frac{m_{ij} - m_{i.}\theta_j}{\theta_j} \cdot \frac{\partial \theta_j}{\partial \theta_r} = \sum_{i=1}^{s} \frac{m_{ir} m_{i.}\theta_r}{\theta_r} = 0$$

$$\text{for } r = 1, 2, \cdots, k - 1$$

The solution of these equations is

(15.5.1.2)
$$\theta_r = p_r = \frac{\sum_{i=1}^{s} m_{ir}}{\sum_{i=1}^{s} m_{i.}} = \frac{m_{.r}}{n} \quad \text{for } r = 1, 2, \cdots, k - 1$$

where

$$m_{.r} = \sum_{i=1}^{s} m_{ir}$$

is the sum of cell frequencies in the rth column and

$$n = \sum_{i=1}^{s} m_{i.} = \sum_{j=1}^{k} m_{.j} = \sum_{i=1}^{s} \sum_{j=1}^{k} m_{ij}$$

the sum of all cell frequencies in the table. Theorem 15.4.3 tells us that the random variable χ^2 obtained by substituting the estimates (15.5.1.2) in (15.5.1.1) has approximately the χ^2 distribution with $ks - (k-1) - s = (k-1)(s-1)$ d.o.f. For this random variable we have the expression

$$(15.5.1.3) \qquad \chi^2 = \sum_{i=1}^{s} \sum_{j=1}^{k} \frac{[m_{ij} - (m_{i.}m_{.j}/n)]^2}{m_{i.}m_{.j}/n}$$

or, by simple algebra,

$$(15.5.1.4) \qquad \chi^2 = n\left(\sum_{i=1}^{s} \sum_{j=1}^{k} \frac{m_{ij}^2}{m_{i.}m_{.j}} - 1 \right)$$

In special cases these expressions may be further simplified. For example, in the case of a $2 \times k$ table, where only $s = 2$ samples are tested for homogeneity, we have the relations $m_{1j} + m_{2j} = m_{.j}$, $m_{1.} + m_{2.} = n$, and (15.5.1.3) reduces to

$$(15.5.1.5) \qquad \chi^2 = m_{1.}m_{2.} \sum_{j=1}^{k} \frac{1}{m_{.j}} \left(\frac{m_{1j}}{m_{1.}} - \frac{m_{2j}}{m_{2.}} \right)^2$$

In another case, when only $k = 2$ events are considered, we have

$$m_{i1} + m_{i2} = m_{i.}, \qquad m_{.1} + m_{.2} = n$$

and

$$p_1 = \frac{m_{.1}}{n}, p_2 = \frac{m_{.2}}{n}$$

so that (15.5.1.3) becomes

$$(15.5.1.6) \qquad \chi^2 = \frac{1}{p_1 p_2} \sum_{i=1}^{s} \frac{m_{i1}^2}{m_{i.}} - n\frac{p_1}{p_2}$$

In the very important case of a 2×2 table (fourfold table) this reduces to

$$(15.5.1.7) \qquad \chi^2 = \frac{n(m_{11}m_{22} - m_{12}m_{21})^2}{m_{1.}m_{2.}m_{.1}m_{.2}}$$

15.5.2. Example. A certain kind of cancer, known to respond to radiation therapy, had been treated either by using radium on the primary tumor, or by using radium on the primary tumor and following this up by x-ray treatment applied to a field surrounding the original focus. Both techniques have been used, and the results obtained are given in Table 15.5.2. Counted as "cured" are patients who remained free of symptoms for at least five years. The homogeneity hypothesis means here that the probabilities of the events "cured" and "not cured" are the same in the populations of those treated with radium alone and of those treated with radium and x-ray. We wish to test this hypothesis on the significance level $\alpha = 0.01$. Using (15.5.1.7) we obtain $\chi^2 = 10.6$ and since for 1 d.o.f. $P(\chi^2 > 10.6)$ is only about 0.001, the homogeneity hypothesis will be rejected. The practical conclusion is that the probability of a lasting cure is greater for radium and x-ray treatment than for radium alone, that is, that the x-ray follow up actually improves the chances of success.

TABLE 15.5.2

Treatment \ Result	Cured	Not Cured	Total
Radium	65	156	221
Radium and x-ray	41	42	83
Total	106	198	304

15.5.3. Example. Table 15.5.3 contains data on hair color of boys and girls. We choose $\alpha = 0.05$ and wish to test the hypothesis that the distribution of hair colors is the same for either sex. If we assume that the number of boys, 2100, and the number of girls, 1783, were determined before the samples were collected, this is the homogeneity hypothesis for a 2×5 table. The computations needed to obtain χ^2 according to (15.5.1.5) are indicated in Table 15.5.3. The value obtained is $\chi^2 = 10.043$. For 4 d.o.f. we have

TABLE 15.5.3

Hair Color j	(1) Fair	(2) Red	(3) Medium	(4) Dark	(5) Jet Black	Totals $m_{i.}$
Sex (i)						
Boys (1)	592	119	849	504	36	2100
Girls (2)	544	97	677	451	14	1783
Totals $m_{.j}$	1136	216	1526	955	50	3883
$\dfrac{m_{1j}}{m_{1.}}$	0.282	0.057	0.404	0.240	0.017	1.000
$\dfrac{m_{2j}}{m_{2.}}$	0.305	0.054	0.380	0.253	0.008	1.000
$\dfrac{m_{1.}m_{2.}}{m_{.j}}\left(\dfrac{m_{1j}}{m_{1.}} - \dfrac{m_{2j}}{m_{2.}}\right)^2$	1.744	0.156	1.414	0.663	6.066	$\chi^2 = 10.043$

$0.05 > P(\chi^2 > 10.043) > 0.02$, which is significant on the 5% level. A glance at the computations shows that this is mainly due to the different proportions of jet black among boys and girls.

15.6 Contingency Tables: Tests of Independence

A contingency-table of $s \times k$ cells may be obtained in a manner which differs materially from that discussed in 15.5. Let $X = (U,V)$ be a two-dimensional random variable; let $U_1, U_2, \cdots, U_s$ be all the possible values of U and $V_1, V_2, \cdots, V_k$ all the possible values of V. Let one sample of X be available, of the total size n. In this sample the value (U_i, V_j) occurred m_{ij} times. The frequencies m_{ij} are arranged in a contingency table which looks exactly like Table 15.4.4 but differs from the contingency tables discussed in 15.5 in that only the total n of all frequencies is given, while all the marginal totals $m_{i.}$ and $m_{.j}$ are random variables. The hypothesis most frequently tested by samples arranged in tables of this kind is the *hypothesis of independence*. This hypothesis H states that U and V are independent, that is, that there exist marginal probabilities

$$\alpha_i = g(U_i) \quad \text{for } i = 1, 2, \cdots, s$$
$$\beta_j = h(V_j) \quad \text{for } j = 1, 2, \cdots, k$$

such that the joint probabilities are

$$f(U_i, V_j) = \alpha_i \beta_j$$

These probabilities α_i, β_j are the parameters which have to be estimated and entered into the expression for χ^2. In view of

$$\sum_{i=1}^{s} \alpha_i = 1, \qquad \sum_{j=1}^{k} \beta_j = 1$$

only $\alpha_1, \cdots, \alpha_{s-1}$ and $\beta_1, \cdots, \beta_{k-1}$ must be estimated. The equations of the modified minimum χ^2 method are

$$\sum_{i=1}^{s} \sum_{j=1}^{k} \frac{m_{ij} - n\alpha_i\beta_j}{\alpha_i\beta_j} \frac{\partial(\alpha_i\beta_j)}{\partial\alpha_r} = \sum_{j=1}^{k} \frac{m_{rj} - n\alpha_r\beta_j}{\alpha_r} = 0 \quad \text{for } r = 1, 2, \cdots, s - 1$$

and

$$\sum_{i=1}^{s} \sum_{j=1}^{k} \frac{m_{ij} - n\alpha_i\beta_j}{\alpha_i\beta_j} \frac{\partial(\alpha_i\beta_j)}{\partial\beta_t} = \sum_{i=1}^{s} \frac{m_{it} - n\alpha_i\beta_t}{\beta_t} = 0 \quad \text{for } t = 1, 2, \cdots, k - 1$$

The solution of these equations is

$$\alpha_r = \frac{\sum_{j=1}^{k} m_{rj}}{n \sum_{j=1}^{k} \beta_j} = \frac{m_{r.}}{n} \quad \text{for } r = 1, 2, \cdots, s - 1$$

(15.6.1)

$$\beta_t = \frac{\sum_{i=1}^{s} m_{it}}{n \sum_{i=1}^{s} \alpha_i} = \frac{m_{.t}}{n} \quad \text{for } t = 1, 2, \cdots, k - 1$$

Since all n determinations of X form one sample, one must apply the special case of Theorem 15.4.3 in which the number of samples is 1 and the number of parameters estimated from the sample is $k - 1 + s - 1$, and one concludes that the quantity

$$(15.6.2) \qquad \chi^2 = \sum_{i=1}^{s} \sum_{j=1}^{k} \frac{(m_{ij} - n\alpha_i\beta_j)^2}{n\alpha_i\beta_j}$$

where the α_i, β_j are computed according to (15.6.1) and

$$\alpha_s = 1 - \sum_{j=1}^{s-1} \alpha_j, \qquad \beta_k = 1 - \sum_{j=1}^{k-1} \beta_j$$

has approximately the χ^2 distribution with

$$ks - (k + s - 2) - 1 = (k - 1)(s - 1) \text{ d.o.f.}$$

Since formally the quantity (15.6.2) with α_i and β_j taken from (15.6.1) is equal to (15.5.1.3), the formulas (15.5.1.4), (15.5.1.5), (15.5.1.6), and (15.5.1.7) may be used to compute χ^2 for testing independence as well as in tests of homogeneity. The number of degrees of freedom is also the same as in 15.5 for a contingency table of the same size, so that the χ^2 test of homogeneity described in 15.5 and the χ^2 test of independence described in the present section are from the manipulative point of view identical, although their logical meaning is entirely different.

15.7 χ^2 Test with Parameters Estimated from Sample: Some Typical Cases

Besides the instances in which the results of observations are readily arranged in contingency tables, there are many other problems which can be treated by an application of the principle stated in Theorem 15.4.3. Some typical cases of this kind will be presented in this section.

15.7.1. If there is reason to assume that a discrete random variable X for which a sample is available has a Poisson distribution, this hypothesis may be tested by estimating the parameter a of this distribution and applying Theorem 15.4.3. The equations (15.4.2.3) are

$$\sum_{j=0}^{\infty} \frac{m_j - na^j e^{-a}/j!}{na^j e^{-a}/j!} \cdot \frac{a^j e^{-a}}{j!} \left(\frac{j}{a} - 1 \right)$$

$$= \sum_{j=0}^{\infty} \frac{m_j - na^j e^{-a}/j!}{n} \cdot \frac{j}{a} - \sum_{j=0}^{\infty} \frac{m_j}{n} + e^{-a} \sum_{j=0}^{\infty} \frac{a^j}{j!}$$

$$= \frac{1}{a} \left(\frac{1}{n} \sum_{j=1}^{\infty} jm_j - ae^{-a} \sum_{j=1}^{\infty} \frac{a^{j-1}}{(j-1!)} \right) - 1 + 1$$

$$= \frac{1}{a} \left(\frac{1}{n} \sum_{j=1}^{\infty} jm_j - a \right) = 0.$$

Use was made here of the equality

$$\sum_{j=0}^{\infty} m_j = n$$

In fact, only a finite number of the frequencies m_j can be different from zero. The resulting estimate for a is

(15.7.1.1) $$a = \frac{1}{n} \sum_{j=1}^{\infty} m_j j$$

which is the arithmetic mean of all the observed values of the variable—the usual estimate for $E(X) = a$.

15.7.2. Example. In Table 10.1.4 the observed frequencies l_s of the discrete variable S are tabulated in column (4). In Example 10.1.4 these values were used to compute an estimate of the form (15.7.1.1), the value $a \sim 4.7$ was obtained, and the expected frequencies corresponding to $a = 4.7$ were tabulated in column (3). To apply the χ^2 test, we need a set of events such that the expected frequency of each event is at least 10. We combine therefore the first two values of S into an event, $S = 0$ or 1, with the total expected frequency 20.8, and the values from $S = 9$ up into an event, $S = 9$ or more, with the total expected frequency 20. The computations in the resulting Table 15.7.2 yield $\chi^2 = 4.39$. The number of cell frequencies is 9, the number of parameters estimated from sample 1, hence the number of degrees of freedom is 7. Since $P(\chi^2 \geq 4.39) > 0.70$, there is no reason to reject our hypothesis at any of the customary significance levels.

TABLE 15.7.2

S	l_s	$E(l_s)$	$\dfrac{[l_s - E(l_s)]^2}{E(l_s)}$
0 or 1	20	20.8	0.03
2	43	40.0	0.22
3	53	62.8	1.53
4	86	74.0	1.95
5	70	69.6	0.00
6	54	54.4	0.00
7	37	36.4	0.01
8	18	21.6	0.60
9 or more	19	20.0	0.05
Total	400	3.996	4.39

15.7.3. Frequently one wishes to test the hypothesis that a sample was obtained from a random variable with a one dimensional normal distribution with neither expectation nor standard deviation assumed known. Let the probability density of X be

$$f(x) = \frac{1}{\sigma\sqrt{2\pi}} e^{-(x-a)^2/2\sigma^2}$$

We consider a sample of size n, grouped in the intervals $(x_1,x_2), (x_2,x_3), \cdots,$ $(x_{k-1},x_k), (x_k,x_{k+1})$ where $x_1 = -\infty$, $x_{k+1} = +\infty$. Let m_j be the observed number of values in (x_j,x_{j+1}). By writing

$$p_j = \int_{x_j}^{x_{j+1}} f(x)dx$$

we have

$$\frac{\partial p_j}{\partial a} = \frac{1}{\sigma^2} \int_{x_j}^{x_{j+1}} (x-a)f(x)dx$$

(15.7.3.1)

$$\frac{\partial p_j}{\partial \sigma^2} = \frac{1}{2\sigma^2}\left[-p_j + \frac{1}{\sigma^2}\int_{x_j}^{x_{j+1}} (x-a)^2 f(x)dx \right]$$

Substituting this in (15.4.2.4), we obtain

$$\frac{1}{\sigma^2}\left[\sum_{j=1}^{k} \frac{m_j}{p_j} \int_{x_j}^{x_{j+1}} xf(x)dx - a \sum_{j=1}^{k} \frac{m_j}{p_j} \int_{x_j}^{x_{j+1}} f(x)dx \right]$$

$$= \frac{1}{\sigma^2}\left[\sum_{j=1}^{k} \frac{m_j}{p_j} \int_{x_j}^{x_{j+1}} xf(x)dx - an \right] = 0$$

and

$$-\frac{n}{\sigma} + \frac{1}{\sigma^3}\sum_{j=1}^{k} \frac{m_j}{p_j} \int_{x_j}^{x_{j+1}} (x-a)^2 f(x)dx = 0$$

The resulting estimates

(15.7.3.2)

$$a = \frac{1}{n}\sum_{j=1}^{k} m_j \frac{\displaystyle\int_{x_j}^{x_{j+1}} xf(x)dx}{\displaystyle\int_{x_j}^{x_{j+1}} f(x)dx}$$

$$\sigma^2 = \frac{1}{n}\sum_{j=1}^{k} m_j \frac{\displaystyle\int_{x_j}^{x_{j+1}} (x-a)^2 f(x)dx}{\displaystyle\int_{x_j}^{x_{j+1}} f(x)dx}$$

are difficult to evaluate exactly. To obtain a first approximation, we replace each integrand by its value at the midpoint of the interval of integration. This procedure fails for the intervals $(-\infty,x_2)$ and $(x_k,+\infty)$; to avoid this difficulty, we choose the intervals so that no value of our sample is $\leq x_2$ or $\geq x_k$ so that $m_1 = m_k = 0$. By writing

$$\frac{x_j + x_{j+1}}{2} = \xi_j$$

we then have the approximate estimates

(15.7.3.3)
$$a_1 = \frac{1}{n} \sum_{j=1}^{k} m_j \xi_j$$

(15.7.3.4)
$$\sigma_1^2 = \frac{1}{n} \sum_{j=1}^{k} m_j (\xi_j - a_1)^2$$

If all class intervals $(x_2, x_3), \cdots, (x_{k-2}, x_{k-1})$ have the same length Δ_1, it can be shown that the approximation

(15.7.3.5)
$$\sigma_2^2 = \frac{1}{n} \sum_{j=1}^{k} m_j (\xi_j - a_1)^2 - \frac{\Delta^2}{12}$$

is closer to the estimate for σ^2 in (15.7.3.2) than σ_1^2 given in (15.7.3.4). The quantity $-\Delta_2/12$ in (15.7.3.5) is known as *Sheppard's correction*. In estimating expectation and variance of a normal variable from a sample grouped in class intervals of equal length, it is customary to use formulas (15.7.3.3) and (15.7.3.5).

15.7.4. Example.   The shape of the frequency distribution of columns (1) and (2) of Table 15.7.4 seems to indicate that it is a sample of a normal random variable. To test this hypothesis by the method described in 15.7.3, we compute the estimates (15.7.3.3) and (15.7.3.5) which yield 145.48 and 2430.63, respectively. Assuming a normal probability distribution with expectation 145.48 and standard deviation $\sqrt{2430.63} = 49.30$, we then obtain $\chi^2 = 5.299$. Since the number of cell frequencies is 10, and 2 parameters were estimated from the sample, we find for 7 d.o.f. $P(\chi^2 \geq 5.299) > 0.50$. There is, therefore, no reason to reject the hypothesis. The data of this example were obtained by taking 500 times three numbers between 0 and 99 from tables of random numbers and writing down their sum. The numbers between 0 and 99, taken at random, are a good approximation to a continuous random variable with uniform probability density in an interval of length 100, and thus the random variable from which our sample was taken has approximately the probability distribution of $X_1 + X_2 + X_3$, where each term is an independent determination of the same random variable with uniform distribution. Comparing this with Exercise 5.7, the reader will observe that the probability distribution of $X_1 + X_2 + X_3$ is not normal but resembles a normal distribution very closely. This resemblance is so close that our application of the χ^2 test to a sample of size 500 did not detect the difference.

15.8 χ^2 Distribution for Large Number of Degrees of Freedom

15.8.1.   According to Theorem 10.3.3 a random variable U which has a χ^2 distribution with n degrees of freedom has the expectation n and the variance

TABLE 15.7.4

(1) X	(2) m	(3) X'	(4) mX'	(5) mX'²	(6) p	(7) e = 500p	(8) $\dfrac{(m-e)^2}{e}$
0–29	2	−4	−8	32	0.009	4.5	1.389
30–59	16	−3	−48	144	0.032	16.0	0.000
60–89	52	−2	−104	208	0.086	43.0	1.884
90–119	87	−1	−87	87	0.171	85.5	0.026
120–149	107	0	−247[a]	0	0.234	117.0	0.855
150–179	108	1	108	108	0.223	111.5	0.110
180–209	79	2	158	316	0.148	74.0	0.338
210–239	34	3	102	306	0.068	34.0	0.000
240–269	13	4	52	208	0.022	11.0	0.364
270–299	2	5	10	50	0.006	3.0	0.333
			430[b]				
Totals	500		183	1459	0.999	499.5	5.299

Provisional mean:

$$C = 30$$
$$\tilde{X} = 134.5$$
$$\Sigma m = 500$$
$$\Sigma mX' = 183$$
$$\Sigma mX'^2 = 1459$$

$$\text{Estimate of variance} = \left[\frac{\Sigma mX'^2}{n} - \left(\frac{\Sigma mX'}{n}\right)^2 - \frac{1}{12}\right]C^2 = 2430.63,$$

$$\sqrt{2430.63} = 49.301$$

$$\text{Estimate of expectation} = \tilde{X} + \frac{\Sigma mX'}{n}\,C = 145.48$$

[a] The total of minus quantities above.
[b] The total of plus quantities above.

$2n$, and the corresponding characteristc function is $C_U(t) = (1 - 2it)^{-n/2}$. Hence the normalized variable is $V = (U - n)/\sqrt{2n}$ and the corresponding characteristic function is

$$C_V(t) = e^{-i\sqrt{(n/2)}t}(1 - i\sqrt{(2/n)}t)^{-n/2}$$

Taking logarithms we obtain

$$\ln C_V(t) = -i\sqrt{(n/2)}t - (n/2) \ln (1 - i\sqrt{(2/n)}t)$$

In view of the expansion

$$\ln \left(1 - i\sqrt{\frac{2}{n}}t\right) = -\sum_{r=1}^{\infty} \frac{1}{r} i^r \left(\frac{2}{n}\right)^{r/2} t^r$$

which converges for $|\sqrt{(2/n)}t| < 1$, this can be written

$$\ln C_V(t) = -\frac{t^2}{2} + \left(\frac{2}{n}\right)^{1/2} \sum_{r=3}^{\infty} \frac{i^r}{r} \left(\frac{2}{n}\right)^{(r-3)/2} t^r$$

We conclude that

$$\lim_{n \to \infty} \ln C_V(t) = e^{-t^2/2} \quad \text{for all } t$$

According to Theorem 7.5.4 it follows that the d.f. of $V = (U - n)/\sqrt{2n}$ converges (uniformly in t in any finite interval) to the d.f. of the normalized normal distribution. Thus we have demonstrated the following theorem.

15.8.2. Theorem. A random variable with the χ^2 distribution with n degrees of freedom is, for large n, distributed approximately as the normal random variable with expectation n and standard deviation $\sqrt{2n}$.

This theorem makes it possible to compute approximately the probabilities $P(\chi^2 \geq t)$ used in testing hypotheses, for numbers of degrees of freedom exceeding the range of the printed tables of χ^2 probabilities.

15.8.3. Example. For $n = 30$ compute $P(\chi^2 \geq 36.25)$ by using the approximation of Theorem 15.8.1. We obtain the value

$$P\left(\frac{\chi^2 - 30}{\sqrt{60}} \geq \frac{36.25 - 30}{\sqrt{60}}\right) = P(X \geq 0.807) \sim 0.21$$

Since $n = 30$ is still in the range of Table III, we read the exact value $P(\chi^2 \geq 36.25) = 0.20$ from that table, and see that the approximation is quite good.

15.8.4. The method of approximating the χ^2 distribution by the normal distribution indicated in Theorem 15.8.2 has the disadvantage that the approximations converge to the exact distribution fairly slowly, that is, that n must be quite large to yield a good approximation. Another disadvantage lies in the fact that the approximating normal random variable has expectation and variance both dependent on n. These disadvantages are considerably reduced if one uses another approximation indicated in the following theorem due to R. A. Fisher.

15.8.5. Theorem. If χ^2 is a random variable which has the χ^2 distribution with n degrees of freedom, then $\sqrt{2\chi^2}$ is distributed approximately as the normal random variable with expectation $\sqrt{2n-1}$ and standard deviation 1.

Proof. For any $s > 0$ and any positive integer n the inequalities

$$\sqrt{2\chi^2} - \sqrt{2n-1} < s$$

and

$$\frac{\chi^2 - n}{\sqrt{2n}} < s + \frac{s^2 - 1}{2\sqrt{2n}} + [\sqrt{1 - (1/2n)} - 1]s$$

are equivalent. We have, therefore, for any fixed $s > 0$

$$\lim_{n \to \infty} P(\sqrt{2\chi^2} - \sqrt{2n-1} < s) = \lim_{n \to \infty} P\left[\frac{\chi^2 - n}{\sqrt{2n}} < s + \frac{s^2 - 1}{2\sqrt{2n}} \right.$$
$$\left. + (\sqrt{1 - (1/2n)} - 1)s\right]$$
$$= \lim_{n \to \infty} P\left(\frac{\chi^2 - n}{\sqrt{2n}} < s\right)$$

and this by Theorem 15.8.2 is equal to

$$\frac{1}{\sqrt{2\pi}} \int_{-\infty}^{s} e^{-t^2/2} dt$$

15.8.6. Example. We again wish to compute $P(\chi^2 \geq 36.25)$ for $n = 30$. According to Theorem 15.8.5 we obtain the approximate value

$$P(X > \sqrt{2 \cdot 36.25} - \sqrt{2 \cdot 30 - 1}) = P(X > 0.834) = 0.20,$$

which is the exact value given by Table III.

15.9 Test of Homogeneity for 2 × 2 Tables: Correction for Continuity—"Exact" Treatment

15.9.1. The random variable with the probability distribution (10.3.2.5) is continuous, while the χ^2 defined by (15.1.1.6) is a discrete random variable with a distribution approximated by (10.3.2.5). This approximation is satisfactory if n is large but cannot be used for n small. A rule of thumb for deciding whether n is large enough to justify the use of the limit-distribution (10.3.2.5), was stated in Section 15.2. In the special case of tests of independence or homogeneity for 2×2 tables, two techniques are available if the expected frequencies are too small to use the limit distribution.

15.9.2. Let our 2×2 table be

(15.9.2.1)

m_{11}	m_{12}	$m_{1.}$
m_{21}	m_{22}	$m_{2.}$
$m_{.1}$	$m_{.2}$	n

The homogeneity hypothesis assumes the existence of p and $1 - p = q$ such that, for given totals $m_{1.}$, $m_{2.}$, we have $E(m_{11}) = m_{1.}p$, $E(m_{21}) = m_{2.}p$, $E(m_{12}) = m_{1.}q$, $E(m_{22}) = m_{2.}q$. By the modified minimum χ^2 method we obtain for p the estimate $m_{.1}/n$, and hence for q the estimate $m_{.2}/n$. The expression (15.5.1.3) for χ^2 then becomes

$$\chi^2 = \frac{\left(m_{11} - \dfrac{m_{.1}m_{1.}}{n}\right)^2}{\dfrac{m_{.1}m_{1.}}{n}} + \frac{\left(m_{12} - \dfrac{m_{.2}m_{1.}}{n}\right)^2}{\dfrac{m_{.2}m_{1.}}{n}}$$

(15.9.2.2)

$$+ \frac{\left(m_{21} - \dfrac{m_{.1}m_{2.}}{n}\right)^2}{\dfrac{m_{.1}m_{2.}}{n}} + \frac{\left(m_{22} - \dfrac{m_{.2}m_{2.}}{n}\right)^2}{\dfrac{m_{.2}m_{2.}}{n}}$$

$$= 2n\left[\frac{\left(m_{11} - \dfrac{m_{.1}m_{1.}}{n}\right)^2}{m_{.1}m_{1.}} + \frac{\left(m_{21} - \dfrac{m_{.1}m_{2.}}{n}\right)^2}{m_{.1}m_{2.}}\right]$$

Here m_{11}, m_{21} are integer numbers. In order to reduce the discrepancy between the resulting discrete values and the treatment of χ^2 as a continuous random variable, it is customary to apply what is known as Yates' correction: all frequencies in (15.9.2.1) are increased or decreased by 0.5, always so as to keep all the marginal totals unchanged, but to reduce the value of the squared quantities in (15.9.2.2). This results in a reduction of the value for χ^2, and hence makes the procedure "safer," that is, less likely to lead to rejection of the hypothesis, than if the correction had not been applied.

15.9.3. Example. A new treatment of a certain disease is to be compared with the treatment currently used. The small clinical material obtained under carefully controlled conditions is summarized in a 2×2 table (Table 15.9.3).

TABLE 15.9.3

Treatment \ Result	Cured	Not Cured	Total
Old	5	8	13
New	9	3	12
Total	14	11	25

Formula (15.5.1.7) yields $\chi^2 = 3.38$ and, for 1 d.o.f., $0.05 \leq P(\chi^2 \geq 3.38) \leq 0.1$. Yates' correction which, as can be seen easily, is equivalent to applying (15.5.1.7) to a table adjusted by decreasing each of the two entries in one diagonal by 0.5 and increasing each of the two entries in the other diagonal by 0.5 yields

$$\chi_Y^2 = \frac{(5.5 \cdot 3.5 - 7.5 \cdot 8.5)^2 0.25}{14 \cdot 11 \cdot 12 \cdot 13} = 2.06$$

Again for 1 d.o.f. this would yield $0.1 \leq P(\chi^2 \geq 2.06) \leq 0.2$.

15.9.4. The following method, known as the "exact" treatment of 2×2 tables, avoids altogether the use of the limiting χ^2 distribution. Under the homogeneity hypothesis, the probability of obtaining the exact frequencies of Table 15.9.3 is

$$P(m_{11}, m_{12}, m_{21}, m_{22}) = \binom{m_{1.}}{m_{11}} p^{m_{11}} (1-p)^{m_{12}} \binom{m_{2.}}{m_{21}} p^{m_{21}} (1-p)^{m_{22}}$$

where p is not known. With the same p, the probability that a sample of the total size n results in the marginal totals $m_{.1}$, $m_{.2}$ is

$$P(m_{.1}, m_{.2}) = \binom{n}{m_{.1}} p^{m_{.1}} (1-p)^{m_{.2}}$$

Hence, under the homogeneity hypothesis, the conditional probability of obtaining $m_{11}, m_{12}, m_{21}, m_{22}$ if the column totals are $m_{.1}$ and $m_{.2}$, is equal to

$$\textbf{(15.9.4)} \quad P(m_{11}, m_{12}, m_{21}, m_{22} \mid m_{.1}, m_{.2}) = \frac{\binom{m_{1.}}{m_{11}} \binom{m_{2.}}{m_{21}}}{\binom{n}{m_{.1}}}$$

$$= \frac{m_{1.}! \, m_{2.}! \, m_{.1}! \, m_{.2}!}{n! \, m_{11}! \, m_{12}! \, m_{21}! \, m_{22}!}$$

a quantity which does not depend on p. Making use of this expression, one can compute exactly the conditional probability that, if in a sample of total size n all four marginal totals are equal to those observed, the frequencies $m_{11}, m_{12}, m_{21}, m_{22}$ deviate from what one would expect in case of homogeneity by more than those observed. If that probability is small, the hypothesis is rejected.

15.9.5. Example. The data in Table 15.9.3 deviate from what one would expect in case of homogeneity by exhibiting more cases cured by the new treatment than by the old. Keeping all four marginal totals constant, one can construct all the 2×2 tables deviating in the same direction as much or more than Table 15.9.3. These tables are:

I		II		III		IV	
5	8	4	9	3	10	2	11
9	3	10	2	11	1	12	0

For each of these four tables the probability (15.9.4) can be computed easily with the aid of tables of logarithms of factorials. One finds

$$\begin{aligned}
P_{\mathrm{I}} &= 0.06352 \\
P_{\mathrm{II}} &= 0.01059 \\
P_{\mathrm{III}} &= 0.00077 \\
P_{\mathrm{IV}} &= 0.00002 \\
\hline
\text{Total } &\ 0.07490
\end{aligned}$$

Hence the total probability that, for the same marginal totals as in Table 15.9.3, the results are in favor of the new treatment as much or more than those observed, is under the homogeneity hypothesis equal to 0.07490. This still would not be significant on the 0.05 significance level.

It should be pointed out that the probability 0.07490 found in Example 15.9.5 cannot be compared directly with the probabilities computed for the same data in Example 15.9.3. It is the probability of obtaining by chance observations apparently favoring the new treatment at least as much as those actually obtained. The probability of obtaining a χ^2 at least as large as the value actually obtained, however, includes the probability of large values of χ^2 because of observations favoring the old treatment as well as those favoring the new treatment. For example, the 2×2 table

$$\begin{matrix} 13 & 0 \\ 1 & 11 \end{matrix}$$

would lead to $\chi^2 = 21.28$ (without Yates' correction), hence the probability of obtaining it would be part of $P(\chi^2 \geq 3.38)$, but has not been considered in our illustration for the "exact" method.

EXERCISES

15.1. For the multinomial probability distribution prove
$$\sigma(m_j, m_k) = E(m_j m_k) - E(m_j)E(m_k) = -np_j p_k.$$

15.2. For $k = 2$, the multinomial distribution reduces to the binomial distribution.
(a) Show that then (15.1.1.6) becomes
$$\chi^2 = \frac{(m - np)^2}{np(1 - p)}$$
where m is the number of times E_1 occurs in n repetitions. What are all the possible values of the random variable χ^2, and what are the corresponding probabilities?
(b) Take $k = 2$, $p = \frac{1}{3}$, $n = 6$, and compute this exact probability distribution of χ^2.
(c) Again take $k = 2, p = \frac{1}{3}$, but $n = 30$, and tabulate all the exact possible values of χ^2. To compute the corresponding probabilities use the DeMoivre-Laplace approximation to the binomial probability. Compare the 10% and 5% point of this distribution with those in the table of χ^2 for 1 degree of freedom.

15.3. There is reason to assume that two pairs of traits, A and a, B and b, are each inherited independently according to Mendel's law. If this is true, the probabilities of occurrence of the possible combinations of these traits are: $P(A,B) = \frac{9}{16}$, $P(A,b) = \frac{3}{16}$, $P(a,B) = \frac{3}{16}$, $P(a,b) = \frac{1}{16}$. In a breeding experiment the following frequencies were obtained:

A,B	A,b	a,B	a,b
161	54	61	36

Use the χ^2 distribution to test on the 5% level of significance the hypothesis of independent Mendelian inheritance.

15.4. A manufacturer claims that his production process is under statistical control and that the length of the units produced has the mean 1.62 inches and the standard deviation 0.02 inch. This is usually understood to mean that the length X is a random variable with a normal probability distribution and $E(X) = 1.62$, $\sigma_x = 0.02$. A sample of 250 units was taken and the following frequency distribution of the actual measurements was obtained:

Length	Frequency
1.56–1.58	10
1.58–1.60	43
1.60–1.62	64
1.62–1.64	75
1.64–1.66	48
1.66–1.68	8
1.68–1.70	2

Test on the 5% level the hypothesis stated by the manufacturer.

15.5. The kind of cancer referred to in Example 15.5.2 has been treated with radium and x-ray in some cases at an earlier stage (Stage II), and in some at a later stage of the disease (Stage III). The results of the same treatment (radium and x-ray) applied at the two different stages are tabulated below:

Stage	Result	
	Cured	*Not Cured*
II	41	42
III	51	87

Result appears centered above the Cured / Not Cured columns.

Test on the 5% level the hypothesis that the chances for a cure are the same when the treatment is begun in Stage III as when it is applied in Stage II.

15.6. Use the data in the following table and test each of the two hypotheses: H_1 the probability of a male child being born is equal to that of a female child being born; H_2 there exists a probability p of a male child being born (and hence a probability $1 - p = q$ for a female child) which is constant through the years.

Births, by Sex, for Birth Registration Areas in the
United States, 1924–1938

Year	Male Births	Female Births
1924	992,431	938,183
1925	966,973	911,907
1926	953,638	902,430
1927	1,099,287	1,038,549
1928	1,147,625	1,085,524
1929	1,114,814	1,055,106
1930	1,131,976	1,071,982
1931	1,084,404	1,028,356
1932	1,063,885	1,010,157
1933	1,068,871	1,012,361
1934	1,112,703	1,054,933
1935	1,105,489	1,049,616
1936	1,099,465	1,045,325
1937	1,130,641	1,072,696
1938	1,172,541	1,114,421

15.7. Test the hypothesis that the following frequency distribution is a sample from a normal population (use Sheppard's correction).

Class	Frequency
0–19	7
20–39	24
40–59	46
60–79	61
80–99	65
100–119	75
120–139	57
140–159	43
160–179	20
180–199	2
	400

15.8. Using Theorem 15.8.5, fill in the values of t_a in the following table so that, approximately, $P(\chi^2 \geq t_a) = \alpha$.

Table of Approximate Values of 100 α Per Cent Points t_a
of χ^2 for Some Large Numbers of Degrees of Freedom n

α \ n	30	40	50	75	100	150	200
0.10							
0.05							
0.02							
0.01							

15.9. Apply the χ^2 test for homogeneity to the following 2×2 tables on the 5% level of significance. Compute the χ^2 (a) without and (b) with Yates' correction.

I		II		III	
4	11	18	8	9	2
9	5	11	41	5	12

15.10. Clinical data like those described in Example 15.9.3 are summarized in the table.

	Results	
Treatment	*Cured*	*Not Cured*
Old	3	21
New	7	14

Apply the "exact" method.

15.11. In a classical book on mathematical statistics, 100 misprints and errors were found and corrected. The distribution of these 100 corrections among the 270 pages of the book was:

No. of Corrections per Page	*No. of Pages*
0	196
1	57
2	12
3	3
4	1
5	0
6	1
	270

Test the hypothesis that this is a sample of a Poisson variable.

15.12. Given a sample of size n, grouped in the intervals (x_1,x_2), (x_2,x_3), $\cdots$, (x_{k-1},x_k), (x_k,x_{k+1}), where $x_1 = 0$, $x_{k+1} = +\infty$. We wish to test the hypothesis that X has a probability density $f(x) = ae^{-aX}$ for $x \geq 0$, with $a > 0$, zero elsewhere. Derive the modified minimum χ^2 estimate for the parameter a.

CHAPTER 16

Some Parameter-Free and Distribution-Free Statistical Techniques

16.1   Concepts and Examples

In setting up confidence intervals or tests of statistical hypotheses, one usually makes some assumptions on the type of the probability distribution of the random variable from which the sample was obtained. For example, the confidence interval (12.3.1.4) was derived under the assumption that the sample was obtained for a normal random variable.

A statistical technique becomes more generally applicable if it assumes less knowledge about the probability distribution. For example, the confidence interval for $E(X)$ given by (13.2.2) was derived by the use of Chebyshev's inequality and requires the knowledge of σ_X, but does not assume any knowledge of the type of the probability distribution of X. Statistical techniques of this kind, which can be applied without the knowledge of the type of the probability distribution will be called "distribution-free." In specific cases additional explanations may be needed, since, while a distribution-free technique is usually applicable to a very general class of probability distributions, some restricting assumptions still may have to be made on that class, and these assumptions must be stated. For example, the confidence interval (13.2.2) can be used for any random variable, with the one restriction that $\sigma^2(X)$ is finite.

The χ^2 test described in the preceding chapter is an important example of a distribution-free technique, since the random variable X introduced in the first lines of 15.1 may have any probability distribution.

The present chapter will be devoted to the discussion of a number of other distribution-free statistical techniques.

16.2   Order Statistics

16.2.1.   Let X be a one-dimensional random variable and $X_1, X_2, \cdots, X_n$ a sample of X of size n. We reorder this sample increasingly and obtain $X_{k_1} \leq X_{k_2}, \cdots, \leq X_{k_n}$. Setting

$$U_1 = X_{k_1}, \qquad U_2 = X_{k_2}, \cdots, U_n = X_{k_n}$$

yields random variables $U_1, U_2, \cdots, U_j, \cdots, U_n$, known as *order statistics*. In particular, U_1 is the 1st order statistic or the *minimum* of the sample, U_n is the nth order statistic or the *maximum*, and if $n = 2m + 1$ the $(m + 1)$st order statistic is the *median* of the sample.

16.2.2. Theorem.   Let $U_{r_1}, U_{r_2}, \cdots, U_{r_k}$ be order statistics such that $1 \leq r_1 < r_2 < \cdots < r_k \leq n$, for a continuous random variable X with the probability density $f(X)$. Then the joint probability element of the k-dimensional random variable $(U_{r_1}, U_{r_2}, \cdots, U_{r_k})$ is

(16.2.2.1)

$$g(U_{r_1}, U_{r_2}, \cdots, U_{r_k}) dU_{r_1} dU_{r_2} \cdots dU_{r_k}$$

$$= \frac{n!}{(r_1 - 1)!\,(r_2 - r_1 - 1)!\,(r_3 - r_2 - 1)! \cdots (n - r_k)!}$$

$$\times f(U_{r_1}) f(U_{r_2}) \cdots f(U_{r_k})$$

$$\times \left(\int_{-\infty}^{U_{r_1}} f(X) dX \right)^{r_1 - 1} \left(\int_{U_{r_1}}^{U_{r_2}} f(X) dX \right)^{r_2 - r_1 - 1}$$

$$\times \left(\int_{U_{r_2}}^{U_{r_3}} f(X) dX \right)^{r_3 - r_2 - 1} \cdots \left(\int_{U_{r_k}}^{+\infty} f(X) dX \right)^{n - r_k} dU_{r_1} dU_{r_2} \cdots dU_{r_k}$$

for $U_{r_1} \leq U_{r_2} \leq \cdots \leq U_{r_k}$ and zero elsewhere

Proof.   To find the joint probability element of $U_{r_1}, \cdots, U_{r_k}$, we consider the intervals $(-\infty, U_{r_1}), (U_{r_1}, U_{r_1} + dU_{r_1}), (U_{r_1} + dU_{r_1}, U_{r_2}), (U_{r_2}, U_{r_2} + dU_{r_2}), \cdots, (U_{r_{k-1}} + dU_{r_{k-1}}, U_{r_k}), (U_{r_k}, U_{r_k} + dU_{r_k}), (U_{r_k} + dU_{r_k}, +\infty)$, which will be denoted by $J_1, J_2, \cdots, J_{2k+1}$, and introduce the notation

$$P(X \in J_j) = q_j \quad \text{for } j = 1, 2, \cdots, 2k + 1$$

The probability element $g(U_{r_1}, U_{r_2}, \cdots, U_{r_k}) dU_{r_1} dU_{r_2} \cdots dU_{r_k}$ is the probability that, in a sample $(X_1, X_2, \cdots, X_n)$, $(r_1 - 1)$ values fall into J_1, one value into J_2, $(r_2 - r_1 - 1)$ values into J_3, one value into $J_4, \cdots$, one value into J_{2k}, $(n - r_k)$ into J_{2k+1}. This, in turn, is the multinomial probability

$$\frac{n!}{(r_1 - 1)!\,1!\,(r_2 - r_1 - 1)!\,1! \cdots 1!\,(n - r_k)!} q_1^{r_1 - 1} q_2^{\,1} q_3^{r_2 - r_1 - 1} q_4^{\,1} \cdots q_{2k}^{\,1} q_{2k+1}^{n - r_k}$$

and this becomes (16.2.2.1) if one replaces $P(U < X < U + dU)$ by $f(U) dU$.

16.2.3. Theorem.   The probability element of the minimum U_1 of a sample of size n is

(16.2.3.1)
$$n\left(\int_{U_1}^{+\infty} f(X)dX\right)^{n-1} f(U_1)dU_1$$

and the probability element of the maximum U_n

(16.2.3.2)
$$n\left(\int_{-\infty}^{U_n} f(X)dX\right)^{n-1} f(U_n)dU_n$$

Proof.   (16.2.3.1) follows immediately from (16.2.2.1) by setting $k = 1$, $r_1 = 1$, and (16.2.3.2) follows similarly for $k = 1$, $r_1 = n$.

16.2.4. Example.   Let X be the random variable with uniform distribution in $(0,1)$. Then (16.2.3.1) becomes

$$n\left(\int_{U_1}^{1} 1dX\right)^{n-1} 1dU_1 = n(1 - U_1)^{n-1}dU_1 \quad \text{for } 0 \leq U_1 \leq 1$$

and zero elsewhere, and the probability $P(U_1 < u)$ is

$$1 - (1 - u)^n$$

This can be verified directly, since it is the probability that not all n values of the sample fall into $(u,1)$.

16.2.5. Example.   Let X have the probability density

$$f(x) = \begin{cases} e^{-x} & \text{for } x \geq 0 \\ 0 & \text{for } x < 0 \end{cases}$$

Then the probability element of the minimum is $ne^{-nU_1}dU_1$ for $U_1 \geq 0$, zero for $U_1 < 0$, and the cumulative probability function is

$$P(U_1 \leq u) = \int_0^u ne^{-nU_1}dU_1 = 1 - e^{-nu}$$

16.2.6. Theorem.   If $n = 2m + 1$, the probability element of the median U_{m+1} is

(16.2.6.1) $\dfrac{(2m + 1)!}{(m!)^2} \left(\displaystyle\int_{-\infty}^{U_{m+1}} f(x)dx\right)^m \left(\displaystyle\int_{U_{m+1}}^{+\infty} f(x)dx\right)^m f(U_{m+1})dU_{m+1}$

Proof.   From (16.2.2.1) by setting $k = 1$, $r_1 = m + 1$.

16.2.7. Example.   For the uniformly distributed random variable of Example 16.2.4, the median $U_{m+1} = M$ has the probability density

$$\frac{(2m + 1)!}{(m!)^2} [M(1 - M)]^m \quad \text{for } 0 \leq M \leq 1, \text{ zero elsewhere}$$

16.2.8. Theorem.   Let $R = U_n - U_1$ denote the *range* of a sample of size n. Then the probability density of R is

(16.2.8.1) $$n(n-1) \int_{-\infty}^{+\infty} \left(\int_s^{s+R} f(x)dx \right)^{n-2} f(s) f(s+R) ds$$

for $R \geq 0$, zero elsewhere

Proof.   The joint probability element of (U_1, U_n) is, according to (16.2.2.1),

(16.2.8.2) $$\frac{n!}{(n-2)!} f(U_1) f(U_n) \left(\int_{U_1}^{U_n} f(x)dx \right)^{n-2} dU_1 dU_n$$

for $U_n \geq U_1$, zero elsewhere

Making the change of variables

$$U_n - U_1 = R$$
$$U_1 = s$$

and integrating with respect to s, we obtain (16.2.8.1).

16.3   Tolerance Limits

16.3.1.   In industrial quality control the following question is of interest. Let X be a dimension of the unit product, subject to random variations. A sample of n units is taken at random and measured, and the smallest and the largest measurements U_1 and U_n are recorded. Is it possible, for given small numbers $\varepsilon > 0$, $\alpha > 0$, to choose n so large that it can be asserted with probability $1 - \varepsilon$ that $P(U_1 \leq X \leq U_n) \geq 1 - \alpha$?

An analogous question often occurs in biological research. How many adult individuals of a species does one have to catch and measure to be reasonably assured (on a given probability level $1 - \varepsilon$) that the range of the sample contains all individuals of the species except for a preassigned small fraction α?

To develop a theory which will make it possible to answer questions of this kind, we will introduce the concept of tolerance limits.

Let L and U be two statistics such that $L \leq U$ for all samples. For a given random variable X, and sample size n, the random variable

(16.3.1.1) $$V = P(L \leq X \leq U)$$

will be called the "coverage" of X by the interval (L,U). Intuitively, the value of V describes the fraction of the total population X contained between the values of the random variables L and U determined by a sample.

The two statistics L and U will be called α *tolerance limits with probability level* $1 - \varepsilon$ for a given random variable X and sample size n, if

(16.3.1.2) $$P(V \geq 1 - \alpha) = 1 - \varepsilon$$

where V is defined by (16.3.1.1), and α, ε are given real numbers such that $0 < \alpha < 1, 0 < \varepsilon < 1$.

Intuitively, again, (16.3.1.2) means that the probability that more than the fraction α of the total population X remains outside of the random interval (L, U) is equal to ε.

Let X be a one-dimensional continuous random variable with probability density $f(X)$, and let the notations be the same as in Section 16.2. We consider the coverage defined by

$$L = U_1 = \text{minimum of sample}$$
$$U = U_n = \text{maximum of sample}$$

Then the fraction of the total population contained between U_1 and U_n, as defined by (16.3.1.1), is

(16.3.1.3)
$$V = \int_{U_1}^{U_n} f(x)dx$$

We will now study this random variable V.

The joint probability element of (U_1, U_n) is given in (16.2.8.2). The change of variables

$$V = \int_{U_1}^{U_n} f(x)dx$$

$$W = \int_{-\infty}^{U_1} f(x)dx$$

has a Jacobian with the absolute value $1/f(U_1)f(U_n)$ and hence transforms (16.2.8.2) into the probability element of (V, W)

(16.3.1.4)
$$h(v,w)dvdw = \frac{n!}{(n-2)!} v^{n-2} \, dvdw$$

$$\text{for } v \geq 0, \, w \geq 0, \, v + w \leq 1, \text{ zero elsewhere}$$

The probability density (16.3.1.4) has the remarkable property of being independent of the original distribution $f(x)$. Integrating out w, we obtain

$$\psi(v)dv = n(n-1)v^{n-2} \int_0^{1-v} dwdv = n(n-1)v^{n-2}(1-v)dv$$

$$\text{for } 0 \leq v \leq 1 \text{ and zero elsewhere}$$

We have proved the following statement due to S. S. Wilks.

16.3.2. Theorem. If X is a one-dimensional continuous random variable with the probability density $f(x)$, then the random variable

(16.3.2.1)
$$V = \int_{U_1}^{U_n} f(x)dx$$

has the probability density

(16.3.2.2) $\psi(v) = n(n-1)v^{n-2}(1-v)$ for $0 \leq v \leq 1$, zero elsewhere

Two properties of the probability distribution (16.3.2.2) are worth noting. First, it is independent of $f(x)$; second, the expectation of V is

$$E(V) = \frac{n-1}{n+1}$$

and the variance

$$\sigma^2(V) = \frac{2(n-1)}{(n+1)^2(n+2)}$$

and since

$$\lim_{n \to \infty} E(V) = 1, \qquad \lim_{n \to \infty} \sigma^2(V) = 0$$

the random variable V converges stochastically to 1 as $n \to \infty$.

From these two properties we see that, for given α and ε such that $0 < \alpha < 1, 0 < \varepsilon < 1$, there exists an integer $N(\alpha,\varepsilon)$ such that

$$P(0 \le 1 - V \le \alpha) \ge 1 - \varepsilon$$

for any $n \ge N(\alpha,\varepsilon)$. This, however, means that for sample size $n \ge N(\alpha,\varepsilon)$ the minimum U_1 and the maximum U_n are α tolerance limits with probability level $1 - \varepsilon$, and these tolerance limits are distribution free.

To obtain a more definite result, we shall determine N so that

$$P(V \ge 1 - \alpha) = N(N-1) \int_{1-\alpha}^{1} V^{N-2}(1 - V)dV = 1 - \varepsilon$$

This equality is equivalent with

(16.3.2.3) $N(1 - \alpha)^{N-1} - (N - 1)(1 - \alpha)^N = \varepsilon$

and $N(\alpha,\varepsilon)$ is the least integer greater than or equal to the solution N of this equation. While (16.3.2.3), for given α,ε, is a transcendental equation and has no simple general solution, it can always be solved by numerical tabulation or by graphical methods. A number of values of $N(\alpha,\varepsilon)$ obtained by solving (16.3.2.3) is given in Table IV at the end of the book.

16.3.3. Example. How large must a sample be so that it can be asserted with a probability of 99% that at least 95% of the population is between U_1 and U_n? Equation (16.3.2.3) becomes

$$N(0.95)^{N-1} - (N - 1)(0.95)^N = 0.01$$

or

$$(0.95)^{N-1} = \frac{1}{5N + 95} \qquad i.e. \ (1-\alpha)^{N-1} = \frac{\varepsilon}{\alpha N + (1-\alpha)}$$

By trial it will be found that $N = 130$ is an approximate solution, and hence $N(0.05, 0.01) = 130$. This can also be read off from Table IV.

solve by $\quad (N-1) \log(1-\alpha) = \log \varepsilon - \log[\alpha N + (1-\alpha)]$

16.4 Distribution-Free Confidence Bands for Cumulative Distribution Functions of Continuous Random Variables

16.4.1. The Integral Transformation. Let X be a continuous random variable with the probability density $f(x)$ and the d.f.

$$F(x) = \int_{-\infty}^{x} f(s)ds$$

We consider the new random variable Y obtained by playing X, substituting its value for x in $F(x)$ and reading off

(16.4.1.1) $$Y = F(X)$$

Equality (16.4.1.1) is known as the *integral transformation* of the random variable X.

16.4.2. Theorem. The random variable Y obtained by the integral transformation (16.4.1.1) has the uniform probability distribution in the interval $0 \leq Y \leq 1$, no matter what $F(x)$.

Proof. We clearly have

(16.4.2.1) $$P(Y < y) = 0 \quad \text{for } y < 0$$
(16.4.2.2) $$P(Y < y) = 1 \quad \text{for } y > 1$$

Since $y = F(x)$ is a continuous non-decreasing function, we may define the inverse function $x = F^{(-1)}(y)$ by setting

$$x = F^{(-1)}(y) = \text{the least value } x \text{ such that } F(x) = y$$

For $0 \leq Y \leq 1$ we obtain

$$P(Y \leq y) = P(F(X) \leq y) = P(X \leq F^{(-1)}(y)) = F(F^{(-1)}(y)) = y$$

and this, together with (16.4.2.1) and (16.4.2.2) proves our theorem.

16.4.3. Let $X_1, X_2, \cdots, X_N$ be a sample of X. We define the *empirical distribution function* (e.d.f.) by

(16.4.3.1) $$F_N(x) = \frac{1}{N} \cdot (\text{number of values } X_j \text{ such that } X_j \leq x)$$

The e.d.f. is a step function with N steps, each of height $1/N$. It depends on the sample, hence may be described as a random function. Obviously $F_N(x) = 0$ for $x < \min(X_1, \cdots, X_N)$ and $F_N(x) = 1$ for $x \geq \max(X_1, \cdots, X_N)$. Intuitively one would expect that, for N large, the e.d.f. should be close to the d.f. $F(x)$. Let us consider the random variable

(16.4.3.2) $$D_N = \underset{-\infty < x < +\infty}{\text{l.u.b.}} \ |F_N(x) - F(x)|$$

that is the largest vertical discrepancy between the graphs of $F_N(x)$ and of $F(x)$. This random variable is known as *Kolmogorov's statistic*, and Theorems 16.4.4 and 16.4.5 below were obtained by Kolmogorov.

16.4.4. Theorem. For any given positive integer N the probability distribution of the random variable D_N is the same for any continuous random variable X and, in particular, is the same as for the random variable X which is uniformly distributed in $0 \leq X \leq 1$.

Proof. The integral transformation (16.4.1.1) ascribes to each sample $X_1, X_2, \cdots, X_N$ of X a sample $Y_1, Y_2, \cdots, Y_n$ of Y, and to the e.d.f. $F_N(x)$ an e.d.f. $G_N(y)$, while the d.f. $F(x)$ is transformed into the d.f. $G(y) = y$ for $0 \leq y \leq 1$, $G(y) = 0$ for $y < 0$, $G(y) = 1$ for $y > 1$. For any sample $X_1, \cdots, X_N$ and the corresponding sample $Y_1, \cdots, Y_N$, we have

$$D_N = \text{l.u.b.} \underset{(x)}{|F_N(x) - F(x)|}$$

$$= \text{l.u.b.} \underset{(y)}{|G_N(y) - G(y)|} = D'_N$$

Hence, for any two real numbers $r < s$, we have

$$P(r < D_N < s) = P(r < D'_N < s)$$

which proves our theorem.

Having thus seen that D_N is a distribution-free statistic, we will proceed to evaluate its probability distribution assuming that X is uniformly distributed in the unit interval, that is, has the d.f.

$$F(x) = \begin{cases} 0 & \text{for } x < 0 \\ x & \text{for } 0 \leq x < 1 \\ 1 & \text{for } 1 \leq x \end{cases}$$

Let $U_1, U_2, \cdots, U_N$ be the order statistics determined by a sample of size N. The e.d.f. then is

$$F_N(x) = \begin{cases} 0 & \text{for } x < U_1 \\ \dfrac{k}{N} & \text{for } U_k \leq x < U_{k+1}, \quad k = 1, 2, \cdots, N-1 \\ 1 & \text{for } U_N \leq x \end{cases}$$

and we have

$$D_N = \text{l.u.b.} \underset{0 \leq x \leq 1}{|F_N(x) - x|}$$

It is easily seen that D_N is a continuous random variable with a d.f. $\Phi_N(\lambda) = P(D_N \leq \lambda)$ such that $\Phi_N(\lambda) = 0$ for $\lambda < 1/2N$.

16.4.5. Theorem. For integer c, $1 \le c \le N$, we have

(16.4.5.1) $$P\left(D_N \le \frac{c}{N}\right) = \phi_N\left(\frac{c}{N}\right) = \frac{N!}{N^N}\, e^N R_{0,N}(c)$$

where $R_{i,k}(c)$ are numbers determined by the recursion formulas

(16.4.5.2) $$R_{0,0}(c) = 1, \qquad R_{i,0}(c) = 0 \quad \text{for } i \ne 0$$

(16.4.5.3) $$R_{i,k}(c) = 0 \quad \text{for } |i| \ge c$$

(16.4.5.4) $$R_{i,k+1}(c) = e^{-1} \sum_{s=0}^{i+c} R_{i+1-s,k}\, \frac{1}{s!}$$

Proof. The values of $F_N(x)$ are multiples of $1/N$, so that

$$F_N(x) = \frac{i}{N}$$

with $i = i(x)$ integer and $0 \le i \le N$. Any x in $[0,1]$ may be written

$$x = \frac{j}{N} + \varepsilon$$

where $j = j(x)$ is an integer, $0 \le j \le N$, and $\varepsilon = \varepsilon(x)$ is a real number such that $0 \le \varepsilon < 1/N$. We have

$$F_N(x) - x = \frac{i - j}{N} - \varepsilon$$

Since $F_N(x)$ is non-decreasing, we obtain for any x

$$F_N\left(\frac{j}{N}\right) - \frac{j}{N} \le F_N(x) - (x - \varepsilon) = \frac{i - j}{N}$$

$$F_N\left(\frac{j+1}{N}\right) - \frac{j+1}{N} \ge F_N(x) - \left(x + \frac{1}{N} - \varepsilon\right) = \frac{i - j - 1}{N}$$

In order that, for a definite x, we have

(16.4.5.5) $$|F_N(x) - x| > \frac{c}{N}$$

either (a) $F_N(x) - x < -\dfrac{c}{N}$ or (b) $F_N(x) - x > \dfrac{c}{N}$ must be fulfilled.

In case (a) we have

$$F_N\left(\frac{j}{N}\right) - \frac{j}{N} \le F_N(x) - x + \varepsilon = \frac{i - j}{N} < -\frac{c}{N} + \varepsilon$$

and since $0 \le \varepsilon < \dfrac{1}{N}$ and $i - j$ is an integer, we must have

(16.4.5.6) $$F_N\left(\frac{j}{N}\right) - \frac{j}{N} \le \frac{i - j}{N} \le -\frac{c}{N}$$

In case (b) we obtain

$$F_N\left(\frac{j+1}{N}\right) - \frac{j+1}{N} \geq F_N(x) - x - \left(\frac{1}{N} - \varepsilon\right)$$

$$= \frac{i-j-1}{N} > \frac{c}{N} - \left(\frac{1}{N} - \varepsilon\right)$$

and again, from $i - j - 1$ being an integer and $0 < 1/N - \varepsilon \leq 1/N$, we conclude

(16.4.5.7) $$F_N\left(\frac{j+1}{N}\right) - \frac{j+1}{N} \geq \frac{i-j-1}{N} \geq \frac{c}{N}$$

Hence if (16.4.5.5) is true for a value x, either (16.4.5.6) or (16.4.5.7) must be true for $j = j(x)$. Therefore

$$P\left(D_N > \frac{c}{N}\right) = P\left(\text{l.u.b.}_{0 \leq x \leq 1} |F_N(x) - x| > \frac{c}{N}\right)$$

$$\leq P\left(\text{l.u.b.}_{j=0,1,\cdots,N} \left|F_N\left(\frac{j}{N}\right) - \frac{j}{N}\right| \geq \frac{c}{N}\right)$$

The inequality

$$P\left(D_N \geq \frac{c}{N}\right) \geq P\left(\text{l.u.b.}_{j=0,1,\cdots,N} \left|F_N\left(\frac{j}{N}\right) - \frac{j}{N}\right| \geq \frac{c}{N}\right)$$

is obvious. Since D_N has a continuous d.f., and hence

$$P\left(D_N > \frac{c}{N}\right) = P\left(D_N \geq \frac{c}{N}\right),$$

we see that

$$P\left(D_N > \frac{c}{N}\right) = P\left(\text{l.u.b.}_{j=0,1,\cdots,N} \left|F_N\left(\frac{j}{N}\right) - \frac{j}{N}\right| \geq \frac{c}{N}\right)$$

$$\phi_N\left(\frac{c}{N}\right) = 1 - P\left(\text{l.u.b.}_{j=0,1,\cdots,N} \left|F_N\left(\frac{j}{N}\right) - \frac{j}{N}\right| \geq \frac{c}{N}\right)$$

and

(16.4.5.8) $$\phi_N\left(\frac{c}{N}\right) = P\left(\left|F_N\left(\frac{j}{N}\right) - \frac{j}{N}\right| < \frac{c}{N}\right) \quad \text{for } j = 0, 1, \cdots, N$$

For any integer i and $k = 0, 1, \cdots, N$, let $E_{i,k}$ be the event

$$E_{i,k}: \begin{cases} \left|F_N\left(\frac{j}{N}\right) - \frac{j}{N}\right| < \frac{c}{N}, & j = 0, 1, \cdots, k \\[2mm] F_N\left(\frac{k}{N}\right) - \frac{k}{N} = \frac{i}{N} \end{cases}$$

and let

$$P_{i,k} = P(E_{i,k})$$

It follows from the definition of $E_{i,k}$ that

(16.4.5.9) $\qquad\qquad\qquad P_{0,0} = 1, \qquad P_{i,0} = 0 \quad \text{for } i \neq 0$

(16.4.5.10) $\qquad\qquad\qquad P_{i,k} = 0 \quad \text{for } |i| \geq c$

and, from (16.4.5.8),

(16.4.5.11) $\qquad\qquad\qquad \Phi_N\left(\dfrac{c}{N}\right) = P_{0,N}$

To obtain a recursion formula for $P_{i,k}$, we consider the expansion

(16.4.5.12)

$$P_{i,k+1} = \sum_{l=-(c-1)}^{c-1} P_{l,k} P(E_{i,k+1} \mid E_{l,k}) \quad \text{for } i = -(c-1), \cdots, c-1$$

We write

$$P_{i,k+1 \mid l,k} = P(E_{i,k+1} \mid E_{l,k})$$

for the conditional probability that

(16.4.5.13) $\quad \left| F_N\left(\dfrac{j}{N}\right) - \dfrac{j}{N} \right| < \dfrac{c}{N} \quad \text{for } j = 0, 1, \cdots, k+1$

and

(16.4.5.14) $\qquad\qquad F_N\left(\dfrac{k+1}{N}\right) - \dfrac{k+1}{N} = \dfrac{i}{N}$

if

(16.4.5.15) $\quad \left| F_N\left(\dfrac{j}{N}\right) - \dfrac{j}{N} \right| < \dfrac{c}{N} \quad \text{for } j = 0, 1, \cdots, k$

and

(16.4.5.16) $\qquad\qquad F_N\left(\dfrac{k}{N}\right) - \dfrac{k}{N} = \dfrac{l}{N}$

Since (16.4.5.13) follows from (16.4.5.14) and (16.4.5.15), $P_{i,k+1 \mid l,k}$ is the probability that (16.4.5.14) if (16.4.5.15) and (16.4.5.16), that is the probability that

$$F_N\left(\dfrac{k+1}{N}\right) = \dfrac{k+i+1}{N}$$

if (16.4.5.16) and

$$F_N\left(\dfrac{k}{N}\right) = \dfrac{k+l}{N}$$

In other words, $P_{i,k+1 \mid l,k}$ is the probability that, if $(k+l)$ sample points fall in the interval $[0, k/N]$ and satisfy (16.4.5.15), exactly $(i+1-l)$ sample points fall in the interval $\left(\dfrac{k}{N}, \dfrac{k+1}{N}\right]$. Since (16.4.5.15) is determined only by the position of the $(k + l)$ sample points in $[0, k/N]$, and this has no effect on the probabilities of the sample points outside $[0, k/N]$, we conclude

$$P_{i,k+1 \mid l,k} = P\Big\{(i + 1 - l) \text{ sample points in } \Big(\frac{k}{N}, \frac{k+1}{N}\Big]$$

$$\text{if } (l + k) \text{ sample points in } [0, k/N]\Big\} =$$

$$\frac{\dfrac{N!}{(l + k)! \, (i + 1 - l)! \, (N - i - k - 1)!}\Big(\dfrac{k}{N}\Big)^{l+k} \Big(\dfrac{1}{N}\Big)^{i+1-l} \Big(\dfrac{N - k - 1}{N}\Big)^{N-i-k-1}}{\dfrac{N!}{(l + k)! \, (N - l - k)!}\Big(\dfrac{k}{N}\Big)^{l+k} \Big(\dfrac{N - k}{N}\Big)^{N-l-k}}$$

$$= \frac{(N - l - k)!}{(i + 1 - l)! \, (N - i - k - 1)!} \cdot \frac{(N - k - 1)^{N-i-k-1}}{(N - k)^{N-l-k}}$$

or

$$P_{i,k+1 \mid l,k} = \binom{N - l - k}{i + 1 - l}\Big(\frac{1}{N - k}\Big)^{i+1-l}\Big(1 - \frac{1}{N - k}\Big)^{N-i-k-1} \qquad \text{for } 0 \leq l \leq i + 1$$

$$P_{i,k+1 \mid l,k} = 0 \qquad \qquad \text{for } i + 1 < l$$

This together with (16.4.5.12) yields

(16.4.5.17)

$$P_{i,k+1} = \sum_{l=-(c-1)}^{\min(c-1,\,i+1)} P_{l,k}\binom{N - l - k}{i + 1 - l}\Big(\frac{1}{N - k}\Big)^{i+1-l}\Big(1 - \frac{1}{N - k}\Big)^{N-i-k-1}$$

From (16.4.5.9), (16.4.5.10), and (16.4.5.17) one can compute all $P_{i,k}$, and (16.4.5.11) will yield $\phi_N(c/N)$. If one introduces the quantities

$$R_{i,k} = P_{i,k}\frac{(N - k - i)!}{(N - k)^{N-k-i}} e^{-k}\frac{N^N}{N!}$$

these relations take the more convenient form (16.4.5.2), (16.4.5.3), (16.4.5.4), and (16.4.5.1), presented in Theorem 16.4.5.

For large N the probability distribution of D_N can be evaluated asymptotically according to the following theorem.

16.4.6. Theorem. For the random variable D_N defined by (16.4.3.2) and for any $z > 0$ we have

(16.4.6.1) $$\lim_{N \to \infty} P(D_N < zN^{-1/2}) = L(z)$$

where

(16.4.6.2) $$L(z) = 1 - 2\sum_{s=1}^{\infty}(-1)^{s-1}e^{-2s^2z^2}$$

The proof of this theorem is too difficult to be presented here. It may, however, be of interest to show how it can be used to set up distribution-free confidence bands for $F(x)$.

Let $\varepsilon > 0$ and $\alpha > 0$ be given. We wish to determine $N_{\alpha,\varepsilon}$ so large that

$$P(\text{l.u.b.}\ |F_N(x) - F(x)| < \varepsilon) = P(D_N < \varepsilon) \geq 1 - \alpha$$

for $N > N_{\alpha,\varepsilon}$. To do this, we determine z_α such that $L(z_\alpha) = 1 - \alpha$, which can be done from Table VI at the end of the book. Then, from $z_\alpha N^{-1/2} = \varepsilon$, we obtain $N_{\alpha,\varepsilon} = (z_\alpha/\varepsilon)^2$, provided this value $N_{\alpha,\varepsilon}$ is large enough to use the approximate equality $P(D_N < z_\alpha N_{\alpha,\varepsilon}^{-1/2}) = L(z_\alpha)$. Intuitively this means that, for $N > N_{\alpha,\varepsilon}$, we have a probability $\geq 1 - \alpha$ that a band contained between $F_N(x) - \varepsilon$ and $F_N(x) + \varepsilon$ will contain all of the d.f. $F(x)$. Such a band is referred to as *confidence band for $F(x)$ with the confidence level* $1 - \alpha$.

16.4.6.3. Example. For $\varepsilon = 0.01$, $\alpha = 0.05$, we have $z_\alpha = 1.36$, hence

$$N_{\alpha,\varepsilon} = \left(\frac{1.36}{0.01}\right)^2 = 18,496$$

16.4.7. The recursion formulas of 16.4.5 make it possible to compute the probability distribution of D_N exactly for finite N not large enough to use the approximation of 16.4.6. Tables of this exact distribution were obtained and some useful values are reproduced in Table V.

16.4.8. Let now $(X_1, X_2, \cdots, X_m)$ and $(X_1', X_2', \cdots, X_n')$ be independent samples of the same continuous random variable X with the distribution function $F(x)$. We consider the corresponding e.d. functions $F_m(x)$ and $F_n(x)$, and the random variable $D_{m,n}$ defined by

(16.4.8.1) $$D_{m,n} = \underset{-\infty < x < \infty}{\text{l.u.b.}}\ |F_m(x) - F_n(x)|$$

known as *Smirnov's statistic*.

16.4.9. Theorem. For any given pair of positive integers m and n, the probability distribution of $D_{m,n}$ is the same for any random variable X, and in particular the same as for the random variable X which has uniform distribution in $0 \leq X \leq 1$.

The proof is quite analogous to that of Theorem 16.4.4. Thus $D_{m,n}$ is a distribution-free statistic. The exact probability distribution of $D_{m,n}$ can be obtained for finite m,n by numerical methods. The following asymptotic theorem is due to Smirnov.

16.4.10. Theorem (Smirnov's Theorem).   Let

$$N = \frac{mn}{m+n}$$

and let

$$m \to \infty, \qquad n \to \infty$$

so that

$$\lim \frac{m}{n} = a$$

where a is a finite positive number. Under these conditions we have

(16.4.10.1) $\lim P(D_{m,n} < zN^{-1/2}) = L(z)$

where $L(z)$ is defined by (16.4.6.2).

Again, the difficult proof of this theorem will not be presented here.

An immediate application of Theorem 16.4.10 is the following test of the hypothesis that two continuous random variables have the same probability distribution:

If samples of size m and size n of X and X', respectively, are available such that $N = mn/(m+n)$ is large and m/n is neither very close to zero nor very large, then (16.4.10.1) may be replaced by an approximate equality. If then, for given significance level α, we determine z_α from Table VI, we have approximately

$$P(D_{m,n} < z_\alpha N^{-1/2}) = 1 - \alpha$$

and if the observed value of $D_{m,n}$ is greater than or equal to $z_\alpha N^{-1/2}$, we will reject the hypothesis.

16.4.10.2. Example.   Available are samples of X and X', of sizes $m = 300$, $n = 600$, so that $N = 200$. For $\alpha = 0.01$, we have $z_\alpha = 1.63$, The observed value of $D_{m,n}$ is $D_{300,600} = 0.16$. Since $z_\alpha N^{-1/2} = 1.63/\sqrt{200} = 0.115$ and the observed $D_{m,n}$ is greater, we reject on the (0.01) level the hypothesis that the continuous random variables X and X' have the same probability distribution.

EXERCISES

16.1. Let X have the probability density $f(x) = (1/2a) \exp(-|x|/a)$ for all real x. Find the probability density of the maximum U_n of a sample of size n. Compute $P(U_n \geq u)$ for $u \geq 0$. For $n = 20$, $a = 1$, tabulate $P(U_n \geq u)$ at $u = 0, 0.5, 1.0, 1.5, \cdots$, until $P(U_n \geq u) < 0.0005$.

16.2. For $f(x) = (1/\sqrt{2\pi})e^{-x^2/2}$ and $n = 2$ find explicitly the probability density of the range.

16.3. Let $U_1, U_2, \cdots, U_{n-1}, U_n$ be the order statistics of a sample of size n of a continuous random variable with probability density $f(x)$. Derive the probability density of the random variable

$$W = \int_{U_2}^{U_{n-1}} f(x)dx$$

Generalize this by deriving the probability density of

$$Z = \int_{U_k}^{U_{n+1-k}} f(x)dx$$

CHAPTER 17

Elements of a General Theory of Statistical Inference

17.1 Up to about twenty years ago the two main classes of problems considered by theoretical statisticians were those of testing hypotheses and of estimating parameters. It has been recognized more recently that these two types of problems do not include many practical situations confronting a statistician, and a more general theory has been developed which deals with so-called decision problems. To illustrate problems of this kind we consider the following examples.

17.1.1. Example. A public health expert is interested in the occurrence of certain microorganisms in a body of water. If the average number of these microorganisms per cubic centimeter is ω, then it may be assumed that, when a sample of v cc is taken, the number X of the microorganisms in the sample is a random variable with the Poisson distribution

$$P(X = x) = \frac{e^{-\omega v}(\omega v)^x}{x!}, \quad x = 0, 1, 2, \cdots$$

The public health official takes a measured volume v_0 of the water, determines the number x of microorganisms in it, and may now be faced with one of the following problems. (*a*) He is instructed to take a certain action, for example, declare the water as polluted, if he decides that ω is greater than a specified value ω_0. In this case he will use the outcome of his experiment either to reject the hypothesis $H: \omega \le \omega_0$ or to accept it, and the statistical procedure used by him will be a test of a hypothesis. (*b*) He has to obtain a number $\hat{\omega}$ which can be considered a reasonable estimate of the true ω, and transmit this $\hat{\omega}$ to his superiors; in this case he performs an estimation of the parameter ω. (*c*) He may have instructions telling him to take action a_1 (e.g., declare the water safe) if $\omega < \omega_1$, take action a_2 (e.g., declare the water safe for swimming but not for drinking) if $\omega_1 \le \omega < \omega_2$, and to take action a_3 (close it for swimming and drinking) if $\omega_2 \le \omega$. He has the choice of three conclusions and corresponding actions, and this is not strictly a problem of estimation or testing hypotheses.

Another question would arise if the public health official had samples of water from k different sources, each of which has its ω_i, $i = 1, 2, \cdots, k$, and had to render an opinion on which source is least polluted. Again he would have to choose one of a number of possible decisions.

17.2   Outcome Space and Parameter Space

17.2.1.   Consider a set Z, with elements (points) z, which in many instances may be a Euclidean space, but sometimes has elements other than n-tuples of numbers; we shall refer to Z as the outcome space, which is consistent with the use of this term in Chapter 2, since we will consider random variables whose possible outcomes are in Z. Furthermore, let Ω be an abstract set of elements ω, such that for each $\omega \in \Omega$ there is a probability distribution P_ω on Z (i.e., a random variable with possible outcomes in Z) which is determined by ω. The set Ω will be called a *parameter space*. We have now three sets: the outcome space Z, the parameter space Ω, and the family P of all probability distributions P_ω such that $\omega \in \Omega$. The collection of any three such sets will be denoted by (Z, Ω, P).

17.2.2. Example.   Consider the following empirical situation. Items coming from a mass production process can be classified into good and defective. A lot of n such items is offered for sale. The purchaser tests m of them $(m < n)$, chosen at random, and finds z defective. A mathematical model for this situation could be this: let p be the true fraction of defectives in the lot $(0 \le p \le 1)$; then the probability of obtaining z defectives in a sample of m, assuming n very large as compared with m, is the binomial probability

$$\binom{m}{z} p^z (1 - p)^{m-z}$$

Here the outcome space Z is the set $Z = \{0, 1, 2, \cdots, m\}$, the parameter space $\Omega = \{p : 0 \le p \le 1\}$, and P consists of all binomial probability distributions with fixed m, corresponding to the values of p in Ω.

17.2.3. Action Space: Decision Functions.   The statistician is usually called upon to recommend a certain action. This is done under the following circumstances. He is provided with a collection A of possible actions (sometimes called decisions) a, of which he has to select one. This set A is called an *action space*. In making his selection, the statistician may use the knowledge that a specific outcome z in Z was observed. This he does according to some rule which tells him for each observed $z \in Z$ which $a \in A$ to choose. Any such rule is a function

$$a = d(z)$$

which maps Z into A, and is called a *decision function*.

A useful interpretation of a decision function is based on the fact that it also ascribes to each action $a \in A$ the set of all outcomes $z \in Z$ such that $d(z) = a$. A decision function may, therefore, also be defined as a partition of Z into the mutually exclusive sets

$$S_a = \{z : d(z) = a\}, \quad a \in A$$

$$\bigcup_{a \in A} S_a = Z$$

It has become an accepted usage to speak of statistical decision procedures as games between Nature and the statistician. In such a game Nature chooses, unknown to the statistician, a point ω in Ω. This point ω is sometimes called the "state of Nature." The statistician has a decision rule d, performs an experiment which yields a point z in Z, and takes action $a = d(z)$. In most practical situations it is up to the statistician to formulate his decision rule, although often he must take one of the rules out of a given set D of possible decision rules. The problem for him to answer is which of the decision rules available to him is most preferable. Rational procedures for selecting one decision rule as preferable to others may be obtained by using the concepts of the loss function and the risk function.

17.2.4. Loss Function.

If ω is the state of nature, then there may be practical considerations which make some actions in A more appropriate than others. For example, in the situation of 17.2.2, where the state of nature is the proportion p of defectives, if p is high it is appropriate to reject the lot and inappropriate to accept it. A way of expressing quantitatively the appropriateness of actions consists in assuming that if the state of nature is ω and the action a is taken, a loss $L(\omega,a)$ will result. This loss may be negative, i.e., a profit, and then one will be inclined to consider a a favorable action, given that ω is the true state of nature. The following is a formal definition.

For given parameter space Ω and action space A, any bounded real-valued function $L(\omega,a)$ defined for $\omega \in \Omega$, $a \in A$ is called a *loss function*.

17.2.5. Risk Function.

Let the triple (Z,Ω,P), an action space A, and a loss function $L(\omega,a)$ be given, and consider a specific decision function $d(z)$. For each state of nature ω, the loss $L(\omega,d(z))$ depends on the outcome z. We assume that $L(\omega,d(z))$ is a random variable, i.e., that it has a probability distribution (this can be proved always to be the case if certain assumptions on measurability are satisfied). Then, since L is by assumption bounded, the mathematical expectation of $L(\omega,d(z))$ always exists, and it depends on the state of nature ω and on the decision rule d; more explicitly: the state of nature ω determines the probability distribution of the outcome z, the observed outcome z determines the action $d(z)$, and ω and $d(z)$ together determine the loss L, so that the expectation of L is determined by Nature's choice of ω and the statistician's choice of d. We define: the mathematical expectation

$$E\{L[\omega,d(z)]; \ P_\omega\} = \rho(\omega,d)$$

is called the *risk function*.

17.2.6. The Minimax Decision Rule.

Let D be a class of decision rules from which the statistician may choose. Using the risk function we may compare different decision rules in D in the following manner.

For each fixed decision rule $d \in D$, the number

$$\sup_{\omega \in \Omega} \rho(\omega,d)$$

is the least upper bound of the risk which Nature may inflict on the statistician by choosing ω in Ω. Sometimes, although not always, there exists an ω_d such that

$$\rho(\omega_d,d) = \sup_{\omega \in \Omega} \rho(\omega,d)$$

In that case ω_d is called the "least favorable" value of ω for given d.

Of two decision rules d and d', we may agree to call d better if

$$\sup_{\omega \in \Omega} \rho(\omega,d) < \sup_{\omega \in \Omega} \rho(\omega,d')$$

In the sense of this agreement the minimax decision rule defined below, if it exists, would be the best rule in D:

For given triple (Z,Ω,P), action space A, loss function $L(\omega,a)$, and class D of decision functions, a decision rule $d\star \in D$ is called a *minimax decision rule* if

$$\sup_{\omega \in \Omega} \rho(\omega,d\star) = \inf_{d \in D} \left[\sup_{\omega \in \Omega} \rho(\omega,d) \right]$$

17.3 Tests of Hypotheses: Hypothesis, Alternative, Critical Region

In this section some of the concepts discussed in Chapter 13 will be more carefully formulated and discussed in some detail within the framework of decision theory.

For a given triple (Z,Ω,P), let H be a proper subset of the parameter space Ω, and H' a non-empty subset of $\Omega - H$. The set H will be called a *hypothesis* and H' an *alternative to H*. If $H' = \Omega - H$, then H' is called the *unrestricted alternative* to H.

We consider an action set A consisting of exactly two actions:

$a_1 = $ reject hypothesis H and accept alternative H'

$a_2 = $ accept H and reject H'

Any decision rule d must now be a partition of Z into two sets

$$W = \{z: d(z) = a_1\}, \qquad Z - W = \{z: d(z) = a_2\}$$

Such a decision rule is called a *test* of hypothesis H against alternative H', and the set W is called the *critical region* or region of rejection (of H against H'). Clearly a test is completely determined by giving W.

As an illustration consider (a) in Example 17.1.1. There

$$Z = \{0,1,2,\cdots\}, \quad \Omega = \{\omega \geq 0\}$$

P consists of all Poisson distributions with parameters $\omega \in \Omega$, $H = \{\omega \leq \omega_0\}$, $H' = \{\omega > \omega_0\}$ (unrestricted alternative), and the tests usually applied are given by critical regions of the form $W = \{x \geq n_0\}$ where n_0 is a critical number appropriately specified.

To state a problem in testing hypotheses one has, therefore, to specify (a) a triple (Z,Ω,P), (b) a hypothesis H and an alternative H'. Tests for such a problem are then sets W in Z, on which we shall still impose the condition that the probability $P_\omega(W)$ is defined for every $\omega \in \Omega$. It is customary to call H a *simple hypothesis* if it consists of one point $\omega \in \Omega$, otherwise H is called a *composite hypothesis*.

17.4   Two Kinds of Error. Power Function

17.4.1.   When we say "H is true" we mean $\omega \in H$ and similarly "H' is true" means $\omega \in H'$. The following four situations can occur in a problem in testing hypotheses when a test W is applied:

(a) $\quad \omega \in H$, $z \in W$, we reject H

(b) $\quad \omega \in H$, $z \in Z - W$, we accept H

(c) $\quad \omega \in H'$, $z \in W$, we reject H

(d) $\quad \omega \in H'$, $z \in Z - W$, we accept H

While in (b) and (c) the action taken is correct (the statistician inferred the true state of nature), the action in (a) and (d) is incorrect. Situation (a), i.e., rejection of H although it is true is called an *error of the first kind;* situation (d), i.e., accepting H although H' is true an *error of the second kind.*

Let the test W be fixed. Then the probability of rejecting H depends on the value of the parameter ω

$$P\{W;\omega\} = \psi_W(\omega), \quad \omega \in \Omega$$

and is called the *power function* of the test W. This terminology is due to the fact that for $\omega \in H'$ the function $\psi_W(\omega)$ is the probability of rejecting H if H' is true hence, intuitively, indicates the "power" of the test to discover the falseness of the hypothesis H. It appears desirable for a test to have a power function $\psi_W(\omega)$ which is small whenever $\omega \in H$ and large whenever $\omega \in H'$. Later on we shall discuss to what extent this can be achieved.

The number

$$\sup_{\omega \in H} \psi(\omega) = \alpha$$

is called the *size* of the test W. It is customary to prescribe for α one of the values $0.10, 0.05, 0.01, 0.001$ and to say that a test with this α has the size or the *significance level* 10%, 5%, 1%, 0.1%.

17.4.2. Comparison of Tests with Regard to Power.

Let (Z,Ω,P) and H and H' be given. If different tests W_1, W_2, $\cdots$ are considered, each of them has a power function which will be accordingly denoted by $\psi_{W_1}(\omega), \psi_{W_2}(\omega), \cdots$, and comparing these power functions may point out some relative properties of the tests. The following are a number of properties of tests, defined in terms of power functions, which are helpful in comparing different tests.

A test W of size α is called *unbiased* if

$$\psi_W(\omega) \geq \alpha \quad \text{for all } \omega \in H'$$

If W_1 and W_2 are two tests of size α, then W_1 is called *uniformly more powerful* than W_2 when

$$\psi_{W_1}(\omega) \geq \psi_{W_2}(\omega) \quad \text{for all } \omega \in H'$$

If strict inequality occurs in this inequality for some $\omega \in H'$, then W_1 is called uniformly more powerful than W_1 *in the strict sense*.

Often one has the choice of one of a class C of tests, all of size α. If there is among them a test which is uniformly more powerful than any other test in C, then it is called the *uniformly most powerful test* in C.

17.5 Likelihood Function and Likelihood Ratio Statistic

17.5.1.   Let Ω be a parameter space. For each $\omega \in \Omega$ there is a probability distribution for the random variable X. If X is a discrete random variable with the possible values ξ_i, $i = 1, 2, \cdots$, the corresponding probabilities will be denoted by

$$P\{X = \xi_i;\omega\} = f(\xi_i;\omega), \quad i = 1, 2, \cdots,$$

and if X is a continuous random variable, its probability density will be called $f(x;\omega)$. When a sample of given size n is obtained, its values X_1, X_2, $\cdots$, X_n determine an n-dimensional random variable $Z = (X_1, X_2, \cdots, X_n)$ with the probability distribution

(17.5.1.1) $$g(z;\omega) = f(x_1;\omega) f(x_2;\omega) \cdots f(x_n;\omega)$$

where $f(x_j;\omega)$ on the right-hand side stands for $P\{X = x_j;\omega\}$ if X is discrete, and for the probability density of X at $x = x_j$ if X is continuous, and clearly both sides of (17.5.1.1) depend on the true value ω of the parameter (the "state of Nature") which determines the distribution of X and which is not known to the statistician.

We now consider, for each $\omega^\star \in \Omega$, the quantity

(17.5.1.2) $$g(Z;\omega^\star) = f(X_1;\omega^\star) \cdots f(X_n;\omega^\star)$$

This quantity $g(Z;\omega^\star)$ is a function of the parameter value $\omega^\star$ which the statistician may choose at will, and of the sample $Z = (X_1, X_2, \cdots, X_n)$ obtained at random. It is therefore itself a one-dimensional, non-negative random variable whose probability distribution depends on both the statistician's choice $\omega^\star$ and on Nature's value ω of the parameter. This quantity $g(Z;\omega^\star)$ will be called the likelihood function or, for short, the *likelihood*.

We now consider the quantity

(17.5.1.3)
$$\lambda(Z) = \frac{\sup_{\omega^\star \in H} g(Z;\omega^\star)}{\sup_{\omega^\star \in H \cup H'} g(Z;\omega^\star)}$$

which is called the *likelihood ratio* (l.r.) or the *likelihood ratio statistic*. Clearly $\lambda(Z) = \lambda(X_1, \cdots, X_n)$ is a statistic such that

$$0 \leq \lambda(Z) \leq 1$$

and its value is determined by the observed value of the sample. The probability distribution of the statistic $\lambda(Z)$ is, therefore, determined by Nature's parameter value ω which determines the distribution of X. Intuitively, the numerator in (17.5.1.3) may be interpreted as the "best explanation" of the observed sample values within H, and the denominator as the best explanation of the observed sample values within $H \cup H'$.

We consider the test for H against H' defined by a critical region of the form

(17.5.1.4)
$$W(c) = \{z \colon \lambda(z) < c\}$$

which will be called a *likelihood ratio* (l.r.) *test* of H against H'. The size of such a test is given by

(17.5.1.5)
$$\alpha = \sup_{\omega \in H} P\{\lambda(Z) < c; \omega\}$$

17.5.2. Example.   We wish to test the simple hypothesis

$$H \colon N(a, \sigma^2)$$

against the unrestricted alternative

$$H' \colon N(\omega, \sigma^2), \quad \omega \neq a$$

with σ^2 and a given, using a sample $Z = (X_1, \cdots, X_n)$. Here the triple (Z, Ω, P) consists of

Z: the n-dimensional Euclidean space

Ω: the real number line

P: all $N(\omega, \sigma^2)$ with the given σ^2

and we have

$$g(Z;\omega^{\star}) = \prod_{j=1}^{n} \frac{1}{\sigma\sqrt{2\pi}} \exp\left[-\frac{(X_j - \omega^{\star})^2}{2\sigma^2}\right] = 2(\pi\sigma^2)^{-n/2}$$

$$\times \exp\left[-\frac{1}{2\sigma^2}\sum_{j=1}^{n}(X_j - \omega^{\star})^2\right]$$

$$\sup_{\omega^{\star}\in H} g(Z;\omega^{\star}) = g(Z;a) = (2\pi\sigma^2)^{-n/2}\exp\left[-\frac{1}{2\sigma^2}\sum_{j=1}^{n}(X_j - a)^2\right]$$

$$\sup_{\omega^{\star}\in H \cup H'} g(Z;\omega^{\star}) = \sup_{-\infty < \omega^{\star} < +\infty}(2\pi\sigma^2)^{-n/2}\exp\left[-\frac{1}{2\sigma^2}\sum_{j=1}^{n}(X_j - \omega^{\star})^2\right]$$

$$= (2\pi\sigma^2)^{-n/2}\exp\left[-\frac{1}{2\sigma^2}\sum_{j=1}^{n}(X_j - \bar{X})^2\right]$$

$$\lambda(Z) = \exp\left\{-\frac{1}{2\sigma^2}\left[\sum_{j=1}^{n}(X_j - a)^2 - \sum_{j=1}^{n}(X_j - \bar{X})^2\right]\right\}$$

$$= \exp\left[-\frac{n}{2\sigma^2}(\bar{X} - a)^2\right]$$

The corresponding l.r. test is therefore

(17.5.2.1) $W(c)$: $\{Z: \lambda(Z) < c\} = \left\{Z: |\bar{X}_n - a| > \frac{\sigma}{\sqrt{n}}\sqrt{2\log(1/c)}\right\}$

$$= \left\{Z: |\bar{X}_n - a| > \tau\frac{\sigma}{\sqrt{n}}\right\}$$

which is the test commonly used for the problem considered.

17.5.3. Power Function of the l.r. Test.   Once one has determined the family of regions $W(c)$: $\{Z: \lambda(Z) < c\}$, the next problems one may study are: (*a*) to obtain the probability distribution of the statistic $\lambda(Z)$ which in general depends on Nature's parameter value of the distribution of X; (*b*) to determine, if possible, c such that the size α in (17.5.1.5) assumes a prescribed value, 0.05, say; (*c*) to find the power function of this test.

17.5.3.1. Example.   For the problem of 17.5.2 and the test (17.5.2.1) we compute the power function

$$\psi(\omega) = P\{z \in W;\omega\}$$

$$= P\left\{|\bar{X}_n - a| > \tau\frac{\sigma}{\sqrt{n}}; \omega\right\}$$

(17.5.3.1.1)

$$= 1 - \frac{1}{\sqrt{2\pi}}\int_{\frac{a-\omega}{\sigma/\sqrt{n}}-\tau}^{\frac{a-\omega}{\sigma/\sqrt{n}}+\tau} e^{-s^2/2}ds$$

If H is true, that is, for $\omega = a$, this becomes

$$\psi(a) = 1 - \frac{1}{\sqrt{2\pi}} \int_{-\tau}^{+\tau} e^{-s^2/2} ds$$

To have a test of preassigned size α one determines from tables of the normal distribution τ_α such that

(17.5.3.1.2) $$\psi(a) = 1 - \frac{1}{\sqrt{2\pi}} \int_{-\tau_\alpha}^{+\tau_\alpha} e^{-s^2/2} ds = \alpha$$

For the so obtained test of size α the power function (17.5.3.1.1) can be written

$$\psi(\omega) = 1 - \frac{1}{\sqrt{2\pi}} \int_{-\tau_\alpha}^{+\tau_\alpha} e^{-s^2/2} ds + \frac{1}{\sqrt{2\pi}} \int_{-\tau_\alpha}^{\Delta-\tau_\alpha} e^{-s^2/2} ds - \frac{1}{\sqrt{2\pi}} \int_{\tau_\alpha}^{\Delta+\tau_\alpha} e^{-s^2/2} ds$$

where

$$\Delta = \frac{a - \omega}{\sigma/\sqrt{n}}$$

hence by (17.5.3.1.2)

$$\psi(\omega) = \alpha + \frac{1}{\sqrt{2\pi}} \left\{ \int_{-\tau_\alpha}^{-\tau_\alpha+\Delta} e^{-s^2/2} ds - \int_{\tau_\alpha}^{\tau_\alpha+\Delta} e^{-s^2/2} ds \right\}$$

$$= \alpha + \psi_1(\Delta)$$

One verifies that $\psi_1(\Delta)$ is an even function, i.e., $\psi_1(\Delta) = \psi_1(|\Delta|)$ and that $\psi_1(|\Delta|)$ is an increasing function of $|\Delta|$ such that

$$\psi(0) = 0, \qquad \psi(+\infty) = 1 - \alpha$$

The graph of the power function has therefore the form indicated in Fig. 17.5.3.2.

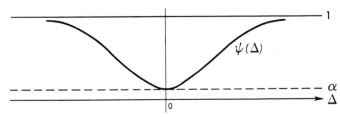

Fig. 17.5.3.2

17.5.4. Example (Binomial Distribution, H Simple, H' Onesided).

Let X be a simple alternative with $P\{X = 1\} = p$, $P\{X = 0\} = 1 - p = q$, and let $z = (X_1, X_2, \cdots, X_n)$ be a sample of X of size n. We wish to test H: $p = p_0$ against H': $p > p_0$. Here the outcome space Z is the set of all n-tuples consisting of 0's or 1's, Ω consists of all p such that $0 \leq p \leq 1$, and P is the family of probability distributions of $z = (X_1,\cdots,X_n)$ given by

$$P\{z;p\} = p\{X_1,\cdots,X_n;p\} = p^{\sum\limits_{j=1}^{n} X_j}(1 - p)^{n - \sum\limits_{j=1}^{n} X_j}$$

Writing

$$S_n = \sum_{j=1}^{n} X_j$$

we have

(17.5.4.1) $$P\{z;p\} = p^{S_n}(1 - p)^{n - S_n}$$

hence

$$\sup_{p \in H} P\{z;p\} = p_0^{S_n}(1 - p_0)^{n - S_n}$$

To obtain

$$\sup_{p \in H \cup H'} P\{z;p\} = \sup_{p \geq p_0} P\{z;p\}$$

we maximize $\log P\{z;p\} = S_n \log p + (n - S_n) \log (1 - p)$ with respect to p. Differentiation yields

$$\frac{S_n}{p} - \frac{n - S_n}{1 - p} = 0$$

and one verifies that the solution $p = S_n/n$ of this equation is the only maximum for $P\{z;p\}$. It follows that

$$\sup_{p \in H \cup H'} P\{z;p\} = \begin{cases} \left(\dfrac{S_n}{n}\right)^{S_n}\left(1 - \dfrac{S_n}{n}\right)^{n - S_n} & \text{if } S_n/n \geq p_0 \\[2ex] p_0^{S_n}(1 - p_0)^{n - S_n} & \text{if } S_n/n < p_0 \end{cases}$$

and

(17.5.4.2) $$\lambda(z) = \begin{cases} \left(\dfrac{p_0}{S_n/n}\right)^{S_n}\left[\dfrac{1 - p_0}{1 - (S_n/n)}\right]^{n - S_n} & \text{if } S_n/n \geq p_0 \\[2ex] 1 & \text{if } S_n/n < p_0 \end{cases}$$

The l.r. test

$$\lambda(z) < c \quad \text{for } 0 < c \leq 1$$

is a set W in z space consisting of those $z = (X_1,\cdots,X_n)$ for which

(17.5.4.3) $$\left(\frac{p_0}{S_n/n}\right)^{S_n}\left(\frac{1 - p_0}{1 - S_n/n}\right)^{n - S_n} < c \quad \text{and} \quad S_n/n \geq p_0$$

All z such that

$$\left(\frac{p_0}{S_n/n}\right)^{S_n}\left(\frac{1 - p_0}{1 - S_n/n}\right)^{n - S_n} \geq c \quad \text{and} \quad S_n/n \geq p_0$$

as well as all z for which

$$\frac{S_n}{n} < p_0$$

belong to $Z - W$.

One verifies that the left side of (17.5.4.3) is a decreasing function of S_n for $S_n \geq p_0 n$, so that (17.5.4.3) is equivalent with

(17.5.4.4) $S_n - np_0 > \tau$ for $\tau > 0$

and this inequality is a simpler way of writing the test W.

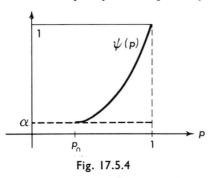

Fig. 17.5.4

To determine τ so that the test (17.5.4.4) has size $\leq \alpha$, for given α, we observe that

$$P\{S_n - np_0 > \tau; H\}$$

$$= \sum_{j > np_0 + \tau} \binom{n}{j} p_0^{j}(1 - p_0)^{n-j}$$

and look for the smallest τ_α such that for $\tau = \tau_\alpha$ the right side still is $\leq \alpha$. It is not always possible to obtain exactly the size α.

Having found this τ_α, one has the power function

$$\psi(p) = P\{S_n - np_0 > \tau_\alpha; p \in H'\}$$

$$= \sum_{j > np_0 + \tau_\alpha} \binom{n}{j} p^{j}(1 - p)^{n-j}$$

Since $\psi(p)$ is an increasing function of p and $\psi(p_0) = \alpha$, $\psi(1) = 1$, the graph of the power function $\psi(p)$ has the form indicated in Fig. 17.5.4.

17.5.5. Some Properties of the l.r. Test.

The l.r. tests have a number of desirable properties. The motivation for these tests is intuitively plausible and the l.r. test is in most classical situations identical with the test well established in practical use. Under certain very general assumptions one can prove that if a uniformly most powerful test exists it must be the l.r. test. It has also been shown that for large sample sizes the l.r. test has certain optimal properties. A great practical advantage of the l.r. test is that, when faced with a new hypothesis testing problem, the statistician has in the l.r. statistic a routine tool which in most practical situations will enable him to construct an appropriate test. This does not mean, however, that the l.r. test is always optimal in every respect. The following example due to H. Rubin and C. Stein shows that the l.r. test may be biased.

17.5.5.1. Example.

Let X be a discrete random variable with the possible values: $-2, +2, -1, +1, 0$, and let our problem be to test a simple hypothesis H against a composite alternative H', where the probability distributions H and H' are of the following form

x:	-2	$+2$	-1	$+1$	0
$P\{x;H\} =$	$\dfrac{\alpha}{2}$	$\dfrac{\alpha}{2}$	$\tfrac{1}{2} - \alpha$	$\tfrac{1}{2} - \alpha$	α
$P\{x;H'\} =$	rc	$(1-r)c$	$\dfrac{1-c}{1-\alpha}(\tfrac{1}{2}-\alpha)$	$\dfrac{1-c}{1-\alpha}(\tfrac{1}{2}-\alpha)$	$\dfrac{1-c}{1-\alpha}\alpha$

The constants α, c, r have the following meaning: α is the required size of the test, and c is a given constant, such that

(17.5.5.1.1)
$$0 < \alpha < \tfrac{1}{2}, \quad \frac{\alpha}{2-\alpha} < c < \alpha$$

while r is a parameter with values $0 \le r \le 1$.
A sample of X of size 1 is used. We have

$$\lambda(X) = \frac{P\{X;H\}}{\max(P\{X;H\}, \sup_{0 \le r \le 1} P\{X;H'\})}$$

This can be evaluated explicitly and one obtains

$$\lambda(-2) = \lambda(2) = \frac{\alpha}{2c}$$

$$\lambda(-1) = \lambda(1) = \frac{1-\alpha}{1-c}$$

$$\lambda(0) = \frac{1-\alpha}{1-c}$$

From (17.5.5.1.1) it follows that

$$\lambda(-2) = \lambda(2) = \frac{\alpha}{2c} < \frac{1-\alpha}{1-c} = \lambda(-1) = \lambda(0) = \lambda(1)$$

so that the inequality

$$\lambda(X) < \frac{1-\alpha}{1-c}$$

determines the critical region

(17.5.5.1.2)
$$W = \left\{X: \lambda(z) < \frac{1-\alpha}{1-c}\right\} = \{-2,2\}$$

of the required size

$$P\{X \in W; H\} = \alpha$$

The power of the test (17.5.5.1.2) is

$$P\{W;r\} = rc + (1-r)c = c < \alpha \quad \text{for all } r$$

hence W is biased. Incidentally, there exist unbiased tests of H against H', of size α, for example the test

$$W^\star: \{x = 0\}$$

which has size $P\{X = 0; H\} = \alpha$ and the power function

$$P\{X = 0; r\} = \alpha \frac{1 - c}{1 - \alpha} > \alpha$$

17.6 Statistical Estimation

17.6.1. For a given triple (Z,Ω,P), we consider an action space A which is identical with Ω, so that any decision function $a = d(z)$ maps Z into Ω. Any such decision function is called a *point estimate* or a *point estimator* of the parameter.

Alternatively, one may consider an action space A' which is a family R of sets in Ω, so that each decision function ascribes to outcomes $z \in Z$ sets in R; such a decision function is called a set estimate or a *confidence set*.

The aim of statistical estimation procedures is, in intuitive terms, to use an observed outcome $z \in Z$ for the purpose of obtaining a reasonable guess of the true value ω of the parameter. In the case of point estimation the decision procedure yields one such value $\hat{\omega} = d(z)$, to be used as an empirical approximation (estimate) of ω. In the case of set estimation the intent is to obtain a set $I \subset R$ which has a certain probability (confidence level) to contain the true value ω.

In the following we will outline some of the general theory of point estimation.

17.6.2. Minimum Variance Unbiased (M.V.U.) Estimates. In order to select from the many possible point estimates those which have some desirable properties, one may proceed within the framework of decision theory by assuming a plausible loss function and then finding a decision rule (estimate) which minimizes the risk within a given class of decision rules.

One of the historically oldest loss functions (Gauss, Laplace) is the *quadratic loss function*

(17.6.2.1) $$L(\omega,\hat{\omega}) = (\omega - \hat{\omega})^2$$

The corresponding risk function is

(17.6.2.2) $$\rho(\omega,\hat{\omega}) = E[(\omega - \hat{\omega})^2]$$

If there exists, in a given class of estimates, one that minimizes (17.6.2.2), then it is called the *least square estimate* in that class.

An estimate $\hat{\omega}$ is called unbiased, consistently with the meaning given this term before, when

(17.6.2.3) $$E(\hat{\omega};\omega) = \omega \quad \text{for all } \omega \in \Omega$$

For an unbiased estimate $\hat\omega$ the risk function (17.6.2.2) becomes

$$\rho(\omega,\hat\omega) = E[(\hat\omega - \omega)^2; \omega] = E\{[\hat\omega - E(\hat\omega;\omega) + E(\hat\omega;\omega) - \omega]^2; \omega\}$$
$$= E\{[\hat\omega - E(\hat\omega;\omega) + \omega - \omega]^2; \omega\} = E\{[\hat\omega - E(\hat\omega;\omega)]^2; \omega\}$$
$$= \sigma^2(\hat\omega;\omega)$$

that is the variance of $\hat\omega$, when ω is the state of Nature. It follows that, among unbiased estimates and for the quadratic loss function, the estimate which has the smallest variance also minimizes the risk function. In other words, in the class of unbiased estimates the least square estimate is the same as the estimate with the smallest variance. If such an estimate exists, it is called a *minimum variance unbiased (M.V.U.) estimate*.

17.6.3. Maximum Likelihood (m.l.) Estimates

17.6.3.1. Let the likelihood function, as in (17.5.1.2), be

$$g(\mathbf{X};\omega^\star) = f(X_1;\omega^\star) \cdots f(X_n;\omega^\star)$$

where $\mathbf{X}$ is the observed sample point $(X_1,\cdots,X_n)$, and $\omega^\star$ a parameter value which the statistician may choose. If g is such that for each $\mathbf{X} \in Z$ there exists a parameter value

$$\hat\omega(\mathbf{X}) = \hat\omega(X_1, X_2, \cdots, X_n)$$

which maximizes $g(\mathbf{X};\omega^\star)$, that is, such that

$$g(\mathbf{X};\hat\omega(\mathbf{X})) \geq g(\mathbf{X};\omega^\star) \quad \text{for all } \omega^\star \in \Omega$$

then $\hat\omega$ is called a *maximum likelihood* (m.l.) point estimate of the parameter ω.

In most practical problems, instead of maximizing $g(\mathbf{X};\omega^\star)$, as function of $\omega^\star$ for the observed $\mathbf{X}$, it is more convenient to maximize

(17.6.3.1.1) $$L(\mathbf{X};\omega^\star) = \log g(\mathbf{X};\omega^\star)$$

17.6.3.2. Example: Simple Alternative. Let X be a simple alternative with the probability distribution $P(X = 1) = p$, $P(X = 0) = 1 - p$, which also can be written

$$f(x;p) = p^x(1 - p)^{1-x}$$

and let $\mathbf{X} = (X_1, X_2, \cdots, X_m)$ be a sample of X. Then

$$g(\mathbf{X};p) = p^{\sum_{i=1}^{m} X_i}(1 - p)^{m - \sum_{i=1}^{m} X_i}$$

$$\log g(\mathbf{X};p) = \sum_{i=1}^{m} X_i \log p + \left(m - \sum_{i=1}^{m} X_i\right)\log(1 - p)$$

$$\frac{\partial \log g}{\partial p} = \frac{1}{p}\sum_{i=1}^{m} X_i - \frac{1}{1 - p}\left(m - \sum_{i=1}^{m} X_i\right)$$

$$= \frac{m}{p(1 - p)}(\bar X_m - p)$$

and equating this to zero and solving for p we obtain

$$\hat{p} = \bar{X}_m$$

One verifies that

$$\frac{\partial \log p}{\partial p} > 0 \quad \text{for } p < \bar{X}_m \quad \text{and} \quad < 0 \text{ for } p > \bar{X}_m$$

so that $\hat{p} = \bar{X}_m$ is the m.l. estimate for p.

17.6.3.3. Example: Normal Distribution. Let X be known to have distribution $N(a,\sigma^2)$, with a and σ^2 both to be estimated from a sample $\mathbf{X} = (X_1,\cdots,X_n)$. We have

$$g(\mathbf{X};a,\sigma^2) = (2\pi\sigma^2)^{-n/2} \exp\left[-\frac{1}{2\sigma^2}\sum_{j=1}^m (X_j - a)^2\right]$$

$$L(\mathbf{X};a,\sigma^2) = -\frac{n}{2}\log 2\pi - \frac{n}{2}\log \sigma^2 - (2\sigma^2)^{-1}\sum_{j=1}^n (X_j - a)^2$$

To maximize L in a and σ^2 for given $\mathbf{X}$ we solve the pair of equations

$$\frac{\partial L}{\partial a} = 2(2\sigma^2)^{-1}\sum_{j=1}^n (X_j - a) = 0$$

$$\frac{\partial L}{\partial(\sigma^2)} = -\frac{n}{2\sigma^2} + 2(2\sigma^2)^{-2}\sum_{j=1}^n (X_j - a)^2 = 0$$

and obtain

$$\hat{a} = \frac{1}{n}\sum_{j=1}^n X_j = \bar{X}_n$$

(17.6.3.3)

$$\hat{\sigma}^2 = \frac{1}{n}\sum_{j=1}^n (X_j - \bar{X}_n)^2$$

One verifies easily that, for any fixed value of σ^2, $L(\mathbf{X};a,\sigma^2)$ is maximized in a for $a = \bar{X}_n$; one also verifies that

$$(2\pi\sigma^2)^{-n/2} \exp\left[-\frac{1}{2\sigma^2}\sum_{j=1}^n (X_j - \bar{X}_n)^2\right]$$

is maximized in σ^2 for

$$\sigma^2 = \frac{1}{n}\sum_{j=1}^n (X_j - \bar{X}_n)^2$$

Therefore the values $\hat{a}$, $\hat{\sigma}^2$ of (17.6.3.3) actually yield the maximum of L, and are the m.l. estimates for a and σ^2. It may be noted that $\hat{\sigma}^2$ is not an unbiased estimate for σ^2.

17.6.3.4. Example (Poisson Distribution). If one wants to estimate the parameter λ of the Poisson distribution

$$P\{X = j\} = e^{-\lambda}\frac{\lambda^j}{j!}, \quad j = 0, 1, 2, \cdots$$

from a sample $\mathbf{X} = (X_1, X_2, \cdots, X_n)$, the m.l. estimate is obtained by considering

$$g(\mathbf{X};\lambda) = e^{-n\lambda}\lambda^{\sum\limits_{i=1}^{n} X_i}(X_1!\, X_2! \cdots X_n!)^{-1}$$

$$L(\mathbf{X};\lambda) = -n\lambda + \sum_{i=1}^{n} X_i \cdot \log \lambda - \log (X_1!\, X_2! \cdots X_n!)$$

and solving the equation

$$\frac{\partial L}{\partial \lambda} = -n + \left(\sum_{i=1}^{n} X_i\right)\bigg/\lambda = 0$$

The solution is

$$\hat{\lambda} = \frac{1}{n}\sum_{i=1}^{n} X_i = \bar{X}_n$$

and one easily verifies that it yields a maximum for $g(\mathbf{X};\lambda)$.

17.6.3.5. Example (Exponential Distribution with Unknown Location Parameter). Let $X = (X_1, X_2, \cdots, X_n)$ be a sample of a continuous random variable known to have the probability density

$$f(x;a,\mu) = \begin{cases} \mu e^{-\mu(x-a)} & \text{for } x \geq a \\ 0 & \text{for } x < a \end{cases}$$

where the scale parameter $\mu > 0$ is given and the location parameter a is to be estimated. We have

$$g(\mathbf{X};a,\mu) = \mu^n \exp\left[-\mu\sum_{j=1}^{n}(X_j - a)\right] \quad \text{if } X_j \geq a \text{ for all } j = 1, \cdots, n$$

otherwise $g(\mathbf{X};a,\mu) = 0$. Clearly, for given $X_1, \cdots, X_n$ and μ, $g(\mathbf{X};a,\mu)$ is maximum when

$$\sum_{j=1}^{n}(X_j - a)$$

is minimum under the condition $a \leq X_j$ for $j = 1, 2, \cdots, n$, so that this maximum is attained for

$$\hat{a} = \min (X_1, X_2, \cdots, X_n)$$

and this is the m.l. estimate for a. One shows easily that this estimate is biased.

EXERCISES

17.1. For the one-parametric family of exponential probability distributions with the probability densities
$$f(x;a) = \begin{cases} ae^{-ax} & \text{for } x \geq 0 \\ 0 & \text{for } x < 0 \end{cases}$$
find the likelihood ratio test of the hypothesis H: $a \geq a_0$, against the unrestricted alternative $a < a_0$.

17.2. For the family of Poisson distributions $f(x;\lambda) = e^{-\lambda}(\lambda^x/x!)$, $x = 0, 1, 2, \cdots$, obtain the likelihood ratio test of the hypothesis $\lambda \geq \lambda_0$ against the alternative $\lambda < \lambda_0$.

17.3. Consider the one-parametric family of the uniform probability distributions with the probability densities
$$f(x;a) = \begin{cases} 1/a & \text{for } 0 \leq x \leq a \\ 0 & \text{elsewhere} \end{cases}$$
Obtain the likelihood ratio test for H: $a = a_0$ against H': $a = a_1 < a_0$.

17.4. For the one-parametric family of uniform distributions
$$f(x;\theta) = \begin{cases} 1 & \text{for } \theta \leq x \leq 1 + \theta \\ 0 & \text{elsewhere} \end{cases}$$
obtain the likelihood ratio test of H: $\theta = \theta_0$ against H': $\theta \neq \theta_0$.

17.5. Find the maximum likelihood estimate for the parameter a of Exercise 17.1.

17.6. Find the maximum likelihood estimate for a in Exercise 17.3.

17.7. Attempt to find the maximum likelihood estimate for the mode b of a Cauchy distribution (5.1.2.2). What are the difficulties?

17.8. A sample $X_1, X_2, \cdots, X_m$ was obtained from $N(x_0, \sigma^2)$ and a sample $Y_1, Y_2, \cdots, Y_n$ from $N(y_0, \sigma^2)$. Use both samples and obtain the maximum likelihood estimate for σ^2.

17.9. Consider the family of discrete random variables with the distributions
$$f(x;p) = (1 - p)p^x, \quad x = 0, 1, 2, \cdots$$
and obtain the maximum likelihood estimate for p using a sample of size n.

Appendixes

Some Elementary Concepts
of the
Theory of Sets

A.I. A finite or an infinite number of things, considered as a whole, is called a *set*. The things of which a set consists are called *elements of that set*. If a set S consists of the elements $a, b, \cdots$, we write

$$S = \{a,b,\cdots\}$$

If a is an element of the set S, we say that *a is contained* in S or that S *contains a* and we write

$$a \in S$$

A set is called *finite* if it consists of a finite number of elements, *infinite* if it consists of infinitely many elements.

A.I.I. Example. Consider the set whose elements are all imaginary roots of the equation $x^5 - x^2 + 2x - 3 = 0$. Since this is an equation of degree 5, it has five roots. By Descartes's rule of signs we see that it has not more than three positive real roots, and no negative real roots at all. There must be, therefore, at least two imaginary roots. Thus, without writing down explicitly the elements of our set, we are able to tell that it is a finite set, containing at least two and at most five elements.

A.I.2. Example. The set of all children born in the United States on December 8, 1944. All we can say about this set offhand is that it is finite.

A.I.3. Example. The set of all prime numbers. Since it has been proved that there are infinitely many prime numbers, this is an infinite set.

A.2. If every element of set A is also an element of set B, we say that set A is *contained* in set B, or that A is a *subset* of B, or that B *contains A*, and we write

$$A \subset B$$

If $A \subset B$ and $B \subset A$, then we call the sets A and B *identical*, and write $A = B$. If A and B are not identical, we call them *different*, and write $A \neq B$.

A.2.1. Example.   Consider the Cartesian plane (x,y), and let A be the set of all points on the straight line bisecting the angle between the positive coordinate axes. Let B be the set of points (x,y) whose coordinates fulfill the equation $x = y$, and C the set of points (x,y) such that $x \geq y$. Then, as one proves in analytic geometry, we have

$$A = B, \qquad B \subset C, \qquad B \neq C$$

The set $\{a,b\}$ consists of two elements, the set $\{a\}$ of one element. For reasons of methodological completeness, we introduce the concept of an *empty set* which will be denoted by 0, a set without elements. We shall agree to consider 0 as contained in every set. Keeping this agreement in mind, we see that, for example, the set with four elements $A = \{a,b,c,d\}$ has the following subsets:

$$0, \{a\}, \{b\}, \{c\}, \{d\}, \{a,b\}, \{a,c\}, \{a,d\}, \{b,c\}, \{b,d\}, \{c,d\},$$

$$\{a,b,c\}, \{a,b,d\}, \{a,c,d\}, \{b,c,d\}, \{a,b,c,d\}$$

All subsets of a set, different from 0 and A, are called *proper subsets* of A. The set $\{a,b,c,d\}$ has, accordingly, fourteen proper subsets.

Many mathematical theorems may be formulated in terms of sets and their subsets. For example, Fermat's conjecture may be thus stated: The set of positive integers $n > 2$, such that the equation with three unknowns $x^n + y^n = z^n$ has a solution consisting of positive integers x, y, z, is the empty set.

It is easily seen that the relationship $\subset$ is transitive, that is that from $A \subset B$ and $B \subset C$ it follows that $A \subset C$.

A.3.   If A is a proper subset of B then there are elements in B which are not contained in A. The set of all these elements is called the *complement of A in B* and is denoted by $B - A$. If $A = B$, the symbol $B - A$ will denote the empty set.

If A and B are two sets, we denote by $A \cap B$ the set of all elements which belong to A and to B, and call this set the *intersection of A and B*.

A.3.1. Example.   Let A be the set of all living men with blue eyes, and B the set of all men living in the United States. Then $A \cap B$ is the set of all blue-eyed men living in the United States.

A.3.2. Example.   If A is the set of all points on the circumference of a circle C_1, and B the set of all points on the circumference of a different circle C_2, then $A \cap B$ is either the empty set (if C_1 and C_2 have no points in common), or consists of one point (if C_1 and C_2 are tangent circles), or of two points (if C_1 and C_2 intersect).

The following statements are easily verified: If $A \subset B$ then $A \cap B = A$; for any sets A, B we have $A \cap B \subset A$, $A \cap B \subset B$; we have $A \cap B = 0$ if and only if A and B have no elements in common.

Two sets A and B such that $A \cap B = 0$ are called *disjoint* or *mutually exclusive sets*. Any finite or countable sequence of sets A, B, C, $\cdots$ such that any two of them are mutually exclusive, that is, $A \cap B = A \cap C = B \cap C = \cdots = 0$, is called a *sequence of mutually exclusive sets*.

If A and B are any two sets, we denote by $A \cup B$ the set of all those elements which belong to at least one of the sets A, B, and call this set the *union of A and B*.

A.3.3. Example.   If A is the set of all men below the age of 40, and B is the set of all men above 25 years of age, then $A \cup B$ is the set of all men.

A.3.4. Example.   Let A be the set of all odd positive integers and B the set of all even positive integers. Then $A \cup B$ is the set of all positive integers.

Clearly, if $A \subset B$, then $A \cup B = B$.

A.3.5. Example.   Let A be the set of all prime numbers greater than 2, and B the set of all odd numbers. Then $A \cup B = B$.

If A and B are not disjoint, it is always possible to write $A \cup B$ as the union of two disjoint sets, namely

$$A \cup B = A \cup (B - A \cap B)$$
$$A \cup B = (A - A \cap B) \cup B$$

The definition of $A - B$ may be extended to the case when B is not a subset of A, by writing

$$A - B = A - A \cap B$$

This means that $A - B$ consists of all those elements of A which are not also elements of B.

A.4.   A set is called *countable* if it contains infinitely many elements and if those elements can be numbered by positive integers, that is, if it is possible to ascribe to each element of the set a positive integer number so that different elements receive different numbers. A countable set S can be written in the form of an infinite sequence

$$S = \{a_1, a_2, a_3, \cdots, a_k, \cdots\}$$

where a_k is the element to which the positive integer number k was ascribed.

Obviously the set of all even positive integers is countable since each of its elements is a number of the form $2k$, and by ascribing to the element $2k$ the number k one can number all elements of the set. Similarly, the set of all odd numbers, the set of all squares of integers, the set of all numbers of the form n^n with positive integer n, are countable sets. Not quite so obvious is the statement proven in the following example.

A.4.1. Example.   Consider the set R of all different rational numbers p/q, where p and q are positive integers. We shall prove that R is countable. For that purpose we arrange all possible quotients p/q in a table with double entry (Fig. A.4.1) and connect them by a line the beginning of which is indicated in the table, and which clearly will, in a finite number of steps, lead to every possible quotient p/q. We then give 1/1 the number 1, 2/1 the number 2, 1/2 the number 3, 1/3 the number 4; the quotient 2/2 we omit since it is equal to 1/1 which had already occurred; 3/1 receives the number 5, 4/1 the number 6, 3/2 the number 7, 2/3 the number 8, etc. Being careful to omit each quotient equal to another one which has already received a number, we shall be able to arrange all different rational numbers with positive numerators and denominators into a sequence beginning with

$$1, 2, \tfrac{1}{2}, \tfrac{1}{3}, 3, 4, \tfrac{3}{2}, \tfrac{2}{3}, \tfrac{1}{4}, \tfrac{1}{5}, 5, \tfrac{5}{2},$$

$$\tfrac{4}{3}, \tfrac{3}{4}, \tfrac{2}{5}, \tfrac{1}{6}, \tfrac{1}{7}, \tfrac{3}{5}, \tfrac{5}{3}, 7, 8, \tfrac{7}{2}, \tfrac{5}{4}, \tfrac{4}{5}, \tfrac{2}{7}, \tfrac{1}{8}, \cdots$$

The law of numbering is, of course, quite complicated.

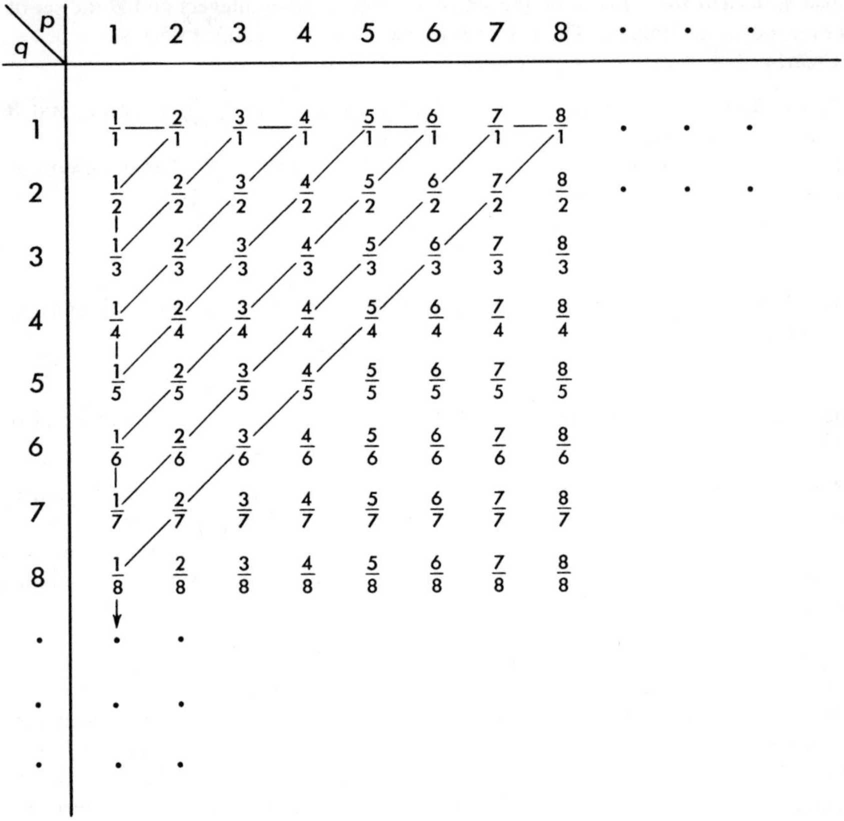

Fig. A.4.1

A.5. It could be considered possible that all sets are either finite, or, if they are infinite, are countable. It will be shown that this is not so and, to prove this statement, we shall give an example of an infinite *non-countable set*.

Let R be the set of all real numbers >0 and <1. Each of those numbers can be written in exactly one way as a decimal fraction with infinitely many digits

$$r = 0.\, a_1 a_2 a_3 \cdots$$

For example

$$\sqrt{0.8} = 0.8944272 \cdots$$

$$\tfrac{1}{2} = 0.4999999 \cdots$$

We shall prove that R is not countable. For, if it were countable, R could be arranged into a numbered sequence $r_1, r_2, \cdots, r_k, \cdots$, and each of these numbers could be written as a decimal fraction with infinitely many digits

$$r_1 = 0.\ a_1^{(1)}\ a_2^{(1)}\ a_3^{(1)} \cdots$$
$$r_2 = 0.\ a_1^{(2)}\ a_2^{(2)}\ a_3^{(2)} \cdots$$
.
.
.
$$r_k = 0.\ a_1^{(k)}\ a_2^{(k)}\ a_3^{(k)} \cdots$$
.
.
.

We then could define a real number s by the following rule: $s = 0.\ b_1 b_2 b_3 \cdots b_k \cdots$, where the digits $b_1, b_2, \cdots, b_k, \cdots$ are such that

$$b_k = 5 \quad \text{if } a_k^{(k)} = 7$$
$$b_k = 7 \quad \text{if } a_k^{(k)} \neq 7$$

The number s clearly would be a real number between 0 and 1, and thus an element of R. However, it would be different from every number in the sequence $r_1, r_2, \cdots, r_k, \cdots$, since it would differ from r_1 in the first digit, from r_2 in the second, $\cdots$, from r_k in the kth digit. Hence the sequence $r_1, r_2, \cdots, r_k, \cdots$ would not contain all elements of R.

The Inequalities
of Schwarz
and Cauchy

B.I. Theorem (Schwarz's Inequality). If $f(x)$ and $g(x)$ are real functions, defined in an interval (a,b), where $-\infty \leq a < b \leq +\infty$, such that

$$\int_a^b f^2(x)dx \quad \text{and} \quad \int_a^b g^2(x)dx$$

are finite, then

(B.I.I) $$\left(\int_a^b f(x)g(x)dx\right)^2 \leq \int_a^b f^2(x)dx \int_a^b g^2(x)dx$$

Proof. (B.1) follows immediately from

$$0 \leq \tfrac{1}{2}\int_a^b \int_a^b [f(x)g(s) - f(s)g(x)]^2 dxds$$

$$= \tfrac{1}{2}\int_a^b f^2(x)dx \int_a^b g^2(s)ds - \int_a^b f(x)g(x)dx \int_a^b f(s)g(s)ds + \tfrac{1}{2}\int_a^b f^2(s)ds \int_a^b g^2(x)dx$$

$$= \int_a^b f^2(x)dx \int_a^b g^2(x)dx - \left(\int_a^b f(x)g(x)dx\right)^2$$

By a simple extension of this proof, which may be left to the reader, one obtains the following generalization of Schwarz's inequality.

B.2. Theorem. For any two real functions $k(x,y)$ and $m(x,y)$, such that

$$\int_c^d \int_a^b k^2(x,y)dxdy \quad \text{and} \quad \int_c^d \int_a^b m^2(x,y)dxdy$$

are finite, we have

(B.2.I) $$\left(\int_c^d \int_a^b k(x,y)m(x,y)dxdy\right)^2 \leq \int_c^d \int_a^b k^2(x,y)dxdy \int_c^d \int_a^b m^2(x,y)dxdy$$

If, instead of integrals, one considers finite or countable sums, one obtains the following theorems, analogous to Theorem B.1 and Theorem B.2.

B.3. Theorem (Cauchy's Inequality).   Let $\sum\limits_{(j)} a_j$ and $\sum\limits_{(j)} b_j$ be either finite real series with the same number of terms, or infinite real series such that $\sum\limits_{(j)} a_j{}^2$ and $\sum\limits_{(j)} b_j{}^2$ converge. Then we have

(B.3.1)
$$\left(\sum_{(j)} a_j b_j\right)^2 \leq \sum_{(j)} a_j{}^2 \cdot \sum_{(j)} b_j{}^2$$

Proof.   We obviously have

$$0 \leq \tfrac{1}{2} \sum_{(j)} \sum_{(k)} (a_j b_k - a_k b_j)^2 = \tfrac{1}{2} \sum_{(j)} a_j{}^2 \sum_{(k)} b_k{}^2 - \sum_{(j)} a_j b_j \sum_{(k)} a_k b_k + \tfrac{1}{2} \sum_{(k)} a_k{}^2 \sum_{(j)} b_j{}^2$$

$$= \sum_{(j)} a_j{}^2 \sum_{(j)} b_j{}^2 - \left(\sum_{(j)} a_j b_j\right)^2$$

B.4. Theorem.   For any two double series $\sum\limits_{(j)} \sum\limits_{(k)} a_{jk}$ and $\sum\limits_{(j)} \sum\limits_{(k)} b_{jk}$, either finite and with the same number of terms in one or both subscripts or infinite in both subscripts and, if infinite, such that

$$\sum_{(j)} \sum_{(k)} a_{jk}{}^2 \quad \text{and} \quad \sum_{(j)} \sum_{(k)} b_{jk}{}^2$$

converge, we have

(B.4.1)
$$\left(\sum_{(j)} \sum_{(k)} a_{jk} b_{jk}\right)^2 \leq \sum_{(j)} \sum_{(k)} a_{jk}{}^2 \sum_{(j)} \sum_{(k)} b_{jk}{}^2$$

Tables

TABLE I. The normal distribution

$$\varphi(x) = \frac{1}{\sqrt{2\pi}}\, e^{-x^2/2}, \qquad \Phi(x) = \int_{-\infty}^{x} \varphi(s)\, ds$$

x	$\varphi(x)$	$\Phi(x)$	x	$\varphi(x)$	$\Phi(x)$
0.0	0.398942	0.500000	2.5	0.017528	0.993790
0.1	0.396952	0.539828	2.6	0.013583	0.995339
0.2	0.391043	0.579260	2.7	0.010421	0.996533
0.3	0.381388	0.617911	2.8	0.007915	0.997445
0.4	0.368270	0.655422	2.9	0.005953	0.998134
0.5	0.352065	0.691462	3.0	0.004432	0.998650
0.6	0.333225	0.725747	3.1	0.003267	0.999032
0.7	0.312254	0.758036	3.2	0.002384	0.999313
0.8	0.289692	0.788145	3.3	0.001723	0.999517
0.9	0.266085	0.815940	3.4	0.001232	0.999663
1.0	0.241971	0.841345	3.5	0.000873	0.999767
1.1	0.217852	0.864334	3.6	0.000612	0.999841
1.2	0.194186	0.884930	3.7	0.000425	0.999892
1.3	0.171369	0.903200	3.8	0.000292	0.999928
1.4	0.149727	0.919243	3.9	0.000199	0.999952
1.5	0.129518	0.933193	4.0	0.000134	0.999968
1.6	0.110921	0.945201	4.1	0.000089	0.999979
1.7	0.094049	0.955435	4.2	0.000059	0.999987
1.8	0.078950	0.964070	4.3	0.000039	0.999991
1.9	0.065616	0.971283	4.4	0.000025	0.999995
2.0	0.053991	0.977250			
2.1	0.043984	0.982136			
2.2	0.035475	0.986097			
2.3	0.028327	0.989276			
2.4	0.022395	0.991802			

TABLE II. Student's t distribution
Values $t_{n,\varepsilon}$ such that, for n degrees of freedom
$$P(|T| \leq t_{n,\varepsilon}) = \varepsilon$$

n \ ε	0.90	0.95	0.98	0.99	0.999
1	6.314	12.706	31.821	63.657	636.619
2	2.920	4.303	6.965	9.925	31.598
3	2.353	3.182	4.541	5.841	12.924
4	2.132	2.776	3.747	4.604	8.610
5	2.015	2.571	3.365	4.032	6.869
6	1.943	2.447	3.143	3.707	5.959
7	1.895	2.365	2.998	3.499	5.408
8	1.860	2.306	2.896	3.355	5.041
9	1.833	2.262	2.821	3.250	4.781
10	1.812	2.228	2.764	3.169	4.587
11	1.796	2.201	2.718	3.106	4.437
12	1.782	2.179	2.681	3.055	4.318
13	1.771	2.160	2.650	3.012	4.221
14	1.761	2.145	2.624	2.977	4.140
15	1.753	2.131	2.602	2.947	4.073
16	1.746	2.120	2.583	2.921	4.015
17	1.740	2.110	2.567	2.898	3.965
18	1.734	2.101	2.552	2.878	3.922
19	1.729	2.093	2.539	2.861	3.883
20	1.725	2.086	2.528	2.845	3.850
21	1.721	2.080	2.518	2.831	3.819
22	1.717	2.074	2.508	2.819	3.792
23	1.714	2.069	2.500	2.807	3.767
24	1.711	2.064	2.492	2.797	3.745
25	1.708	2.060	2.485	2.787	3.725
26	1.706	2.056	2.479	2.779	3.707
27	1.703	2.052	2.473	2.771	3.690
28	1.701	2.048	2.467	2.763	3.674
29	1.699	2.045	2.462	2.756	3.659
30	1.697	2.042	2.457	2.750	3.646
40	1.684	2.021	2.423	2.704	3.551
60	1.671	2.000	2.390	2.660	3.460
120	1.658	1.980	2.358	2.617	3.373
∞	1.645	1.960	2.326	2.576	3.291

SOURCE: Abridged and adapted from Table III of Fisher and Yates, *Statistical Tables for Biological, Agricultural and Medical Research*, 5th ed., published by Oliver & Boyd Ltd., Edinburgh, 1957, by permission of the authors and publishers.

TABLE III. χ^2-distribution

Values $\chi^2_{n,\varepsilon}$ such that, for n degrees of freedom,

$$P(\chi^2 \leq \chi^2_{n,\varepsilon}) = \varepsilon$$

n \ ε	0.10	0.30	0.50	0.70	0.80	0.90	0.95	0.98	0.99	0.999
1	0.0158	0.148	0.455	1.074	1.642	2.706	3.841	5.412	6.635	10.827
2	0.211	0.713	1.386	2.408	3.219	4.605	5.991	7.824	9.210	13.815
3	0.584	1.424	2.366	3.665	4.642	6.251	7.815	9.837	11.345	16.266
4	1.064	2.195	3.357	4.878	5.989	7.779	9.488	11.668	13.277	18.467
5	1.610	3.000	4.351	6.064	7.289	9.236	11.070	13.388	15.086	20.515
6	2.204	3.828	5.348	7.231	8.558	10.645	12.592	15.033	16.812	22.457
7	2.833	4.671	6.346	8.383	9.803	12.017	14.067	16.622	18.475	24.322
8	3.490	5.527	7.344	9.524	11.030	13.362	15.507	18.168	20.090	26.125
9	4.168	6.393	8.343	10.656	12.242	14.684	16.919	19.679	21.666	27.877
10	4.865	7.267	9.342	11.781	13.442	15.987	18.307	21.161	23.209	29.588
11	5.578	8.148	10.341	12.899	14.631	17.275	19.675	22.618	24.725	31.264
12	6.304	9.034	11.340	14.011	15.812	18.549	21.026	24.054	26.217	32.909
13	7.042	9.926	12.340	15.119	16.985	19.812	22.362	25.472	27.688	34.528
14	7.790	10.821	13.339	16.222	18.151	21.064	23.685	26.873	29.141	36.123
15	8.547	11.721	14.339	17.322	19.311	22.307	24.996	28.259	30.578	37.697
16	9.312	12.624	15.338	18.418	20.465	23.542	26.296	29.633	32.000	39.252
17	10.085	13.531	16.338	19.511	21.615	24.769	27.587	30.995	33.409	40.790
18	10.865	14.440	17.338	20.601	22.760	25.989	28.869	32.346	34.805	42.312
19	11.651	15.352	18.338	21.689	23.900	27.204	30.144	33.687	36.191	43.820
20	12.443	16.266	19.337	22.775	25.038	28.412	31.410	35.020	37.566	45.315
21	13.240	17.182	20.337	23.858	26.171	29.615	32.671	36.343	38.932	46.797
22	14.041	18.101	21.337	24.939	27.301	30.813	33.924	37.659	40.289	48.268
23	14.848	19.021	22.337	26.018	28.429	32.007	35.172	38.968	41.638	49.728
24	15.659	19.943	23.337	27.096	29.553	33.196	36.415	40.270	42.980	51.179
25	16.473	20.867	24.337	28.172	30.675	34.382	37.652	41.566	44.314	52.620
26	17.292	21.792	25.336	29.246	31.795	35.563	38.885	42.856	45.642	54.052
27	18.114	22.719	26.336	30.319	32.912	36.741	40.113	44.140	46.963	55.476
28	18.939	23.647	27.336	31.391	34.027	37.916	41.337	45.419	48.278	56.893
29	19.768	24.577	28.336	32.461	35.139	39.087	42.557	46.693	49.588	58.302
30	20.599	25.508	29.336	33.530	36.250	40.256	43.773	47.962	50.892	59.703

SOURCE: Abridged and adapted from Table IV of Fisher and Yates, *Statistical Tables for Biological, Agricultural and Medical Research*, 5th ed., published by Oliver & Boyd Ltd., Edinburgh, 1957, by permission of the authors and publishers.

TABLE IV. Sample size $N(\alpha,\varepsilon)$ for Wilks's distribution-free α-tolerance limits with probability level $1-\varepsilon$

ε \ α	0.20	0.10	0.05	0.01	0.001
0.10	18	38	77	388	3889
0.05	22	46	93	473	4742
0.02	27	56	115	581	5832
0.01	31	64	130	662	6636

TABLE V. Exact distribution of Kołmogorov's D^N
Values $\varepsilon_{N,\alpha}$ such that

$$P\{D_N > \varepsilon_{N,\alpha}\} = \alpha$$

N \ α	0.05	0.01
2	0.8419	0.9293
3	0.7076	0.8290
4	0.6239	0.7341
5	0.5633	0.6685
10	0.4087	0.4864
15	0.3375	0.4042
20	0.2939	0.3524
25	0.2639	0.3165
30	0.2417	0.2898
40	0.2101	0.2521
50	0.1884	0.2260
60	0.1723	0.2067
70	0.1597	0.1917
80	0.1496	0.1795
90	0.1412	
100	0.1340	

TABLE VI. Asymptotic distribution of Kolmogorov's D_N
Values z_α such that, for N large, one has
approximately

$$1 - L(z_\alpha) = P\{D_N > z_\alpha N^{-\frac{1}{2}}\} = \alpha$$

α	z_α
0.50	0.83
0.45	0.86
0.40	0.90
0.35	0.93
0.30	0.97
0.25	1.02
0.20	1.07
0.15	1.14
0.10	1.22
0.05	1.36
0.02	1.52
0.01	1.63
0.001	1.95

INDEX

Absolute probability density, 52
Absolute probability distribution, 31, 33, 38
Action space, 287
Addition theorem for mathematical expectations, 78
Addition theorem for variances, 84
Alternative (in testing hypotheses), 289

Bartlett, M. S., 230
Bayes' formula, 36, 53, 59
Bernoulli, 44, 45
Bernoulli's coefficient of correlation, 148
Bernoulli's law of large numbers, 90
Beta distribution, 156, 159
Beta function, 154
Binomial distribution, 44
Bivariate normal distribution, 55, 143, 223
Bivariate population, 174
Boole's inequality, 14
Borel field, 13

Cauchy's distribution, 62, 76, 187
Cauchy's inequality, 311
Cell frequencies, observed, 253
Central limit theorem, 117
Characteristic function, 98
Chebyshev's inequality, 87
Chi-square distribution, 158, 192, 243
Chi-square variable, 158
Coefficient of correlation, 134
Complement of a set, 306
Composite hypothesis, 210, 290
Conditional expectation, 133
Conditional probability, 31, 33, 39
Conditional probability density, 52
Confidence band for $F(x)$, 283

Confidence coefficient, 185
Confidence interval, 185
Confidence set, 298
Consistent estimate, 165
Contingency table, 253, 257
Continuous probability distributions, 17
Convergence in distribution, 118
Convergence in probability, 165
Correlation, 133
Correlation of attributes, 146, 147
Correlation coefficient, 134
Correlation matrix, 234
Countable sets, 307
Covariance, 134
Covariance matrix, 234
Cramér, H., 41, 118, 240, 253
Critical region (region of rejection), 290
Cumulative distribution function, 22

Daly, J., 197
De Moivre-Laplace approximation to binomial probability, 117
Decision function, 287
Degrees of freedom of chi-square distribution, 158
Degrees of freedom of F distribution, 207
Degrees of freedom of Student's distribution, 199
Diagonalization of a positive definite quadratic form, 129
Discrete probability distribution, 15
Disjoint events, 13
Disjoint (mutually exclusive) sets, 306
Distribution-free techniques, 271
Drawings with replacement, 45, 176, 185
Drawings without replacements, 48, 176, 185

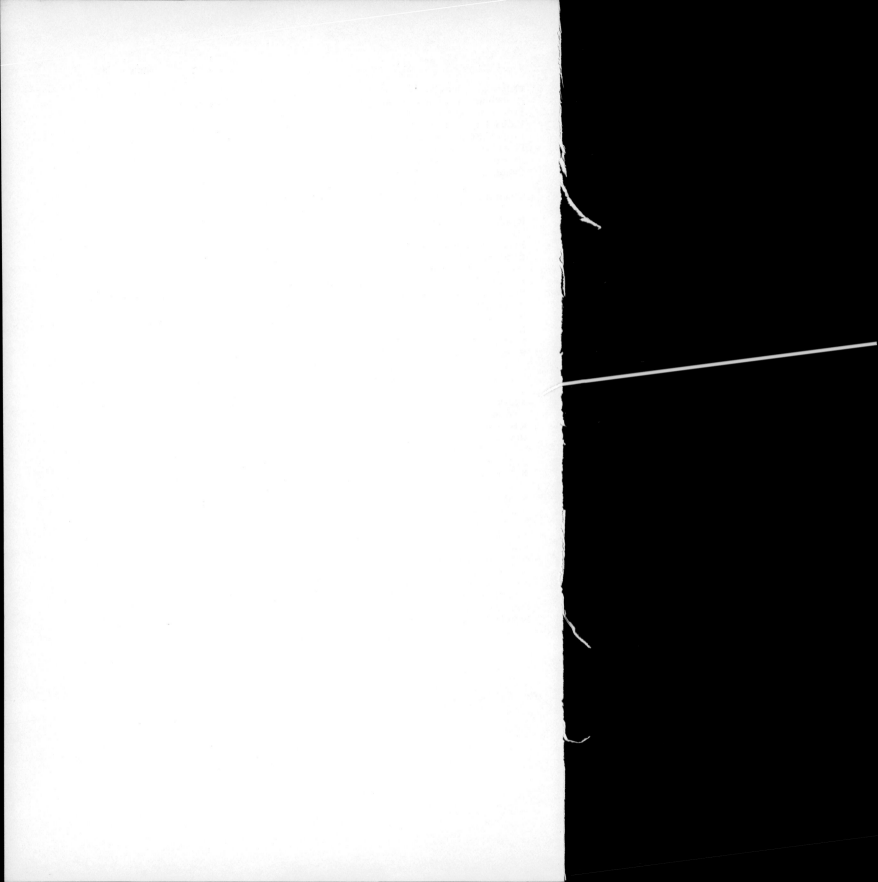